ON THE EVE OF THE

REFORMATION

"Letters of Obscure Men"

harper ✦ torchbooks

EDITORS' NOTE: *A check-list of Harper Torchbooks, classified by subjects, is printed at the end of this volume.*

ON THE EVE OF THE
REFORMATION

"Letters of Obscure Men"

ULRICH VON HUTTEN, ET AL.

TRANSLATED BY FRANCIS GRIFFIN STOKES

New Introduction by

HAJO HOLBORN

HARPER TORCHBOOKS
THE UNIVERSITY LIBRARY

HARPER & ROW, PUBLISHERS
NEW YORK, EVANSTON, AND LONDON

ON THE EVE OF THE REFORMATION:
'Letters of Obscure Men'

Introduction to the Torchbook edition copyright © 1964
by Hajo Holborn.

Printed in the United States of America.

This book, translated and edited by Francis Griffin Stokes, was first
published September 23, 1909, by Chatto & Windus, London, and is
here reprinted by arrangement. The Torchbook edition omits the Latin
text and the 1909 Preface and Introduction.

First HARPER TORCHBOOK edition published 1964 by
Harper & Row, Publishers, Incorporated
49 East 33rd Street
New York 16, N.Y.

CONTENTS

INTRODUCTION TO
THE TORCHBOOK EDITION

by Hajo Holborn

The *Letters of Obscure Men* are the contribution of six-teenth-century German humanism to the great satires of world literature. While few of the scholarly and poetic works of the German humanists will arouse more than a historical interest among modern readers, the *Letters of Obscure Men* can still be enjoyed as humorous literature. Seldom has human stupidity among scholars been so wittily depicted and a degenerate philosophy so cleverly held up to ridicule.

German humanism developed under Italian influence in the late fifteenth century, but soon tried to emancipate it-self from the Italian models. The German humanists ac-cepted the program of a new education that was to be built on classical poetry, eloquence, and philosophy rather than on theology. But the Germans felt that the new ideal of *humanitas*, that to the Italians naturally was one of restored *Romanitas*, ought to be given a different character in accord-ance with German historical traditions and sentiments. The studies of the German humanists centered largely around the search for a definition of the historic nature of the Ger-man people and a philosophy that would express its highest aspirations. The answers found, though varying a great deal, on the whole tended to emphasize simplicity as the true German virtue, which also implied a simple piety unaffected by the artificial and abstruse ideas of the theologians.

In contrast to Italian humanism, which gained its chief supporters at the courts, German humanism was predomi-nantly a movement in the universities and schools. The hu-manist poets, as they were called, often migratory students and teachers, invaded the faculties of liberal arts and presented their new poetry and eloquence as the ideal education. They clearly challenged the traditional forms of teaching and study, although they were careful not to dispute the substance of the old faith. A free thinker, such as Mutianus Rufus, who cultivated a Platonic pantheism, while inviting friends and students to his home, avoided the academic halls.

It was only the Reuchlin feud that saw the schoolmen on one side and the poets on the other close ranks and begin a common battle. In 1507-8 a Jewish convert, Johannes Pfefferkorn, had denounced in four books the usurious practices of the Jews and their hatred of the Christians. He had demanded that the Hebrew books, particularly the "mendacious, fraudulent, and false" Talmud, which inculcated this spirit, should be taken from the Jews. The four books by Pfefferkorn soon appeared in Latin, at least two of them translated by the Cologne scholar, Ortvinus Gratius. In August 1509 Pfefferkorn succeeded in getting a mandate from Emperor Maximilian authorizing him to collect the Jewish books in the presence of local officials. The archbishop of Mainz objected to this procedure, whereupon the Emperor turned the matter over to the archbishop and directed him to call for the opinions of the universities of Mainz, Cologne, Erfurt, and Heidelberg, as well as of special experts. The university of Cologne at once came out in favor of Pfefferkorn, followed by Mainz and Erfurt, whereas Heidelberg evaded the issue. Among the experts, Jakob von Hochstraten, the Dominican inquisitor general in the archdioceses of Cologne, Mainz, and Trier concurred with the judgment of Cologne University in the drafting of which he had participated.

But one of the experts spoke out clearly and firmly against the suppression of the Hebrew books. It was Johannes Reuchlin, a prominent lawyer in Württemberg, who had won general renown as the foremost Hebrew scholar and had written the books that made a systematic study of the Hebrew language and literature for the first time possible. Reuchlin recommended that whereas patently slanderous books should be taken away from the Jews, all others should be left in their hands. Unfortunately, Reuchlin attempted to make his statement more effective by questioning the motives happened to Reuchlin now might befall any of them in the future. The German humanists formed a single phalanx ready to protect the new learning and education against the ignorance and malevolence of the old-school theologians.

At the time of the Speyer judgment Reuchlin published a collection of letters written by prominent humanists in support of his scholarship. He had called the volume *Epistolae Clarorum Virorum*. About one-and-a-half years later a seemingly similar collection, containing forty-one letters addressed to Ortvinus Gratius, was published under the title *Epistolae Obscurorum Virorum*. This edition of October 1515 was followed a year later by a new edition that contained an appendix of seven additional letters. In the spring of 1517 a further augmented edition appeared, in which a second section of sixty-two letters had been added. All letters were fictitious, while their writers and publishers remained anonymous.

The documentary evidence strengthened by literary criteria leaves no doubt that the idea of lampooning the Cologne theologians originated with Crotus Rubeanus and Ulrich von Hutten. Crotus Rubeanus, a Thuringian peasant's son, received most of his academic training in Erfurt, where he spent the years from 1498 to 1509 with few interruptions as student and tutor. In 1505 an epidemic of the plague drove him temporarily to Fulda, where he met Ulrich von Hutten, who was just leaving the school of the famous monastery against the wishes of his family. In the winter of 1505 both studied in the liberal arts faculty of Cologne, but soon moved on to Erfurt. Although Crotus's long study made him very proficient in scholastic argumentation and disputation, he came to dislike scholastic manners. It was important for his growing contempt of the old theology that he found access to the circle that Mutianus Rufus assembled in near-by Gotha. Here mockery of the scholastic theology and its representatives in Church and school was carried to great length.

In 1509 Crotus Rubeanus went to Fulda as principal of the monastery's school and stayed there till the summer of 1516. In 1512 he was for a while in Cologne, where incidentally he met Pfefferkorn. The wish to help Reuchlin by the public disparagement of his enemies was expressed by

Crotus Rubeanus as early as January 1514. Probably the conception of the *Letters of Obscure Men* came to him almost immediately after the appearance of Reuchlin's *Letters of Distinguished Men* in March 1514, and he must have started work soon thereafter. Whether his friend Ulrich von Hutten was from the outset a partner we do not know, but he undoubtedly approved the plan and promised cooperation.

Ulrich von Hutten, scion of a family of imperial knights, who had chosen the career of a "poet," had left Erfurt as early as 1506 and led the life of an itinerant scholar with all the insecurities and adversities it entailed. In 1513 Hutten gained a position at the court of the Elector and Archbishop Albert of Mainz. Since his new lord and his own relatives wanted him to finish his law studies, Hutten spent the period from the end of 1515 to the summer of 1517 in Italy. But his law study did not keep him from humanistic pursuits, particularly his involvement in the Reuchlin feud. He was able to show Erasmus of Rotterdam, whom he met in the summer of 1515, some of the pieces of the first part of the *Letters of Obscure Men,* among them his own contribution, the first letter that opened the collection. In all likelihood he wrote some more letters before he received rather belatedly, in August 1516, a copy of the first edition of the *Letters of Obscure Men.* The edition with the appendix of seven new letters was already distributed in early October 1516, and it is improbable that Hutten wrote all seven letters in such a brief time.

The appendix shows a shift in the tone of the letters. Crotus in his letters had attempted to draw satirical pictures of schoolmen and monks and make merry with their moral frailty, their self-deceit, and their intellectual ineptitude. Though not without biting sarcasm, Crotus's letters were intended as literary badinage, and the author himself so familiar with this world seems to smile at least at some of the characters on the stage. The writer of the appendix, in contrast, mixes polemics with satire and relates the academic controversy to the acute political problems of the day. He presents letters supposedly written by Jakob von Hochstraten and Arnold von Tungern instead merely by unknown people. He draws in Erasmus as a supporter of the humanistic cause. And in the second part of the *Letters of Obscure Men* this belligerency has been further enhanced.

Ulrich von Hutten, the knight among the German humanists, lived in a political arena. His national pride made him judge the conflict between scholasticism and humanism as a struggle for the future greatness of Germany. For half a year he followed with burning interest the activities of Hochstraten in Rome, and this prompted him to write the letters, or at least most of the letters, which were to form the second part of the *Obscure Men*. This humanist in armor did not merely wish to rise in laughter above his literary adversaries, as Crotus Rubeanus did, but wanted to smash the public enemies.

Six letters of the second part—11, 13, 17, 29, 42, 61, 62 —do not clearly show the imprint of Hutten's mind. Some of them may be contributions of a German humanist who, together with Hutten, attended the university of Bologna, while the two last letters were probably added by a friend of Crotus and Hutten, Hermann von dem Busche, who looked after the publication of the second part of the *Letters of Obscure Men* and managed to do so right in Cologne.

Nobody ought to look in the *Letters* for a truthful likeness of the persons portrayed. The assertions of an immoral conduct of Arnold von Tungern and Ortvinus Gratius, for example, are outright slanders. But it is true that the German clergy at the beginning of the sixteenth century had fallen rather low, and although men of devotion and unimpeachable character were found in its ranks, it had lost the leadership of the people. In an atmosphere of popular criticism of the religious, moral, and intellectual state of the church the *Letters of Obscure Men*, which were widely read in spite of their immediate ban by the Church, intensified the clamor for a reform of the Church. In this respect they belong to the events which were instrumental in preparing the ground if not for the Lutheran reformation at least for the popular response to Luther's revolt against the politico-ecclesiastical order. However, it needed a new religious faith to shake the foundations of the medieval Church.

Luther called the author of the *Letters*, who was unknown to him, a "clown." Erasmus, though greatly amused by some early samples of the *Letters*, was unpleasantly surprised by the licentiousness of the whole book. Reuchlin, far from being happy about the *Letters* written to support him, seems to have been fearful that they were rather harmful to his cause. Crotus Rubeanus, originally a follower of Luther, ultimately made his peace with the old Church. Hutten, however, saw in Luther the liberator of the Germans not only from scholasticism but also from the yoke that Rome had imposed on Germany. To him the Reuchlin affair became the first test in the struggle for German freedom.

Yale University
December 1, 1963

LETTERS OF OBSCURE MEN

TO

MAGISTER ORTWIN GRATIUS
OF DEVENTER

For the first time done into English

PART I

I

℄ *THOMAS LANGSCHNEIDER, duly qualified, albeit unworthy, Bachelor in Theology,
sendeth greeting to the supereminent and high-
scientifical Herr Ortwin Gratius of Deventer,
Poet, Orator, and Philosopher—Theologian too,
and whatsoever else he listeth*

SINCE, as *Aristotle* hath it, " To enquire concerning
all and singular is not unprofitable "; and, as we
read in *The Preacher*, " I purposed in my soul to seek
and ensearch wisely of all things that are made under
the sun," so I, therefore, am purposed to propound to
your worship a question about which I have a doubt.

But first I call the Lord to witness that I seek not
to craftily entangle your excellence or your reverence ;
I do but heartily and sincerely crave of you that you
will instruct me on this perplexful matter.   For it is
written in the Evangel, " Thou shalt not tempt the
Lord thy God," and *Solomon* saith, " All wisdom is of
God."

Now, it was you who imparted to me all the learning that is mine—and all right learning is the beginning
of wisdom—therefore, to speak as a Poet, you stand to
me, as it were, in the place of a god, because it was
you who imparted to me this beginning of wisdom.

Now, the aforesaid question arose after this manner :
—The other day a *Feast of Aristotle*[1] was celebrated
here—the Doctors, the Licentiates, and the Magisters
were in high feather, and I too was present.   To
begin with, by way of a whet, we drank three bumpers
of Malmsey, and for the first course we had fresh
wastel-bread and made sops ; and then we had six
dishes of meat, and chickens, and capons—and one of

5

fish; and between the courses we ceased not to drink Kotzberger and Rhine wine, and beer of *Eimbeck*, and *Torgau*, and *Naumburg*; and the Magisters were full pleased, and vowed that the new-fledged graduates had acquitted themselves right well, and greatly to their credit.

Then began the Doctors over their cups to argue canonically concerning profundities. And the question arose, whether "magister nostrandus" or "noster magistrandus" is the fitter to denote a candidate eligible for the degree of Doctor in Divinity. (As is now, for example, the mellifluous Father *Theodoric* of *Gouda*,[2] friar of the Order of Carmelites, most reverend legate[3] of the benign University of *Cologne*—most sagacious Artsman, Philosopher, and syllogiser—and withal Theologian pre-eminent.)

Forthwith made answer Magister *Warmsemmel*, my compatriot—a right subtle Scotist,[4] and a Master of eighteen years' standing. (He was, in his time, twice rejected and thrice impedited, for the Master's degree, and yet he resided until, for the honour of the University, he was graduated.)

He knoweth his business right well, and hath many pupils, high and low, young and old; and, speaking with ripeness of knowledge, he held that we should say "nostermagistrandus"—in one word—because "magistrare" signifies to make Master, and "baccalauriare" to make Bachelor, and "doctorare" to make Doctor (whence come the technical terms "magistrand," "baccalauriand," and "doctorand"). Now Doctors in Divinity are not styled "Doctors," but on account of their humility and sanctity, and by way of distinction, are named and styled "Magistri Nostri," because in the Catholic Faith they stand in the room of our Lord *Jesus Christ*, who is the fount of life, and the "Magister" of us all: wherefore are they styled "Magistri Nostri" because it is for them to instruct us in the way of truth—and God is truth.

Rightly, he argued, are they called "our masters," for it is the bounden duty of us all, as Christians, to hearken to their preachments, and no man may say them nay—wherefore are they the masters of us all.

But " nostro-tras-trare " is not in use, and is found neither in the Vocabulary *Ex Quo*, nor in the *Catholicon*, nor in the *Breviloquus*, nor even in the *Gemma gemmarum*, notwithstanding that this containeth many terms of art.

Thereupon uprose Magister *Andreas Delitzsch*, a very subtle scholar—on the one hand a Poet, and on the other, an Artsman, Physician, and Jurist—who lectureth in ordinary upon *Ovid* in his *Metamorphoses*, and explaineth all the fables allegorically and literally (I myself have attended his lectures, by reason that his exposition is mightily fundamental), and he lectureth privately on *Quintilian* and *Juvencus*—and he held, in opposition to Magister *Warmsemmel*, that we should say " magisternostrandus "; for, as there is a difference between " magisternoster " and " noster magister," so there is a like difference between " magisternostrandus " and " nostermagistrandus." Because " magisternoster " signifieth a Doctor of Divinity, and is one word, but " noster magister " consisteth of two words, and is used for a Master in any Liberal Science, whether it concern handicraft or braincraft.   And it booteth not that " nostrotras-trare " is not in use, for we may devise new words—and on this point he quoted *Horace*.

Then the company marvelled greatly at his subtilty, and a tankard of Naumburg beer was handed to him. Quoth he, " Now I wait awhile—but, with your leave ! " and, laughing heartily, he touched his cap and pledged Master *Warmsemmel*, saying, " Marry, Herr Magister, think not that I am out with you ! "   He made but one draught of it, and bravely did Master *Warmsemmel* respond thereto, for the honour of the Silesian " Nation."[6]

Then all the Magisters waxed merry, till at last the bell rang to Vespers.

I beseech your excellence, therefore, to set forth your opinion, seeing that you are mightily profound, and, as I said at the time, " Magister *Ortwin* will easily unfold the truth of the matter, for he was my teacher at *Deventer*, when I was in the third class."

Let me know, too, how standeth the strife between Doctor *Johann Reuchlin* and yourself.   I have heard, indeed, that the scoundrel, albeit a Doctor and a Jurist, will not yet recant.

Send me also, I prithee, Mag. N. *Arnold von Tongern's*[7] book of " *Articles*," which he hath drawn up; for it is vengeance subtle, and treateth of many theological profundities.

Farewell—and take it not amiss that I write to you thus familiarly, for you told me once on a time that you loved me as a brother, and desired to advance me in all things, even if it should cost you a pretty penny.

LEIPSIC.

II

❦ *MAGISTER JOHANNES PELZER*, to *Magister Ortwin Gratius, Greeting*

CORDIAL greeting, and homage beyond belief. Reverend Herr Magister, since, as saith *Aristotle* in his *Categories*, to doubt concerning all and sundry is not unprofitable, know then that there is a matter that giveth me great searchings of heart.

I was lately at *Frankfort* fair, and as I walked along the street with a certain Bachelor, two men met us, who, to all outward appearance, were reputable, and they wore black cassocks and great hoods with lappets. Now, heaven be my witness, I took them for two Doctors of Divinity, and I saluted them, taking off my cap. Thereupon the Bachelor nudged me, and said, " God-a-mercy ! what doest thou ? Those fellows are Jews, and thou uncoveredst to them ! "

Then was I aghast, as though I had seen a devil ! And I said, " Herr Bachelor, may the Lord forgive me, for in ignorance I did it ! But how think you, is it a heinous sin ? " And at first he said that it seemed to him that the sin was mortal,[8] inasmuch as it fell under the head of idolatry, and broke the first commandment of the Ten—" Thou shalt believe in one God." "Because, when any one payeth respect to a Jew or to a heathen, as though he were a Christian, then he withstandeth Christianity, and seemeth to be a Jew or a Pagan himself : the Jews, too, and the Pagans, say, ' Lo, ours is the better way, for the Christians do us reverence—and unless we were of the better way they would not do us reverence.' And thus they are confirmed in their own creed, and despise the Christian faith, and will not be baptized." Then I replied, "That is true enough, when the deed is done wittingly; but I did it in ignorance, and ignorance excuseth sin. For if I had known them to be Jews, and had nevertheless done them reverence, then I should have been deserving of the stake, for it would have been heresy. But, heaven knoweth, neither from word or gesture did I gather that they were Jews, but I thought that they were Doctors."

Still he declared that it was, nevertheless, a sin, and he added, "I myself was once walking in a church where there was placed a Jew, of wood, before the Saviour, grasping a hammer; and I took it for *St. Peter* with a key in his hand, and I made a genuflexion, and took off my biretta. Then I saw that it was meant for a Jew, and immediately I repented; nevertheless at my confession, when I made it at the monastery of the *Predicants*, my confessor told me that the sin was mortal, because we must ever be heedful; and he told me that he could not have shriven me unless he had had episcopal powers, because it was a reserved case. And he said that if I had erred wilfully, and not through ignorance, it would have been a papal case.[9] Nevertheless I received absolution, because he had episcopal powers. And, by the Lord, I think that if you desire to salve your conscience you ought to make confession to an Official of the Consistory. Ignorance cannot excuse that sin, because you ought to have been vigilant, and the Jews always wear a round yellow patch on their cloaks in front,[10] which you could have seen as well as I; wherefore your ignorance is crass, and of no avail towards absolution of your sin."

All this the Bachelor told me.

Now, seeing that you are a profound theologian, I beg of you, earnestly and humbly, that you will deign to resolve this my question, and tell me whether this sin is mortal or venial, and mine an ordinary, or an episcopal, or a papal case? Tell me, too, whether it seemeth to you that the citizens of Frankfort do well in having such a custom as to allow Jews to walk abroad in the garb of Doctors of Divinity.[11] It seemeth to me that it is not right, but a great scandal, that no distinction should be made between Jews and the Doctors; it is mockery of holy Theology. And his Serene Highness the *Emperor* ought in no way to countenance it, that a Jew, who is a dog, and an enemy of *Christ*, should strut about like a Doctor of holy Theology.

I send you herewith a missive from Magister *Bernhard Plumilegus*, commonly called *Federleser*, that he sent me from *Wittenburg*. You know him, for he was your crony at *Deventer*, and he told me that you were right good company. He is still a boon-companion, and sings your praises; and so, farewell, in the name of the Lord.

LEIPSIC.

III

¶ *MAGISTER BERNHARD FEDERLESER*
sendeth many greetings to Magister Ortwin Gratius

"WRETCHED is the mouse that hath but one hole;" and this saw, by your favour, I can apply to myself, Reverend Sir, for I should be undone if I had but one friend, and when he betrayed me there was none other to play a friend's part.

You must know that there is a certain Poet here, *Georg Sibutus* by name, who is reckoned among the Secular Poets, and lectureth publicly on the Humanities, and is withal a boon-companion. However, as you know, these Poets, when they are not theologers too, as you are, are ever carping at others, and vilifying the Theologians. Now it fell out at a junketing at his house, when we sat drinking Torgau beer till the third hour, that I was half-seas-over because that same beer had risen into my head.

Now there was a fellow there who was at loggerheads with me, but I pledged him in a modest cup, and he took the greeting, but, after, he would not do me right. Thrice I challenged him, and he would not respond, but sat mute and mumchance. Then think I to myself, "See now, of Pfefferkorn's conversion to the Christian faith. Pfefferkorn replied rudely with his *Hand Mirror*, which appeared in the spring of 1511 and was dedicated to Arnold von Tungern, one of the heads of the theological faculty in Cologne. In this pamphlet it was asserted that Reuchlin was not the true author of his own books and had been bribed by the Jews.

Highly agitated, Reuchlin, in August 1511, issued his *Eye Mirror*, in which he hotly inveighed not only against Pfefferkorn but also against the theological faculty of Cologne. The latter thereupon openly attacked Reuchlin. In September 1512 Arnold von Tungern published a pamphlet in which he pilloried a number of "articles and propositions" from the *Eye Mirror* as heretical. Moreover in the following month the theological faculty of Cologne secured an imperial order prohibiting the sale and print of the *Eye Mirror*. Shortly thereafter Pfefferkorn issued still another highly venomous pamphlet against the Jews and Reuchlin, entitled the *Brand Mirror*. But Reuchlin answered with his equally slanderous *Defense*, presented to the Emperor. He not only berated Pfefferkorn, but even made bad insinuations against the wife of the hated adversary. Ortvinus Gratius was belittled as a man who knew neither Latin or Greek, while Arnold von Tungern was accused of having deliberately twisted Reuchlin's statements.

Incensed, the Cologne theologians used their powerful influence to have Reuchlin's *Defense* suppressed by imperial mandate. In addition they requested their own theological faculty and the faculties of Louvain, Mainz, and Erfurt to pass judgment on the *Eye Mirror*. All four faculties condemned the work, although Erfurt at least pleaded the author's good intentions. Jakob von Hochstraten boldly moved to defeat Reuchlin by citing him before his court of inquisition in Mainz, where the Dominican intended to act both as prosecutor and judge. Thanks to the intervention of the archbishop of Mainz, who declared the proceedings of the court improper, Reuchlin was allowed to appeal to Pope Leo X. The Roman curia then commissioned the bishop of Speyer to adjudicate the case. The young bishop, Count Palatine George, after lengthy argument, passed judgment wholly favorable to Reuchlin. On March 29, 1514 he pronounced all accusations directed against the *Eye Mirror*, on account of heresy, disrespect of the Church and its doctrine or illicit favoritism toward the Jews, undeserved, unjust, and untruthful. He imposed "eternal silence" on Hochstraten and his followers and charged him with the cost of the Mainz and Speyer trials. Hochstraten at once appealed to the Pope.

By now the conflict between Reuchlin and the Cologne theologians had become a *cause célèbre* in Europe. Emperor Maximilian, who originally had taken action against Reuchlin's *Eye Mirror* and *Defense*, now recommended Reuchlin in Rome, whereas his grandson, King Charles I of Spain, expressed his disapproval of the book. The strongest vituperation came from France. The Dominican Wilhelmus Parvus, the confessor of King Louis XII, succeeded in having the University of Paris issue a scathing condemnation of the *Eye Mirror* in August 1514. The book was to be confiscated and burned and so was the Talmud. Francis I, who ascended the French throne in the following year, exercised his influence in Rome in the same direction.

Yet the litigation at the curia did not seem to go badly for Reuchlin. In the summer of 1516 it was expected that the court would fully clear him. But in July 1516 a papal mandate suspended its deliberations. Hochstraten remained another year in Rome attempting to win a decision. The curia, however, was obviously not wishing to disappoint any of the mighty persons interested in the case. Actually sentence was passed only in 1520, simultaneously with the ban against Luther. Now Hochstraten and the Dominicans were believed when they asserted that the leniency shown toward Reuchlin had encouraged Luther's obstinacy. Reuchlin submitted to the sentence.

When in 1513 Emperor Maximilian had ordered the suppression of Reuchlin's *Defense* and Hochstraten had summoned Reuchlin before his court of inquisition, the German humanists had endeavored to come to the rescue of the eminent scholar. The defense of the Hebrew books had not been popular among the German humanists, some of whom in the beginning openly applauded Pfefferkorn's anti-Semitism. But once the Dominicans began to persecute the great Reuchlin, the humanists pulled together, fearful that what this fellow smoketh you, he giveth himself airs, and is always seeking to put you down!" And I was so moved with wrath that I took up the tankard and smote him on the pate.

Then the Poet flew into a rage, and said that I made a tumult in his house; and he bade me begone in the Devil's name.

Then quoth I, "What care I tho' you are my enemy? I have had enemies to the full as curst as you, and yet I've worsted them. And what tho' you are a Poet? I have Poets who are friends of mine, and they are just as good as you. To the jakes with your poetry! What do you take me for? Thinkest thou I'm a gowk, or that I grew on a tree, like an apple?"

Thereupon he called me an ass, and said that I had never seen a Poet.

Then cried I, "There's an ass in your own hide! I've seen a sight more Poets than you!"

Then I held forth about you, and about Doctor *von Zutphen* of *Kuijk* Hostel, who compiled the Commentary,[2] and about Domine *Roger* the Licentiate in Divinity at *De Monte* Hostel—and with that I flung out of the house, and we are at feud to this day.

Now, therefore, I beg most earnestly that you will send me but an exemplar of your art, and I will flourish it before that Poet and the rest, and I will make boast that you are my friend, and a sight better Poet than he.

Be sure you tell me what Domine *Johann Pfefferkorn* is doing; whether he still maintaineth his quarrel with Doctor *Reuchlin*, and whether you still take up the cudgels on his behalf, and send me some news. Farewell in Christ.

IV

❦ *MAGISTER JOHANN KANNEGIESZER
to Magister Ortwin Gratius hearty greetings*

REVEREND HERR MAGISTER—seeing that we have oftentimes played the fool in company, and that it irketh you not a whit to hear tell of a pleasantry such as that I have in store for you, I have no fear that you will take it amiss if I relate a merry jest—for you send the like to me.

You will laugh, I trow, for it is a mighty fine affair. There was here of late one of the Preaching Friars—he was not ill-versed in Theology, a cunning syllogiser, and he had many patrons.

This Predicant, Herr *Georg* by name, was formerly at *Halle*, and then he came hither and held forth for full half a year, upbraiding in his preachments men of all sorts and conditions, even the Prince¹⁹himself and his courtiers. He was, nevertheless, at the board a hail-fellow and of good cheer, who tossed off his drams and bumpers with the rest; but whenever of an evening he drank deep with us, he failed not the next morning to preach about us, saying, " Thus do the Magisters in this University sit swilling the live-long night, fleering and fooling with their boon-companions, whose ways they ought to mend, whereas they do but entice them to evil: " and before now he hath put me to very shame.

At the last I waxed wroth with him, and cast about in my mind how I might be even with him—but I could not devise a means.

One day it was told me how that Predicant was wont to go by night to a certain woman, and abuse her, and, after, sleep with her. Hearing this, I straightway collected a band of collegers, and at about ten of the clock we went to the house, and brake into it; whereupon the monk, desiring to escape, found no time to bear away his garments, but leapt stark from the window; and I laughed till I had well-nigh pickled myself, and cried out, " Herr Predicant, take thy pontificals with thee ! "

Then my comrades without rolled him in the mire and in the water, till I stayed them and told them to use moderation. Nevertheless I lent them my aid ; and we all had knowledge of the wench.

And thus was I even with that monk, and never again hath he preached about me !

But you must not blab this forth to others, for the *Preaching Friars* are now your allies against Doctor

Reuchlin, and they are the defenders of the Church and the Catholic Faith against those secular poets.

I could wish that the monk had been of some other Order, seeing that of all the Orders 'tis the one that worketh the greatest marvels.

Now must you, in turn, indite a merry tale, and be not angered with me.   Fare thee well.

WITTENBERG.

V

❧ *JOHANNES STRAUSZFEDER to Ortwin Gratius*

ABUNDANT greetings—and gooddens as many as there are stars in heaven and fishes in the sea.

I would have you know that I am hearty, and my mother too.   Right glad should I be to hear the like concerning you, for at least once in every day do I think of your worship.

And now you shall learn, an it please you, of the incredible carryings-on of a certain nobleman[14] here. May the devil confound him world without end—for he vilified Herr Magister *Peter Meyer*,[15] at table, before many gentlemen and noblemen; and not one drop of deference did he manifest, but he was that haughty that I marvelled.   " Go to ! " said he, " Doctor *Reuchlin* hath deeper learning than thou ! " and he snapped his fingers at him.

Then Magister *Peter* replied : " I'll be hanged if that is true !   Holy Mary !   Doctor *Reuchlin* is a mere child in theology—a child knows more theology than Doctor *Reuchlin*.   Holy Mary !   mark my words, for I have experience, and he knows not a whit of the Book of Sentences.[16]   Holy Mary !   there's subtle stuff for you ! Thou canst not pick that up like grammar and poetry ! I could easily become a poet if I would, and I should know well enough how to turn a verse, because at *Leipsic* I heard read *Sulpitius*[17] on the quantities of syllables.   But what is that to the purpose ?   Let him propound me a thesis in theology, and argue *pro et contra.*" Then he shewed by a multitude of proofs that no man could attain a perfect knowledge of theology save through the holy spirit, and that the holy spirit was the well-spring of that art, and that poetry is the food of the devil, as saith *Jerome* in his Epistles.

Then the zany declared that to be a lie, and that Doctor *Reuchlin* had the holy spirit too, and was duly qualified in theology, seeing that he had written a right theological book (I know not what its name may be), and thereafter he called Magister *Peter* a beast. And then he swore that Magister *Hoogstraten* was naught but a mumping, cheese-begging friar, and so set the table on a roar; but I cried that it was a shameful thing that a mere student should behave so irreverently towards a Doctor of Divinity.

Thereupon Doctor *Peter* was so wrath that he rose from the table, and, quoting the Evangel, said: "Thou art a Samaritan, and hast a devil!" And I cried: "Swallow that!" and was overjoyed because he had so roundly trounced that braggart.

You must persevere in your undertaking, and must defend theology as you were wont—and you must have no respect for any man, for are you not qualified?

If I knew how to write verses as thou dost, I would not heed even the prince if he went about to slay me.

I hate those Jurists, too, who strut up and down in red boots and marten-fur cloaks, and make not the obeisance, that would be fitting, to the Magisters and Doctors.

Now I entreat you, humbly but affectionately, that you will explain to me how the matter standeth at *Paris* concerning the *Augenspiegel.* God grant that the University of *Paris*, that *alma mater*, will hold with you, and will burn that heretical book—for it containeth many heretical things, as Magister *von Tongern* hath declared.

I have heard that Magister *von Zutphen*, of *Kneck* Hostel, who compiled the notable commentary on the four parts of *Alexander*, is dead. I trust, however, that this is not true, for he was an eminent man and a profound grammarian, and was far more skilled than these new poetising grammaticasters.

14

Be pleased to salute, on my behalf, Magister *Remigius*, for he was formerly my class-master, and ofttimes would chide me roundly, saying: "You are a goose, and will not study how to become a good disputant." And I would say: "Most excellent Herr Magister, I will do better in future." And then he would sometimes send me away, and sometimes give me sound chastisement: in those days I was so submissive that I would willingly endure correction for my faults.

And now I have no more to write, save that I hope you will live for a hundred years. Fare thee well in peace.

MAINZ.

VI

⁋ *NIKOLAUS ZIEGENMELKER*, Bachelor, to *Magister Ortwin Gratius*

ABUNDANT greetings, with mighty respect to your worthiness, as is but meet in addressing your magistrality.

Reverend Herr Magister, you must know that there is a notable question that I desire, or entreat, to be by you magistrally determined.

There is a certain Grecian here who readeth in *Urban's* Grammar, and whenever he writeth Greek he always putteth tittles atop.

Thereupon I said, a little while ago, "Magister *Ortwin* of *Deventer* also handleth Greek Grammar, and he is as well qualified therein as that fellow, and yet he never maketh tittles so: and I trow he knoweth his business as well as that Grecian—ay, and can put him to rights." Nevertheless some distrusted me in this matter, wherefore my friends and fellow-students besought me to write to your worthiness so that you might make it known to me whether we ought to put tittles or no. And if we ought not to put them, then, by the Lord, we will roundly harry that Grecian, and bring it to pass that his hearers shall be but few!

Of a truth I took note of you at Cologne, in *Heinrich Quentell's* house,[18] when you were reader, and had to correct Greek, that you would strike out all the tittles that were above the letters and say, "Of what use are these fiddle-faddles?" And it hath just come into my mind that you must have had some ground for this, or you would not have done it.

You are a marvellous man, and God hath given you a large measure of grace, so that you know somewhat of all things knowable. You must praise God, therefore, in your metrification, and the Blessed Virgin, and all the Saints.

Prithee, take it not amiss if I weary your mightiness with such questions as these, seeing that it is for edification that I propound them. Farewell.

LEIPSIC.

VII

❡ *M. PETRUS HAFENMUSIUS sendeth Greetings innumerable to M. Ortuinus Gratius*

REVEREND HERR MAGISTER, an I had pelf and great substance, I would give you, believe me in good earnest, no small guerdon to resolve for me the question that I am going to propose.

Nevertheless, since, at present, I possess not "sheep and oxen and all the beasts of the field," but have not a doit, I cannot recompense you for your exposition. Yet I pledge my word that when I am beneficed—and I am even now a candidate for a vicarship—I will do you signal honour.

Tell me, then, whether it be necessary to eternal salvation, for scholars to learn their grammar out of the profane poets, such as *Virgil, Tully, Pliny,* and the rest?

Methinks that to study in this wise is blameworthy, for, as saith *Aristotle* in the First of *The Metaphysics,* "Many are the feignings of the poets." But those who feign, sin ; and those who base their learning upon falsehoods, base it upon sin ; and whatsoever is based upon sin, resisteth God, because God is the enemy of sin.

Now poetry containeth falsehoods, and therefore those who commence their studies with poetry cannot advance in virtue, for from an evil root springeth an

evil plant, and a corrupt tree bringeth forth corrupt
fruit, according to the Evangel, wherein the Saviour
saith, "A good tree bringeth not forth corrupt fruit."

I well remember the monition that Doctor *Valentin*[19]
von Geltersheim, of *De Monte* Hostel, gave me when I
was his pupil, and desired to attend lectures on *Sallust*.
"Wherefore art thou fain to read *Sallust*, thou rebel?"
he asked. And I told him that Magister *Johann* of
Breslau said that one could learn to write correct theses
out of such like poets.

Then said he, "A fiddlestick! You must needs be
well drilled in *Alexander's* 'Parts,' and the Epistles of
Carolus,[20] which are taught in the Grammar School. I
never read *Sallust*, and yet I can write theses in verse
and prose."

And so Doctor *Valentin* brought it about that I
never read the Poets. And now these humanists pester
me with their new-fangled Latin, and laugh to scorn
the good old books—*Alexander*, and *Remigius*, and
Joannes de Garlandia, and the *Cornutus*, and the *Composita Verborum*, and Master *Paul Schneevogel* his
Complete Letter-writer. They tell such thumping
lies, too, that I cross myself when I hear them. Just
now one of these fellows said that in some country there
is a river called the *Tagus*, which hath golden sands!
But I whistled to myself, for that could not be.

Now I well know you to be a poet, but I cannot
tell whence you learned that art. I have heard say that
when you are so minded you can turn out a screed of
verses in an hour. But I suppose that your intellect is
illuminated by the grace of the Holy Spirit from above,
so that you know this art and all else, for you have ever
been a steadfast theologer and have trounced those
heathens.

Gladly would I send you some news if I knew any,
but I have heard none, save that the Dominican friars
and priests here can give absolution, *a poena et a culpa*,[21]
to any one who hath confessed and is contrite; and
they hold papal letters as well.

Write to me, for I am thy humble servant. Farewell.
Nuremberg.

VIII

❦ *FRANZ GÄNSEPREDIGER* to *Magister Ortwin Gratius*

GREETING, of ponderosity to make a thousand talents kick the beam.

Reverend Herr Magister, you must know that there is a mighty buzz here concerning you, and the theologers applaud you hugely because you pay no heed to any man, and have written in defence of the faith against Doctor *Reuchlin*.

Howbeit certain doltish fellows here—and those jurists too who are not enlightened in the Christian faith—scoff at you and say all manner of things against you ; but they are of small account, for the Faculty of Theology upholdeth you. And lately, when those books found their way here which are intituled "*Acta Parisiensium*," straightway almost all the Magisters bought them and were mightily pleased. Thereupon I myself bought the books and sent them to *Heidelberg*, that they may be read there.

And I trow that when the Heidelbergers see them they will rue that they did not join hands with the benign University of *Cologne* against Doctor *Reuchlin*. Moreover I learn that the University of *Cologne* hath made a statute ordaining that never, world without end, will it grant a degree to any man who has qualified as Bachelor or Master at *Heidelberg*. And a good thing too ; for this will learn them what the University of *Cologne* is, and to take part with her another time. Would that you had dealt so with the rest, but I ween the other Universities knew naught of the matter, and you spared them on the score of ignorance.

A friend has given me some mighty pretty verses which you must have published in the University of *Cologne*. I have shewn them to the Magisters and Doctors, and they were highly lauded. And to your glory I have sent them to many parts, for am I not on your side ?

18

And here they follow, that you may know what
I mean:—

> " Pravities heretical—fain are you to learn 'em ?
> Phrases Latinistical—vultis you to turn 'em ?
> Then by you buyenda the Parisians' *Acta,*
> And the scripta newly in *Lutetia* facta !
> Telling how Herr *Reuchlin* from the Faith erravit,
> As Magister noster *Arnold* well probavit :
> And Magister *Ortwin* soon will lecture, gratis,
> On them, to the members Universitatis.
> Et cum on the textum he hath done enlarging,
> Tum the pretty postils jotting in the margin.
> Pro he first will argufy—contra then, profoundly,
> Sicut the theologers who in Paris roundly
> Swore Doctorem *Reuchlin* and his dissertation,
> *Oculare Speculum,* worthy of damnation !
> This the brethren understand—fratres *Carmelitae*—
> Sciunt too the others—clept the *Jacobitae.*"

I marvel how you can conceive such things. You
are wondrously skilful in your craft, and there is in
your compositions such a dulcitude that I snicker for
very joy when I read aught that you have written. I
ever hope that your life may be long and that your
fame may continue to wax as it hath to this day, inasmuch as your writings are of much profit.

May God keep you and quicken you, and not
deliver you into the hands of your enemies, as saith the
Psalmist : " Grant thee thy heart's desire, and fulfil all
thy mind."

Write also to me concerning your doings, for joyfully do I hear and regard all your deeds and actions.
And so, farewell.

Freiburg.

IX

¶ *MAGISTER CONRAD OF ZWICKAU*[22]*to*
Magister Ortwin Gratius

GREETING. Seeing that it is written in *Ecclesiastes XI.:* " Rejoice, O young man, be glad in
thy youth," I therefore am of jocund heart ; and you
must know that I have prospered in love affairs,

and have had much dalliance. Doth not *Ezekiel*
say: "Nunc fornicabitur in fornicatione sua"? And
wherefore may I not sometimes purge my reins? I
am no angel, but a man—and to err is human. Even
you go a-wenching now and then, albeit you are a
Theologer, for you cannot always lie alone; as saith
Ecclesiastes III.: "If two lie together, then they have
heat, but how can one be warm?"

Give me tidings of your doxy, how she doth. A
fellow told me lately that when he was at *Cologne* you
were at odds with her, and beat her because she, by ill
hap, was not of your opinion. I marvel, indeed, that you
could thus smite a comely woman: I should have wept
to see it. You ought rather to have told her to do so
no more, and she would have turned over a new leaf and
been all the more buxom at even-tide. When you expounded *Ovid* to us you told us that we should never
strike women, and you cited the Scriptures concerning
this matter.

I am well content if my wench is blithe and not
grudging to me; and when I visit her I am the like, and
we make good cheer, and drink beer and wine—for wine
maketh glad the heart of man, but grief drieth up the
bones. Now and then I am angered with her—but she
giveth me a buss, and straightway we are at one, and
she crieth, "Be of good cheer, Herr Magister!"

Not long ago it had come into my mind to pay her
a visit, when I met a young chapman quitting her house
—his points untrussed, and beads on his brow—and me-
thought he had had dealings with her. This, in some
measure, irked me, but she swore that the chapman had
not laid hands on her, and had but desired to sell her
some linen to make shifts. "Good," said I, "and when
are you going to give me a shirt?" Thereupon she
asked me to give her two florins, wherewith to pay for
the linen, and then she would give me a shirt. Just
then I had no money, but I sought out a friend who lent
it to me, and I gave it to her.

Let a man ever be merry, say I. The physicians
say it is wholesome for a man to be merry without
ceasing. There is a certain Magister here who is always
crabbed and never merry, and hence it falleth out that he is

always sick. He is for ever chiding me, and telling me that I ought not to set my affections on women, for that they are devils, and bring men to destruction, and are abominable, and that no woman is chaste, and that to consort with a woman is as bad as consorting with a devil, and that they allow a man no peace. Then said I, "Cry you mercy, Herr Magister, but your mother was a woman!" And with that I left him.

He hath been preaching too, of late, that priests should in no wise maintain concubines,[23] and he declared that bishops are guilty of mortal sin when they take milk-tithes, and wink at priests consorting with their hand-maidens, whereas they ought to drive them forth one and all.

Be this as it may, we must sometimes be merry and have to do with a wench, when nobody is the wiser; after, we can make confession; and the Lord is merciful, wherefore we hope for forgiveness.

Herewith I send you a certain writing in defence of *Alexander Gallus*—that grammarian time-honoured and trusty, notwithstanding that the "Poets" of to-day scoff at him: but they know not what they say, for *Alexander* is the best of all, as you were wont to tell me when we were at *Deventer*. A certain Magister here gave me the tractate, but I wot not where he obtained it. Would that you might have it printed, and then would you make the "Poets" rage furiously, for the author trounces them roundly. And it is so poetically composed that it passeth! He that wrote it was a pretty poet and Theologer withal, and he holdeth not with the secular poets —such as Doctor *Reuchlin, Buschius*,[24] and the rest.

No sooner had that document been put into my hands than I promised myself to send it to you, that you might read it. If you have any news give me knowledge of it　Farewell, in love unfeigned.

Leipsic.

21

X

❡ *JOHANN ARNOLDI* sendeth many greetings to Magister Ortwin Gratius

FORASMUCH as, and seeing that, you at all times would fain learn the news, according to that dict of *Aristotle:* " All men by nature crave after knowledge "; wherefore I, therefore, *Johann Arnoldi*, your disciple and humble servant, send herewith to your mightiness, or your honour, a libel that a certain cullion here hath clouted up to malign Herr *Johann Pfefferkorn* of Cologne—a man beyond all doubt of properest probity.

I was mightily wrath, but could not hinder him so that he should not print it, because the rascal hath here many patrons, even nobles, who strut about the streets like mountebanks, girt with long swords. Nevertheless I averred that this thing was not seemly, because, mark my words, these same secular poets will stir up branglings without end with their metrifications, if our Magisters do not take heed, and do not straightway cite them before the Roman Court, by the hand of Magister *Jakob van Hoogstraten*. I fear, moreover, that there will arise a mighty pudder among the faithful.

I entreat you, therefore, to write a book against this scandalmonger, and put him to confusion : and another time he will not be so foolhardy as to molest the Magisters.

The fellow is a mere student, neither graduated nor qualified in Jurisprudence or Arts—but he hath kept residence at *Bologna*, where there are herds of these same secular poets, neither enlightened in the faith nor defenders thereof. A little while ago he sat at the board and averred that the Magisters at *Cologne* and *Paris* were persecuting Doctor *Reuchlin*. Then I argued in the contrary sense, whereupon he turned upon me with many objurgations and railings, so that I rose from the table and called all the company to witness how I was shent—and I had no stomach for a morsel of victuals.

Now, prithee, give me counsel in the matter afore-said, for you are even, in some sort, a jurist.

I have made up some verses, and I send them to you herewith. *A Choriambi - hexametri - sapphiambic-asclepiadic-endecasyllabic-elegiac-dicolic Distrophe :—*

> " He who a perfect Catholic would be,
> Must aye with the Parisians agree—
> Because
> Of every other
> Their University is mother;
> *Cologne* the sacred, ranks as second,
> And bulwark of the Faith is reckoned—
> To this
> If any man say ' Nay,'
> He the penalty must pay ;
> Doctor *Reuchlin*, to wit,
> *Augenspiegel* who writ;
> Whom *Arnold* of *Tongern*, magisternoster,
> Unmasked as an heretical impostor—
> As did Master *Hoogstraten*, not least though the last,
> Who into the fire *The Eyeglass* did cast ! "

Had I but materials, I would compose a tome against that windbag, and prove that he is *de facto* excommunicate.

I have no further leisure for writing, for I must needs hie to lecture, where a Magister handleth *pro et con* very subtle opinions on ancient philosophy, and I listen—to finish my course.

Fare ye well, above all my comrades and friends here and everywhere and in all places of honest report.

XI

☙ *CORNELIUS FENSTERMACHER* to *Magister Ortwin Gratius, many greetings*

GREETINGS as many as are the stars of heaven and the sands of the sea. Reverend Herr Magister, I encounter here much strife and brangling with certain lewd fellows who boast that they are lettered, and yet have read not Logic, the Science of Sciences.

And I have lately said mass with the brethren, "*De Spiritu Sancto*," that God might give me his grace and a good memory for syllogisms in disputing with these fellows that only know Latinizing and how to compose themes. And into that mass was foisted a collect for Magister *van Hoogstraten*, and Magister *Arnold von Tongern*, Regent of *St. Lawrence* Hostel, that they may conduct to the goal of refutation a certain Doctor of Laws hight *Johann Reuchlin*, a secular poet and an arrogant man withal, who putteth himself, in opposition to four Universities, on the side of the Jews, and frameth propositions most scandalous and offensive to pious ears—as *Johann Pfefferkorn* hath demonstrated, and Magister *Arnold*. And all the while he is not grounded in speculative Theology, nor versed in *Aristotle*, nor in *Petrus Hispanus*. And on this account the Doctors of the *Sorbonne* have condemned him to the stake—failing recantation. I have seen the missive and the seal of the Dean of the Holy Faculty of Theology at *Paris*.

One of the Magisters, deeply versed in Sacred Theology and enlightened in the faith, who is member of four universities, and who hath more than a hundred treatises on "The Sentences," in the which he groundeth himself, hath openly declared that Doctor *Johann Reuchlin* cannot escape, and that the Pope himself dareth not give a decision adverse to so pious a University, seeing that his Holiness is no theologian[26] and doth not understand the "Contra Gentiles"[27] of the blessed *Thomas*—albeit it is rumoured that he is versed in poetics. A Magister who is a priest at St. Martin's showed me a letter in which that University promiseth in most friendly fashion real and earnest help to her sister of *Cologne*. And yet these Latinists presume to run counter to them.

A little while ago I sojourned at *Mainz*, at the sign of "The Crown," where two braggarts annoyed me greatly, calling the Doctors of *Paris* and *Cologne* idiots and fools! And they said that the books written on The Sentences were mere moonshine, and in like manner they declared that the "Processus" and the "Copulata," and the "Reparationes" were all balderdash! There-

upon I was so wroth that I knew not how to reply.
Moreover they twitted me with having made pilgrimage
to *Treves* to see the holy coat, which they averred was
perchance not the Lord's garment.   This they would
fain prove by a dilemmatic syllogism, thus: "That
which is torn should not be shown as the Holy Coat,
but this is torn, therefore, &c."   Thereupon I con-
ceded the major but denied the minor premiss.   Then
they argued thus: "Saint *Jerome* saith, 'By its ancient
schism the Eastern Church hath rent in pieces the
Lord's coat, woven without seam throughout.'"   But
I retorted that *Jerome's* style differs from that of the
Evangelist, and is not idiomatically apostolic.   And, so
saying, I arose from the table and left those windbags.

You must know that so irreverently do these fellows
talk concerning the Magisters, that certainly and without doubt they can be excommunicated therefor by
the Pope.   If the authorities at *Rome* but heard of it
they would summon them to the Court, and confiscate
their benefices—or, at the least, saddle them with costs.
Who ever heard of such a thing as that mere students,
neither graduated nor qualified in a single Faculty,
should dare to calumniate men so exalted, so profoundly
immersed in all knowledge, as our Magisters!

I too have learned how to fashion theses and verses,
for I have been studying the "*Novum Latinum Idioma*"
of Magister *Lorenz Rabe*, and *Kohlburger's* Grammar,
and *Valerius Maximus*, and other poets.   And as I
went along I just now constructed a metrical composition against those rascals.   It followeth:—

> In *Mayence* town there standeth
> > a hostel cleped *Corona*,
> And there I lay, the other day,
> > in propria persona,
> But two buffoons, irreverent loons,
> > 'gainst Doctors of Theology
> Began to bray, though graduates they
> > not even in Philosophy!
> Unknown to them the solemn disputation,
> And multifold corollary formation
> From one small "ergo": as *Duns Scotus* taught—
> (Who scorns him to confusion will be brought)—
> Unknown the *Quodlibets* of *Alexander*,[28]
> Of all the foes of learning a withstander;

Unknown to them the *Seraph Doctor*[29] he
Without whose lore none can Physician be;
The *Holy Doctor* is to them unknown,[30]
Who *Porphyry* and the *Stagirite* alone[31]
Expoundeth with a comment ever true—
Predicaments and predicables too,
The Universals five, and Moral Rules
Of *Aristotle* fitting for the Schools.

Such things new-fangled Poets all ignore,
And hence inanely jabber all the more;
As did these windbags, braggart and loquacious,
Against our Masters, with words contumacious:
Let but *Hoogstraten* nab them, and 'tis plain
The faithful they will never plague again!

Fare ye well, and salute for me with all reverence the worshipful Magisternosters *Arnold von Tongern, Remigius, Valentin von Geltersheim,* Herr *Jakob von Gouda,* of the order of Preachers—most subtle poet—and the rest.

XII

❦ *MAGISTER HILDEBRAND MAM-MACEUS to Magister Ortwin Gratius, Greeting*

DEARLY beloved Herr *Ortwin!* I cannot indite to you an epistle curiously composed according to the precepts of "The Art of Letter-writing," for time doth not allow of this; wherefore I am constrained briefly, and in a few words, to make manifest the nature of the matter in hand—for I desire with your aid to disentangle a prodigious difficulty. The affair standeth thus: —You must know that there is a terrifying rumour afoot here, and it is in all men's mouths, that at the Roman Court the cause of the Theologers is in evil case. For they say that the Pope is minded to confirm the sentence pronounced a year agone at *Spires* in favour of Doctor *Reuchlin!* [32]

When this came to my ears I had such a fright that I could not utter a word, but became like a dumb man, and I slept not for two whole nights. But *Reuchlin's* friends make merry, and strut hither and thither, bruiting this report. As for me, I should not have given heed to the thing without I had seen a letter from one of the Order of Preachers—a Magister—in which he related the tidings in sore anguish. He wrote withal that the Pope hath allowed the *Augenspiegel* to be printed at Court, and the booksellers to vend it, and every man to read it! Thereupon Magister *Hoogstraten* made petition to leave *Rome*, and would fain plead poverty. But the Judges would not let him go, declaring that he must await the issue, and, moreover, that he could not plead poverty, seeing that he arrived at *Rome* with three horses, and while at the Court had guests at his table, and dispensed much money, and had bestowed many gifts upon the Cardinals and Bishops and Assessors of the Consistory—wherefore it was not possible for him to plead destitution.

Holy Mary! what are we to do next, if Theology is thus insulted, so that a single Jurist is able to prevail against all the Theologers? I verily fear me that the Pope is no good Christian—for if he were a good Christian it would be impossible for him not to uphold the Theologers. If, moreover, the Pope pronounceth judgment against the Theologers, it seemeth to me that an appeal to a Council might be made; for a Council is above a Pope, and, in a Council, Theology hath a precedence over the other faculties. And then I trust the Lord will show his loving-kindness, and look upon his servants the Theologers, and not permit their foes to triumph over them, and will give us the grace of his holy spirit to enable us to surpass the fallacies of these heretics.

A certain Jurist lately declared that it hath been prophesied that the *Order of Preachers* would perish, and that out of that Order would proceed grievous offences against the Christian Faith—such as never were heard of before. But grant that this may be far from the truth! For that Order is right profitable, and if it were not for that Order I know not how Theology would endure—for the *Dominicans* are more deeply immersed in Theology than the *Minorites* or the *Augustinians*, and follow the way of the *Holy Doctor*, who never erred. They have, too, many saints of their Order, and are bold in disputation against heretics.

I marvel how it cometh about that Magister *Jakob*

van Hoogstraten cannot plead poverty, seeing that he is one of a mendicant Order, who are all manifestly poor. If it were not that I fear excommunication, I would say that the Pope erred on this point. Moreover I do not believe it to be true that Magister *Jakob* dispensed money in that fashion, or bestowed gifts, because he is a mighty zealous man; and it is my belief that those Jurists and the rest concoct this gossip, and that Doctor *Reuchlin* knoweth how to wheedle them, for I have heard that many burgs, and princes, and persons of quality have written letters on his behalf.

Now the reason of this is that they are not grounded in Theology, and do not understand how the case standeth —otherwise they would bid the devil take that heretic— for a heretic he is, though the whole world should hold the contrary. You must forthwith explain matters to the Magisters at *Cologne*, that they may take counsel. Write and tell me what they intend to do. Farewell in Christ.

TÜBINGEN.

XIII

☙ *MAGISTER CONRAD OF ZWICKAU* to *Magister Ortwin, Greeting*

YOU have sent me word that you no longer have any mind to wantonness, nor to consort with woman-kind—save once in a month, or, maybe, twice—yet I marvel that you can write such things. Full well do I know to the contrary. There is a student here who hath just arrived from *Cologne*—you know him right well, he was ever in your company—and he saith that you are intimate with *Johann Pfefferkorn's* wife. He declared this to be true, and made oath, and I believe him. For you are a squire of dames, and know how to wheedle them—besides, you have *Ovid's* " Art of Love " by rote! A certain merchant did tell me, too, that Magister *Arnold von Tungern* was in the lady's good graces as well. But this is false, for I know of a truth that he is a virgin, and hath never bussed a wench. But even if he had done, or were to do, what I cannot believe of him, that would not make him a bad man, for to err is human. You send me whole screeds about that sin—which is not the worst sin in the world—and you quote texts without end. I very well know that it is not a virtue, and yet it is recorded in Holy Writ that certain men thus erred, and yet were saved. *Samson*, to wit, had dealings with a bona-roba, and nevertheless the spirit of the Lord afterwards came upon him. I can syllogize against you thus:—"Whosoever is not unrighteous receiveth the holy spirit; but *Samson* was not unrighteous, ergo, he received the holy spirit." I can prove the major premiss—for it is written, "Into an unrighteous soul the spirit of wisdom shall not enter; but the holy spirit is the spirit of wisdom, ergo, &c." The minor premiss is manifest, for if that sin of incontinence is so grave, then the spirit of the Lord would not have come upon *Samson*, as it is told us in the *Book of Judges*. We read, too, of *Solomon*, how he had three hundred queens, and concubines without number—and he was prince of gallants to his dying day. Nevertheless, the Doctors, with one accord, declare that he found salvation. What then? I am not stronger than *Samson*, nor wiser than *Solomon*, and so I must needs be wanton, once and again. Moreover the physicians say it is sovran against melancholy. Fie! what booteth it that you cite those dumpish fathers! What saith *The Preacher*? "I know that there is nothing better than that a man should rejoice in his own works." Wherefore, with *Solomon*, I say to my doxy: "Thou hast ravished my heart, my sister, my spouse: thou hast ravished my heart with one of thine eyes, with one chain of thy neck. How beautiful are thy breasts, my sister, my spouse. Thy bosom is fairer than wine—" and so forth.

By the Lord, courting the lasses is merry sport! As that Ode of *Samuel* the poet saith:—

> " Fail not, jolly cleric, merry maids amare,
>   Flattering busses knowing how to you praestare—
>   So contriving, many a day, youth's flower conservare ! "

"Amor is love, and God is love—therefore Amor is not a bad thing!" Answer me that argument. And *Solomon* saith: "If a man would give all the substance of his house for love, it would utterly be contemned."

But enough of this; let us turn to other matters.

You bid me send you some news—so you must know that there were high jinks here in Lent. There were joustings, and the Prince himself rode in the *Platz*, and he had a fine horse, and a fine saddle-cloth too, upon which was painted a woman in brave attire, and near her sitting a youth, with curly locks, who played an organ to her, as saith the *Psalmist*: "Young men and maidens, old men and children, praise the name of the Lord." And when the Prince had entered the town, the University enthroned him with great pomp, and the burghers brewed lashings of beer, and set forth toothsome fare, and royally feasted the Prince and all his train. And afterwards they fell to dancing, and I stood on a scaffold to look on. I can call to remembrance nothing else, save that I wish you all good wishes. So fare ye well, in the name of the Lord.

LEIPSIC.

XIV

℃ *MAGISTER JOHANN KRABACIUS sendeth greeting to Magister Ortwin Gratius*

SEEING that I was formerly for two years with your Excellency at *Cologne*, and that you bade me always write to you, wheresoever I might be, I therefore now make bold to announce to you that I have heard of the death of a most illustrious Theologian—denominated Magister *Heckman* of *Franconia*. He was a topping Divine, and in my time was Rector there [at Vienna]. He was a profound dialectician after the school of the Scotists, and was the foe of all the secular poets; he was a man of zeal withal, and right willingly would celebrate a mass. Moreover, when he held the Rectorship at *Vienna* he ruled the undergraduates with a rod of iron, and therein was most laudable. A certain fellow[33] once came from *Moravia* when I was at *Vienna*, who was by way of being a poet, for he wrote verses, and he must needs teach the art of metrification—but he was not matriculate. Thereupon Magister *Heckman* inhibited him; but the rascal was so impudent that he paid

30

no heed to the mandate. Then the Rector inhibited the undergraduates that they should not attend his lectures; and then the fellow forced his way to the Rector and said many insolent words to him, and thou'd him! Then the Rector sent for the University beadles, and essayed to imprison him, because it was mightily scandalous that a mere student should "thou" the Rector of a University and a Doctor of Divinity: besides I hear that the fellow is neither Bachelor nor Master,[34] and is in no way either qualified or graduated, though he strutted about like a warrior who was going to march to war, and he wore a helmet, and a long knife by his side. Nevertheless, by the Lord, he would have been clapped in gaol if he had not had friends in the city. I greatly grieve if it be true that such a man as Magister *Heckman* is dead, for he did me many a good turn when I was at *Vienna*, and so I have written an epitaph on him, as followeth :—

> He who in this tomb doth lie
> Was the Poets' enemy,
> Minded aye to send them flying,
> When their craft they would be plying!
> One from out *Moravia* came,
> Who could no precedence claim,
> Metre-spinning fain to teach,
> And, his lawless end to reach,
> *Thou'd* the Rector to his face—
> Jail for him the proper place!
> Now that the good Rector's dead,
> And in *Wien* is buri-ed,
> Grudge not, of your charity,
> Paternosters two or three.

A messenger hath brought us tidings which, if true, are ill indeed—to wit, that your cause goeth amiss at the Roman court. This I cannot believe, for these messengers tell a pack of lies.

The Poets murmur sorely against you, and say that they will defend Doctor *Reuchlin* with their verses. But since you are likewise a poet—when you are so minded—I think you will easily get the better of them. Nevertheless, prithee let me know how the business goeth; and then, if I can aid you, you will find in me a faithful helpmate. Farewell.

NUREMBERG.

31

XV

❦ *WILHELM SCHERENSCHLEIFER*
sendeth greeting to Master Ortwin Gratius

I MARVEL greatly, Reverend Sir, why you write not to me, and nevertheless write to others who write not to you as often as I write to you.

If you are in dudgeon with me, and will not write to me again, at the least write and tell me why you will not write to me again, that I might know why you write not, although I am ever writing to you— as I am writing to you now, although I know you will not write back.

But I beseech you from my heart's core that you will yet write to me ; and when you have written to me once then I will write ten times to you, because I gladly write to my friends, and I love to exercise myself in writing, so as to be able to finely indite tractates and letters.

I cannot think what is the reason why you write not to me. Lately, when there were some folk here from *Cologne*, I groped them and asked them, " What is Master *Ortwin* about, that he doth not write to me ? He hath not written for two years ; but bid him write to me, for I would rather read his letters than eat honey. And on a time he was my chiefest friend."

I asked them, too, how you sped in that controversy with Doctor *Reuchlin*. And they replied that that Jurist well knew how to circumvent you with his craft. And then I wished that the Lord would give you his grace that you might triumph.

If you do write to me, you might write to me about that affair, for I would gladly know more concerning it. The Jurists strut about here and say, " Doctor *Reuchlin* doeth well, and the Theologians at *Cologne* have used him ill."

And, by the Lord, I fear me that a great scandal will befall the Church if that book, " *The Eyeglass*," be not burnt.

For it containeth many irreverent propositions in opposition to the Catholic faith. And if that Jurist is not compelled to recant them, then others will try to write after the same fashion about questions of Theology, although they know naught of the matter, and follow neither *Thomas*, nor *Albertus*, nor *Scotus*, and are not enlightened in the faith by the Holy Spirit.

For every one should cleave to his own business, and none should put his sickle into another man's corn. Because a cobbler is a cobbler, and a tailor is a tailor, and a smith is a smith; and it would go ill with a tailor who tried to make shoes and slippers.

You must stoutly defend both yourself and sacred Theology, and I will pray on your behalf that God will grant you his grace, and will enlighten your mind, as he did that of the Fathers of old, lest the Devil and his meiny should prevail against justice.

Nevertheless for God's sake write to me, and tell me how you speed. You cause me great anguish, albeit there is no need. And now I commend you to the Lord. Farewell, in Christ.

FRANKFORT-ON-MAIN.

XVI

ⓒ *MATTHÄUS HONIGLECKER to*
Magister Ortwin Gratius, Greeting

INASMUCH as I have ever been your worship's adherent, and have ever wrought on your behoof, I now take upon myself to premonish you in a time of trouble—for in your prosperity will I rejoice, and in your adversity will I lament. Are you not my friend? And it beseemeth us to exult when our friends prosper, and to sorrow when they mourn—as saith *Tully*, notwithstanding that he is a pagan and a poet.

I must tell you, therefore, that you have here a most malicious enemy, who uttereth many slanders against your worship, and he noiseth abroad many matters, exalting himself in his pride. And he averreth to all and sundry that you are a bastard—that your mother is a drab, and your father a priest. But I stood up for you and said: "Herr Bachelor—or whatever your degree may be—you are still a young man, and you ought not to slander the Magisters. For what saith the scripture? 'The disciple is not above the master,' and you are yet a disciple, while Herr *Ortwin* is a Master of eight or ten years' standing. You are therefore not competent to slander one who is a Magister and in such an exalted position; but you will find some one to slander you, notwithstanding that you are so high and mighty. You should use more modesty, and not be of such behaviour." Then quoth he: "I am speaking sooth, and I can prove my words, and I heed you not a whit; I say that *Ortwin* is a bastard, and a fellow-countryman of his told me so of a truth, because he knew his parents; and I am resolved to write and unfold the matter to Doctor *Reuchlin*, who is not yet apprized of it. But on what grounds could you censure me, a man unknown to you?" Then quoth I: "See, gentlemen, this fellow boasteth himself a saint, and saith that he is above censure, and that he hath done no evil, like that Pharisee who boasted that he fasted twice in the week." Then the fellow waxed wrath, and cried: "I said not that I had never sinned, because that would be contrary to the words of the Psalmist, 'All men are liars,' which the gloss expounds as 'sinners.' What I said was that you have no right, nor are you able, to censure me as touching my parentage. But *Ortwin* is a bastard, and not true-born—therefore he is reprobate, and reproach him I will for ever and a day!" Then said I: "You cannot, for Herr *Ortwin* is an eminent man, and can protect himself." Thereupon the fellow reeled off many scandalous tales concerning your mother—how she had been in the company of priests, and monks, and soldiers, and rustics, in the meadow and in the byre. You would not credit how great was my shamefacedness.

Notwithstanding, I cannot be active in your defence, for I never saw your father and mother: however, I firmly believe them to be worthy and decent folk.   But write and tell me how this matter standeth, and any glad tidings I will scatter broadcast.

I said furthermore to your calumniator: "You ought not to say such things, for even if Herr *Ortwin* be base-born, he may have been legitimised; and if he is legitimised then he is no longer a bastard, seeing that the sovereign pontiff hath power to bind and to loose, and can make a bastard legitimate—and contrariwise.   Moreover, I can prove from scripture that you are blameworthy; for it is written, 'With what measure ye mete, it shall be measured to you again;' but you mete with the measure of abuse, therefore abuse shall be meted to you.   Or I can prove it thus: the Lord said: 'Judge not, that ye be not judged,' but thou judgest others, and slanderest them, therefore shalt thou be judged and slandered."   Then he replied that my arguments were all flapdoodle and led nowhither; and he was so stubborn as to declare that if the pope himself begat a son out of wedlock, and afterwards legitimised him, the child would nevertheless in the sight of heaven be a bastard and not true-born.

I trow the devil must be in these vagabonds, that they slander you thus.   I beseech you, therefore, write to me, so that I may defend your good name; of a truth it would be scandalous for Doctor *Reuchlin* to be apprized that you were a bastard.   But even if you are, the fellow cannot certainly prove it, and if it seem good to you, we will hale him before the Court at *Rome*, and we will compel him to recant—the Jurists know the way; and we will harry him at law, and we will seize his benefices when he incurs deprivation—for he holds a canonry here at *Mainz*, and a living elsewhere.   Take it not amiss that I write to tell you what I have heard.   My intent is of the best.   Farewell in the Lord, who shall keep thee in all thy ways.

MAINZ.

XVII

⁊ *MAGISTER JOHANN HIPP* to *Mag. Ortwin Gratius, greeting*

"**B**E glad, O ye righteous, and rejoice in the Lord: and be joyful, all ye that are true of heart."— *Psalm xxxi.*

Now, take this not amiss, saying within yourself, "What aileth this fellow with his texts?" But hearken rather, with glee, to a piece of news that will mightily tickle your lordship.

You shall have it in a nut-shell. There was a poet here, calling himself *Joannes Aesticampianus*[35] a bumptious fellow, ever girding at the Masters of Arts, and decrying them in his lectures. He would dub them dunces, and aver that one Poet was worth ten Masters, and that Poets should always take precedence of Masters and Licentiates in processions. He lectured on *Pliny* and other poets, and declared that the Magisters were not Masters of the Seven Liberal Arts,[36] but of the Seven Deadly Sins, and that they were not grounded in their rudiments, and knew naught save *Peter of Spain* and his Logical Primer. The rantipole was much run after, even by the gentleman-commoners. He used to say that the Scotists and Thomists were piddlers alike, and he uttered blasphemies against the Angelic Doctor himself!

But the Magisters bided their time, to avenge themselves by the help of the Lord. And by the Lord's will, at last he made a speech, and railed at the Magisters, and the Doctors, and the Licentiates and the Bachelors, and extolled his own Faculty, and reviled sacred Theology.

Thereupon mighty indignation arose among the heads of the Faculty. And the Masters and Doctors took counsel together, saying, "What shall we do? For this man hath done many notable things; and if we send him away, all men will believe that he is more learned than we. And mayhap the Moderns will come

and say that their way is better than that of the
Ancients, and our University will be defamed, and will
become a laughing-stock."

Then Magister *Andrew Delitzsch*, who is a fine poet
himself, said that *Aesticampianus* at the University was
like a fifth wheel to a coach—for he thwarted the other
Faculties, so that the students could not graduate
therein. And the other Masters were of the same
mind, so the long and the short of it was that they
determined to either expel or inhibit that poet, at the
risk of his everlasting dudgeon. Thereupon they cited
him before the Rector, and nailed the citation on the
doors of the church.

Then the fellow put in an appearance—an advocate
with him—and made as though he would defend himself, nor was he without friends to support him, but the
Masters told them to stand aside, if they would not
commit perjury in opposing the University. And the
Masters waxed valiant in fight, and stuck to their
guns, and swore they would spare nobody—for justice'
sake.

Nevertheless certain jurists and courtiers pleaded for
the fellow. But the Magisters said that this was out of
the question, for they had statutes, and by the statutes
he ought to be expelled. Then the marvel was that
even the Duke put in a word for him; but to no effect,
because they replied that he himself ought to observe
the statutes of the University, inasmuch as its statutes
are to a University as is the binding to a book. If
there be no binding, the leaves fall hither and thither;
and if there were no statutes order would cease in the
University, and the students would be at sixes and
sevens, and Chaos would come again—therefore should
the Duke work for the good of the University, as did
his father before him.

Then the Duke was persuaded, and avouched that
he might not oppose the University, and that it was
expedient that one man should be expelled, rather than
that the whole University should suffer disgrace. The
Magisters then were fully content, and cried: " Heaven
be thanked, Lord Duke, for this thy righteous judgment!" Then the Rector fastened a decree to the

church doors, that *Aesticampianus* should be banished for ten years.

But his disciples murmured much, and declared that the Lords of the Council had done grievous wrong to *Aesticampianus*. But the Doctors swore that they cared not a doit for that.

Some gentlemen-commoners, indeed, have spread it abroad that *Aesticampianus* will avenge the injury, and cite the University before the Roman Curia. But the Magisters laughed, and said : " Pish ! what can that vagabond do ? "

And now great peace reigneth in the University. Mag. *Delitzsch* lectureth on the humanities, and so doth a Magister from *Rothenburg*, who hath compiled a book full three times as large as all the works of *Virgil ;* and in that book he hath put many mighty fine things, both in defence of holy Mother Church and in praise of the saints. And he most of all hath praised our University, and sacred Theology, and the Faculty of Arts—and he hath reproved the secular and heathen poets. The Masters say that his verses are as good as *Virgil's*, and have no faults at all, because he knoweth quite perfectly the Art of Metrification, and hath been a good metrist these twenty years. Therefore the Lords of the Council have allowed him to lecture on that book instead of on *Terence*, because it is more necessary than *Terence*, and is not all about drabs and clowns, as *Terence* is.

You must spread abroad these tidings in your University, and then peradventure *Buschius* will be served in like manner as was *Aesticampianus*. When will you send me your book about *Reuchlin* ? You say much, and nothing cometh of it. You promised faithfully that you would send it, but you have sent it not. The Lord forgive you in that you do not love me as I love you, for you are my heart's core. Nevertheless fail not to send it, for with desire have I desired to eat this passover with you—I mean, to read that book. Send me some news—and, just for once, write a little treatise, or some verses, about me, if I am worthy thereof.

And now farewell, *in Chr. D. D. nost.*, world without end. Amen.

XVIII

⫷ *MAGISTER PETER NEGELIN* to *Magister Ortwin Gratius, greeting*

NOTWITHSTANDING that I am mightily afeared to be so bold as to show you a composition of my own devising—seeing that you have great cunning in the making of metres and lyricisms, while I am but a dabbler (as saith *Jeremy*, "Ah, ah, Lord! Behold I cannot speak : for I am a child"), for I am not yet fully grounded in my fundaments, nor am I perfectly skilled in poetistical art and Rhetorick.

Nevertheless, since you once said that I should by all means construct a poem and send it to you, that you might botch it up, and show forth its faults—a little while ago quoth I to myself, "See now, *Ortwin* was your teacher, and he meaneth well by you, and you should do what he biddeth you. He can advance you in this matter, and in all else besides. And you will grow up to be a learned clerk, an it please God, and will prosper in all your affairs. Is it not written in the *First Book of Kings*: "To obey is better than sacrifice"?

And thus it hath fallen out that I send you a poem fashioned by myself in praise of *Saint Peter*, and a composer who excels in plainsong and descants hath set it to music in four parts. Indeed I took great pains to rhyme it in the way it is rhymed—because songs sound best to four parts, just as *Alexander's* Grammar is in four parts.

I know not whether the poem hath any faults. Scan it, I pray you, according to the Rules of Metrification, and mend it if you will.

Here beginneth Peter Negelin's new ditty
in praise of Saint Peter

Good Saint Peter, pity me !
Since the Lord hath given thee
Power—and, by peculiar grace,
'Midst the saints the topmost place ;

39

By prepollence of the keys,
Tying, loosing, as thou please,
Things on earth and things on high :
Hear me, as to thee I cry !
For my sins entreat—for the
Sake of th' Universitie !

They say that Dr. *Reuchlin* (who is named in the Hebrew tongue *Joannes Capnion*)[37] hath obtained a judgment in his favour at *Spires*—but the Magisters of the *Friars Preachers* say that this irketh them not, for the Bishop there hath no comprehension of sacred Theology.[38] Dr. *Hoogstraten* is at the Roman Court, and is in high favour with the Apostolic Chair. He hath plenty of money and other necessaries. I would give a groat to learn the truth of the matter. You must write to me. Good Lord! what is the reason that you will not now send me one single syllable? And yet when you do write to me I am full fain.

Farewell, and deign to salute for me Dr. *Valentinus von Geltersheim*, and Dr. *Arnold von Tongern* of *Lawrence Hostel*, and Dr. *Remigius*, and Herr *Roger* the licentiate of *De Monte Hostel*, and first of all, Herr Doctor *Johann Pfefferkorn*, that man of zeal, and all others who are learned in Theology and the Arts.

Farewell, once more, in the name of the Lord.

TRIER.

XIX

❡ *STEPHAN GLATZKOPF*, Licentiate, to *Mag. Ortwin Gratius*

GREETING, with all humility, to your loftiness. Reverend Herr Magister, a fellow hath come hither bringing with him certain verses, which he averred you had written and published at *Cologne*. Thereupon, a Poet of this place, who is held in high esteem, but is no good Christian, read them and declared that they were poor stuff, and full of blunders. Then quoth I, " If Master *Ortwin* composed them they have no faults—be sure of that." And I offered

to wager my coat that if those verses contained any
faults you had not composed them, and that if you had
composed them they contained no faults.   Accordingly
I send you the lines, that you may judge whether you
contrived them, or not, and let me know.   The poem is
written concerning the death of Doctor *Gerhard von
Zutphen* of *Kneck Hostel*, who composed the commentary but now, alas, is dead and gone.   May he rest in
peace.   Thus it beginneth:—

> A famous scholar here doth lie lamented,
> To th' University by heaven presented;
> He o'er *Kneck Hostel* erst did Regent sit,
> And pieced the *Copulata* bit by bit.
> Oh! that he might upon the hither shore
> Have lingered, and of comments written more!
> To adjuvate the University,
> And teach her students fair Latinity!
> But now, his life by death untimely lost,
> With half the *Alexander* still unglossed,
> The University deplores her limb,
> Who, like a shining lantern, or the glim
> Of candle in a candle-stick a-burning,
> Lit far and wide the darkness with his learning.
> What man than his could better periods round?
> He joyed the upstart Poets to confound,
> Who in their foolish grammars scorn reliance
> On Logic—of all Sciences the Science.
> So, in the Faith being unillumined, they
> From Mother Church aye wander, all astray.
> But if to think aright they are not willing,
> Soon will *Hoogstraten* set them all a-grilling!
> Who Doctor *Johann Reuchlin* lately cited,
> Before the Court, and grievously indicted.
> Almighty, to thy suppliant lend an ear,
> Who humbly thee invokes, with many a tear,
> To grant our member dead thy grace eternal,
> And pack the Poets off to realms infernal!

This seemeth to me an excellent poem, though I know
not how to scan it, because it is of an unwonted kind,
and I have only skill to scan hexameters.   You must
suffer no man to spurn your verses; so write to me,
and I will defend you even at the risk of single combat.
Fare ye well.

MÜNSTER IN WESTPHALIA.

XX

❦ *JOHANNES LUCIBULARIUS* to
Magister Ortwin Gratius

GREETINGS that no man can number.
Reverend Herr Magister, inasmuch as you formerly promised me that you would be my help in time of need, and that you would fain advance me before all others; and inasmuch as you told me boldly to seek your aid, and that you would then stretch out a helping hand to me as to a brother, and would not desert me in adversity—I therefore now entreat you, for the love of God, to succour me, as you are well able.

The Rector here hath dismissed an assistant teacher, and desireth to appoint another—will you therefore on my behalf write a letter of recommendation, praying him to be pleased, or to deign, to appoint me? I have no more money, since I have spent it all, for I have even bought me some books and some shoes.

You are well aware that, by God's grace, I am competent; for when you were at *Deventer* I was in the second class, and I afterwards stayed in residence at *Cologne* for a year, so that I qualified for the Bachelor's degree, and I should have graduated at Michaelmas if I had had the money. I know how to expound the Boys' Exercise-book to learners, and the *Opus Minus* (*Part II.*), and I know the art of Scansion as you taught it me, and *Peter of Spain* in all his works, and the *Parvulus* of Natural Philosophy. I am a singer too, and am skilled in plain-song and prick-song, and I have a bass voice withal, and can sing one note below contra-C.

I call these things to your mind in no vainglorious spirit; pardon me, therefore—and so I commend you to God Almighty.

ZWOLLE.

42

XXI

ℭ MAGISTER CONRAD OF ZWICKAU
sendeth greeting to Magister Ortwin Gratius

INASMUCH as you have written to apprize me of
all things concerning your mistress—how dearly
you dote upon her, and how she cherisheth you, and
sendeth you posies and kerchiefs and girdles and the
like, and taketh no guerdon from you, as is the
wont of venal hussies — and how, when her spouse
goeth abroad, you visit her to her great content—and
how you thrice embraced her in succession, and once
on the threshold behind the door, chanting "*Attolite
portas!*"—and how when her husband returned you
fled privily by way of the garden—I therefore will in
turn now relate how I have fared with my lady-love.

She is a topping dame, and a wealthy, and I scraped
acquaintance with her by a strange chance, for a certain
gentleman-commoner, a friend of the Bishop's, was our
go-between. Straightway I fell over head and ears in
love with her, till by day I knew not what I did, and at
night I could not sleep. But when I would have
slumbered I cried aloud from my bed, "*Dorothea!
Dorothea! Dorothea!*" so that the students in the
hostel heard me, and ran to me, saying, "Herr Magister,
what would you, that you thus cry aloud? If you
would fain make confession, we will fetch you a priest"
—for they thought I was at the point of death and
cried upon *S. Dorothea* with other saints. Thereupon
I was mightily abashed. Nevertheless when I visited
my beloved I was always so terrified that I durst not
regard her, but grew red from head to foot. Then
quoth she, "Prithee, Herr Magister, why so shy?"
Then I said that I was afeared to tell her. But she
must needs have an answer, and would not let me go
until I told her—she said, moreover, that she would not
be out with me, tho' my words were downright roguish-
ness. Then at last I grew bold and opened my heart
to her. Can you call to mind how that you explained
long ago, when you expounded *Ovid* in his "Art of

43

Love," that lovers ought to be as bold as warriors, else it availed them not?

Then said I to her, "Reverend mistress mine, forgive me for God's love, and for your honour's sake—but I love you, and I have chosen you from among all the children of men; for you are fair among women, and there is no spot in you. You are the goodliest that there is in the whole world." Then she laughed, and said, "Pardy! you talk full loverly—if I could but trust you!" And after that I often visited her at her house, and drank with her. And when I was in the church I always stood where I could see her, and in turn she looked me through and through. At last I earnestly asked her to keep me in her thoughts—whereupon she declared that I loved her not. But I swore that I loved her as my own mother, and that I would dare all things in her service, though it should cost me my life. Then answered the lady fair: "I would fain learn if that be so," and she made a cross with chalk upon the door of her house, and said: "If you love me, you will kiss that cross, for my sake, every evening after dark." This I did for many days, but at last came some one and smeared the cross with filth, and when I kissed it I defiled my lips and teeth and nose. Then was I full of wrath against the lady; but she swore by the Holy of Holies that she had no hand in the matter. And I believe her, for she is in all else an honourable woman.

I have suspicion of a student here, that the deed was his. Can I but bring it home to him—verily I say unto you, he shall have his reward! But she useth me in more friendly wise than formerly, and I trust I shall yet gain her favours. She heard of late that I was a poet. Then quoth she: "I have been told that you are a jolly rhymer—so you must write me a ballad!" This I did, and I sang it in the street at even-tide that she might hear; and afterwards I rendered it for her into German. It runneth thus:—

Venus benign! of love the fountain and the queen!
Why frownest thou on me with such a hostile mien?
Oh, *Dorothea* mine! whom I for mistress choose,
Me for thy leman true, in turn, do not refuse!

Fairest of maidens all that in this city are,
Thy smile is like a rose, thy twinkle like a star!

She said that she would keep this as long as she
lived, for my sake.　I pray you give me counsel how to
comport myself, and how to make her love me.　Forgive
me for having so grossly written to your worthiness.　It
is my wont to unbosom myself to my friends.　Farewell,
in the name of the Blessed.

From LEIPSIC.

XXII

❡ *GERHARD SCHIRRUGEL to*
Magister Ortwin Gratius

*Manifold greeting to thee, in the glorious name of our Master,
Who from the dead arose, and now is enthroned in heaven.*

HONOURED Sir, I would have you know that I
abide here reluctantly, and it irketh me that I
remained not at *Cologne* with you, where I should have
made fairer progress.　You, indeed, would have been
able to make me a good syllogiser, and even in some
sort a poet.　In *Cologne* folk are devout, and gladly
visit the churches, and on Sundays they flock to the
sermon.　The arrogance of this place is not to be
seen there.　Here the students show no deference to
the magisters, and the magisters pay no heed to the
students, but let them go wheresoe'er they will; and
they wear no hoods.　When they are in their cups they
take God's name in vain, and blaspheme, and do many
unseemly things.　A little while ago, for instance, a
fellow said that he did not believe the Holy Coat of
Treves to be our Lord's Coat, but a lousy old rag; and
he said that he did not believe that a single hair of the
Blessed Virgin remained in the world.　Another further
said that like enough the Three Kings at *Cologne* were
three boors from *Westphalia,* and that the sword and
shield of *St. Michael* were not *St. Michael's.*　He swore,
too, that the indulgences of the Preaching Friars were

45

only fit for the jakes, and that the Friars themselves
were a pack of jack-puddings, who deceived women and
churls. Then cried I, "To the stake, to the stake with
such a heretic!"

But he laughed in my face. Then said I, "Thou
rascal, if thou shouldest but say such things in the ears
of Doctor *Hoogstraten* of *Cologne*, the Inquisitor of
Heretical Pravity!" Quoth he, "*Hoogstraten* is a vile
and damnable beast," and thereupon he railed against
him, and said "*Johann Reuchlin* is an upright man, but
the theologians are devils, and unjustly have they given
sentence that his book, the *Augenspiegel* should be
burned."

Then I answered, "Say not so, for it is written
in the eighth chapter of *Ecclesiasticus:* 'Deem thou
not against the judge, for after that is righteous he
deemeth.' Knowest thou not that the University
of *Paris*, where the theologians are learned and
zealous and cannot err, hath decided as *Cologne* hath?
Wherefore wilt thou fight against the universal
Church?" Then he averred that the theologians
of *Paris* were unjust judges, and that they took
from the Predicant Friars a bribe which — so the
lying rascal said—was conveyed to them by that most
zealous and learned man Herr *Theodoric von Gouda*,
legate of the University of *Cologne*. Moreover he
swore that the church I spake of was not God's
Church, but that of which the *Psalmist* spake, "I have
hated the congregation of evil doers, and will not sit
with the wicked." And he reviled the Doctors of *Paris*
for all that they did; saying that the University of
Paris was the mother of all foolishness, which, taking
there its rise, spread into *Germany* and *Italy*, and that
that University sowed broadcast superstition and folly.
He said too that, as a rule, all students of *Paris* were
wrong-headed and in a manner numskulls. In conclusion he declared the *Talmud* not to be under the ban of
the Church.[39] Then Doctor *Peter Meyer*, parish priest of
Frankfort, who was seated hard by, said, "I will prove
to you that this fellow is no good Christian and holdeth
not with the opinion of the Church. By'r lady! you
fellows talk much about theology, and know nothing.

Reuchlin even doth not know where it is written that the Talmud is a forbidden book."

" And where is it written ? " asked the fellow.

Then Doctor Peter told him that it was written in " *The Fortress of Faith.*" Then the braggart made answer that " *The Fortress of Faith* " was a dung-hill book, and of no account, and that none save a ninny or a dunce cited that book. Then I was overcome with fear, for Doctor *Peter* was so wroth that his hands trembled, and I feared lest he should do the fellow an injury, but I said to him, " Good Sir, prithee have patience, for ' Who is patient is governed with much wisdom.'—*Proverbs xiii.* Let him alone and he will perish like the dust before the wind. He speaketh much, yet knoweth nothing. As it is written in *Ecclesiasticus,* ' A fool multiplieth words,' so doth he." And then, oh shame ! the fellow began to say many things against the *Order of Preachers*—how that those pious friars did a deed of wickedness at *Berne*[40] that I would not credit to save my life—how that they were burned at the stake—and how that the *Preachers* once mingled poison in the Eucharistic Sacrament and thus murdered an Emperor.[41] He declared that the whole Order should be blotted out—for otherwise great scandals would be caused in the Church, since from that Order proceedeth all malice—and many other such like things he said. Know then of a truth that I earnestly desire to return to *Cologne,* for what can I do among such accursed men as these ? " May death come upon them, and may they go down alive into the pit," as saith the *Psalmist,* for they are sons of *Belial.* If it seemeth good to you, I will first of all take my degree—but if not, I will depart immediately. Speedily therefore send me your opinion : therewith will I be governed. And now I commend you to the Lord. Farewell.

MAINZ.

XXIII

❦ *JOHANN WICKELTRÄGER, Humble Professor of sacred Theology, sendeth greeting to Magister Ortwin Gratius, Poet, Divine, and what not*

INASMUCH as you were once my pupil at *Deventer*, where I loved you before all my scholars, in that you were a youth of good parts and very towardly, I therefore am ever mindful to give you good counsel whensoever it lieth in my power.

But you must take it in good part, for God who seeeth the heart knoweth that I speak but for love of you, and for the saving of your soul.

There were here of late certain folk, hailing from *Cologne*, and they declared that there is a woman in that city who is oft at your house, and that you are oft at hers, and have commerce with her. Now when I heard these sayings I was smitten with great dread, for if this be true, it is a grievous scandal, seeing that you are a graduate and will in due time rise to higher things, to wit, a degree in sacred Theology. Moreover, when such doings of yours are noised abroad, a bad example is set to the young, who are thereby corrupted. You know how that the son of *Sirach* saith : " For many have perished by the beauty of a woman ; for hereby lust is enkindled as a fire ; " *The Preacher*, too, toucheth the matter : " Turn away thy face from a woman dressed up, and look not upon another's beauty ; " and again : " Gaze not upon a maiden, lest her beauty be a stumbling-block to thee." Full well you know that incontinence is a grievous sin. Moreover, what is worse, I hear that this woman liveth in lawful wedlock with her husband. For the Lord's sake send her packing, and have regard to your own good name. It is a disgrace that men should say of a theologian that he is an avouterer ; and yet in other matters your repute is fair enough, and all deem you a competent scholar—as I well know you to be. Once every day you must devoutly call to remembrance the Lord's Passion, for that is a powerful remedy against

48

the wiles of the Devil and the thorn in the flesh; seek,
too, in your prayers that you may be preserved from all
evil thoughts.　It is my belief that you have been reading about such things in the heathen poets, and are
corrupted thereby.　Would that you might cast away
all their works, for you know that *St. Jerome* himself was
smitten by an angel for reading a book of poetry.　At
Deventer I often urged you not to become a Poet or a
Jurist, for such men are evil-affectioned towards the
Faith, and almost all are loose livers.　Concerning them
the *Psalmist* saith : "Thou hast hated them that regard
vanities to no purpose."

There is another matter on which I have a mind to
counsel you.　The rumour goeth that you have written,
in defence of the Faith, against *Johann Reuchlin*.　This
is well enough, if you would use to your profit the talent
that God hath given you.　But it is reported here that
Johann Pfefferkorn, the man whom you buttress, is a
worthless knave, and became not a Christian for love of
the Faith, but, because the Jews would have fain have
hanged him for his wrong doings—for they say he is a
thief and a traitor—he was baptized to save himself.　And
all aver that at heart he is a sorry Christian, and will not
abide in the Faith.　Therefore take heed what you do.
Already they have burnt at *Halle* another baptized Jew,
also named *Johann Pfefferkorn*, for his many evil deeds.
I fear me that this fellow will tread in his steps, and
then you will be in a quandary.

Nevertheless, continue to defend Theology, and take
in good part my brotherly counsel.　Fare ye well, in all
prosperity.

MAGDEBURG.

XXIV

❦ *PAUL DAUBENGIGEL sendeth goodly*
greeting to Mag. Ortwin Gratius

SEE now whether I am a liar, as you lately said I was,
in that I was always promising to write to you and
yet wrote not.

Hereby I will prove that I keep faith with you—for

a discreet and upright man should make no promise that he doth not keep. It would be the height of fickleness in me not to keep my promises to you, and I should be a deceiver.

You must write back to me, and then we will often send, or address, letters in turn to each other.

Now you must know that Doctor *Reuchlin* hath published a book entitled "*A Defence*," in which he is scandalously abusive, and calleth you an ass. And I felt greatly ashamed as I read that book—not that I read it all, for I threw it against the wall when I found that it was full of malice against the Theologians and Artsmen.

You may read it, an you will, because I am sending it to you herewith. It seemeth to me that the author and the book ought to be burned together, for it is a monstrous scandal that anybody should compile such a volume.

I was lately at the horse-market, for I wanted to buy a horse to take me to *Vienna*, and it was then that I saw the book exposed for sale, and I thought to myself that you ought to see it, so that you might write a rejoinder to its falsehoods—and if I could do you some greater service I would not delay, for in me you have a humble servant and adherent.

You may know that hitherto I have had weak eyes, but a certain Alchemist came here who said he knew how to heal eyes—even if a man were stark blind with that malady. In other leechcraft too he had much experience, for he had roved through *Italy* and *France*, and many provinces. Every Alchemist, as you know, is either a leech or a quack-salver—but this fellow was something out at elbows. You ask me how I thrive in general. I thank you for asking, and you must know that, by God's grace, I am doing well. At the last vintage I pressed much wine, and of crops I have an abundance.

By way of news I may tell you that our most serene Lord, the Emperor, is sending a great force into *Lombardy*, against the *Venetians*, and intendeth to chastise them for their insolence. I saw full two thousand men with six standards; half had spears, and half, culverins or arquebuses; they were indeed right formidable, and had slashed hose, and they wrought much scathe to the country-folk and villagers. Folk said that they hoped they would all be slain, but I trust they will all return safe and sound. Send me, I pray you, by the carrier, what *Brulifer*[42] has written concerning *Scotus*, his *Formalitates et Distinctiones;* and also " *The Shield*" of the Thomists in the Aldine character, if you can come by it.

I greatly desire also to see your tractate on the *Method of Versifying*.[43]

Buy for me, too, *Boethius* in all his works, but especially his *De Disciplina Scholarium*,[44] and his *De Consolatione Philosophica* with the Commentary of the *Holy Doctor*.

And now, farewell, and hold me not in disesteem.

AUGSBURG.

XXV

ℂ *MAGISTER PHILIPP STEINMETZ to Mag. Ortwin Gratius, greeting*

A S I have ofttimes told you, I chafe bitterly because that vile raff, to wit the Faculty of Poets, groweth and extendeth throughout every province and region. In my time there was only one poet—and his name was *Samuel*—but now in a single burg a good score may be found, to harass us who cling to the ancients. Just now I sharply snibbed one who said that " scholaris " did not mean a person who went to school to learn, for, quoth I, " Thou ass ! Wouldst thou correct the *Holy Doctor* who useth that word ? " But forthwith he wrote a lampoon against me, with many scurrilities therein, and vowed that I was no sound grammarian, in that I had not rightly expounded certain words when I treated of *Alexander*, his First Part, and of the book *De modis significandi*.

Now therefore I will set down in due form those words, that you may see that I have rightly expounded them according to all the vocabularies, and I can moreover cite canonical writers, even in Theology. First, I maintained that "seria" sometimes meaneth a pot, and in that case is derived from *Syria* as being first made in that country; or from "serius," because useful and necessary; or from "series," because pots stand in a row. Again, "patricians" were so called as being the fathers of senators. "Currus" is derived from "currendo" because therewith things within run out. "Jus, juris" signifies justice, but "jus, jutis," broth, as the verse runneth :—

> "Jus, jutis, mando : jus, juris, in agmine pando."

Again, "Lucar" signifies money culled from a grove or forest. "Mantellus" means a cloak, and hence proceedeth the diminutive "manticulus." "Mechanicus" means adulterous, and hence the "mechanical arts" are named, as being adulterine, when compared with the liberal arts, which are true-born. "Mensorium" means that which appertains to a table, "mensa." Again, *Polyhistor* signifies one who knows many histories, whence cometh *Polyhistoria*—that is a multitude of histories. *Polysenus* means "possessing many senses."

These, and such-like teachings the fellow declared to be false, and he put me to shame before my pupils. Then I alleged that it sufficed for a man's eternal salvation that he should be a simple grammarian, and at least know how to express his thoughts. But he replied that I was neither a simple nor a duplex grammarian, and knew nothing at all. Thereat I rejoiced, for now I shall cite him for breach of the privileges of the University of *Vienna*, where he will have to answer me—for there by God's grace I have graduated Magister : and if I proved learned enough in the eyes of a whole university, I am learned enough for a single poet. Is not a university greater than a poet? Believe me I would not forego that slander for twenty florins.

The rumour goes that all the Poets here will take Doctor *Reuchlin's* part against the Theologians, and that one of them hath composed a book entitled "*The Triumph of Capnion* "[45] which contains many libels upon you. Would that all the poets were where the pepper groweth, and would let us rest in peace, for it is to be feared that the Faculty of Arts will perish through these same poets! For they say that the Artsmen decoy youths, and take their money, and make Bachelors and Doctors of them though they know nothing. And they have brought it about that students no longer desire to graduate even in Arts, but all wish to became Poets. I have a friend who is a worthy youth, and talented withal; and his parents sent him to *Ingolstadt*, and I gave him a letter of introduction to a Magister there who is duly qualified in Arts and intendeth to graduate Doctor of Divinity—but the youngster must needs quit the Magister and attend the lectures of *Philomusus* the poet.[46] Of a truth I am woundily grieved for that young man, as it is written, *Prov. xix.*, "He that hath pity upon the poor lendeth unto the Lord"; for if he had but stayed with the Magister he would have been Bachelor by this time. And now his labour is in vain—if he were to study Poetry for ten years.

I know that these profane poets harass you greatly, notwithstanding that you are a poet yourself—but not of that kind: for you hold with the Church and are moreover well grounded in Theology. When you indite verses they deal not with vanities, but with the praises of the Saints. Most earnestly do I desire to know how that affair of Doctor *Reuchlin's* standeth. If I can be of any service to you therein prithee let me know, and tell me all things concerning it. Farewell.

XXVI

❡ *ANTON RÜBENSTADT* amicably and with hearty affection wisheth weal to Magister Ortwin Gratius

VENERABLE Herr Magister, I would have you know that at this present I have not the leisure for writing to you concerning matters that press not urgently, but solely that you may reply to a single question that I will propound forthwith: whether, namely, a Doctor of Laws is bound to make obeisance to a Magister-noster who weareth not his rightful habit. The garb of a Doctor of Divinity, as you know, consisteth of a large cope with a liripoop. Now there is a Doctor here, a graduate in Canon and Civil Law, who hath a grudge against Magister-noster *Peter Meyer* the parish priest. Lately the Jurist met in the street Magister *Peter*, who was not garbed in his canonicals, and he made him no obeisance. Then it was said that he had not done well, for even if he were out with him, yet he should have done him reverence for the honour of sacred Theology. We may be at odds with a person without insulting his Faculty, and the Magisters stand in the Apostles' place, of whom it is written, "How beautiful are the feet of them that preach the gospel of peace, and bring glad tidings of good things." If, therefore, their feet are beautiful, how much fairer are their heads and their hands. It is meet, therefore, for every man, even a prince, to do reverence and honour to the Theologians and Magisters. But the Jurist made reply, and cited in a precisely opposite sense the Laws, and many passages in Scripture, where it is written, "I will judge you according to your ways"; and he argued that we need do reverence to no man who doth not go about in his proper habit, even if he were a prince. "When a priest," quoth he, "is detected in some disgraceful act, while he is not garbed as a priest should be, but is in lay attire, then the secular judge can hale him and treat him as a layman, and sentence him to corporal punishment, benefit of clergy notwithstanding." This is what the Jurist said, but, I pray you, unfold your opinion, and if of yourself you cannot tell, there are jurists and theologians in the University of *Cologne* with whom to take counsel. I would fain know the truth, for God is truth, and whoso loveth truth loveth God also.

You might likewise send me word how matters stand in that suit of yours against Doctor *Reuchlin*. I hear that he is beggared by reason of the great law costs, and right glad of it I am. But I trust that with the Theologians and you will rest the victory. Farewell, in the Lord's name.

FRANKFORT.

XXVII

❡ *JOHANN STABLER* of *MILTENBERG* sendeth greeting to Magister Ortwin Gratius

YOU have ever been minded to learn the news from me, and just now I can, and will, send you tidings, though I grieve that they are ill.

You must know, then, that the Friars of the *Order of Preachers* here held certain indulgences which they procured from the Roman Court at a great price, and that therefrom they derived no small gain. And then by night some thief broke into the Church, filched more than three hundred florins, and made off with them. Thereupon the Friars, men full of zeal, and warmly affectioned in the Christian Faith, were sad at heart, and bewailed concerning that thief. And the citizens sent hither and thither and could not find him, for he had escaped and taken the money with him. Great is the wickedness of such a crime, committed against the papal indulgences and in a holy place, and the robber is excommunicate wherever he may be. The folk who had been absolved, and had paid their fees into the chest now believe that they are unshriven : but this fear is groundless—they are just as truly shriven as if the Predicants still possessed the money.

You must know, too, that certain fellows who support Doctor *Reuchlin* have come hither, and spread abroad many rumours, and aver that the Friars obtained those indulgences from *Rome* that with their price they might harry the Doctor, and in the cause of the Faith trouble him ; and that folk should give them not a doit, whatever their condition—high or low, rich or poor, religious or secular. Not long ago I was present at the proceedings at *Mainz* that the Magisters instituted against *Reuchlin ;* now there is a certain preacher there, in the Cathedral, who graduated Doctor of Divinity at Heidelberg, *Bartholomew Zehender* by name—or, in the Latin, *Decimarius*—and from the pulpit he enjoined all men to come on the morrow to see the "*Augenspiegel*" burnt, inasmuch as he deemed it impossible that Doctor *Reuchlin* could devise any quibble to prevent that being done. But a fellow here, a Poet by repute, went about uttering foul words against the aforesaid Doctor of Divinity, and when he met him glared at him with snaky and venomous eyes : and he cried openly, " That preacher is not worthy to sit at the same table with honest men ; and I can prove that he is a vile poltroon, for in the pulpit of your church, before all the congregation, he lied against the good report of an illustrious man, and said that which is not." Then he cried, " Out of envy do they torment the good Doctor ! " And he called *Decimarius* a beast and a dog, and swore that no heretic was ever so malicious and envious. Now this saying came to the ears of the preacher, and he excused himself—sufficiently as it seemeth to me—saying that although the book had not been burnt, perhaps nevertheless it would be burnt later on ; moreover he quoted Scripture in many places to prove that nothing any one may say in defence of the Catholic Faith is a lie. He declared, moreover, that the bailiffs and officers of the Bishop of *Mainz* had hindered the execution of the sentence, contrary to all justice, but that folk would see what would happen yet, for he would venture a prophecy that the book would be burnt, though the *Emperor*, and the *King of France*, and every Prince and Duke maintained Doctor *Reuchlin's* cause. I deem it well to inform you of these things, that you may be forewarned—and I beg of you to walk warily in all your ways, lest you incur reproach. And so, farewell.

MILTENBERG.

XXVIII

℃ *FRIAR CONRAD DOLLENKOPF to Mag. Ortwin Gratius, greeting, with the humblest devotion, and daily intercessions to our Lord Jesus Christ*

TAKE it not amiss, Reverend Sir, if I write to you concerning affairs of my own, albeit you have weightier matters to give heed to.

But you told me erstwhile to keep you acquainted

with my studies, and never to weary of learning, but to press forward, seeing that I had rare capacities, and might, by God's help, excel if I were fain.

You must know, then, that for the present I have betaken myself to the University of *Heidelberg*, where I am studying Theology. But I attend likewise a daily lecture on Poetics, and in this art I am making, by God's grace, notable progress.

I already know by rote all the fables of *Ovid* in his *Metamorphoses*, and these I can expound quadruply— to wit, naturally, literally, historically, and spiritually— and this is more than the secular poets can do.

Just now I asked one of those fellows whence "Mavors" is derived. Whereupon he put forth a conjecture, but it was false.

Then I set him right, and told him that *Mavors* was so named as being, so to speak, "mares vorans," a man-eater—and he was put to confusion.

I next demanded of him what is signified allegorically by the Nine Muses. And again he was at fault. Then I told him that the Nine Muses signify the Seven Quires of Angels.[47]

Thirdly, I asked him whence "Mercurius" is derived. But he did not know, and I showed him that *Mercurius* was so named as being "mercatorum curius"—for he is the god of merchants, and curious concerning them.

You will hence understand that nowadays these Poets do but study their art literally, and do not comprehend allegorizing and spiritual expositions: as saith the Apostle, "The natural man receiveth not the things of the spirit of God."

Now you may ask whence I have obtained this subtle skill. I reply that I lately bought a book composed by a certain English Doctor, of our Order, *Thomas of Wales* by name; and this book is all writ concerning *Ovid's Metamorphoses*, explaining each story allegorically and spiritually, and its profundity in Theology passeth belief.

Most assuredly hath the Holy Spirit inspired this man with so great learning, for in his book he setteth forth the harmonies between the Holy Scriptures and the fables of the Poet, and of these you may judge from the instances subjoined :

Of the Python that *Apollo* slew, the *Psalmist* saith, "This dragon which thou hast formed to play therein." And, again, "Thou shalt walk upon the asp and the basilisk."

Concerning *Saturn*—who is always feigned an old man, and the father of the gods—devouring his own children, *Ezekiel* saith : "The fathers shall eat the sons in the midst of thee."

Diana signifieth the Blessed *Virgin Mary*, going hither and thither with a virgin company. And therefore it is written in the *Psalms*, "The virgins that be her fellows"; and, elsewhere, "Draw me, we will run after thee in the savour of thine ointments."

Concerning *Jupiter*, who after the defloration of *Callisto* returned to heaven, it is written, *Matt. xii.*, "I will return to my house from whence I came out."

Of the lapidification of the maiden *Aglauros*, whom *Mercury* turned into a stone, *Job* hinteth, "Whose heart is as firm as a stone."

Also, it is related in Holy Writ how *Jupiter* had commerce with the virgin *Europa*, though formerly I knew it not, for he spake to her thus, "Hearken, O daughter, and consider, and incline thine ear, because the King hath pleasure in thy beauty."

Cadmus, too, seeking for his sister, is a figure of *Christ* who seeketh for his sister, to wit, the soul of man ; and he buildeth a city, that is, the Church.

Concerning *Actaeon*, who beheld Diana naked, *Ezekiel* prophesied, saying, "Thou wast bare and full of confusion, and I passed by thee and saw thee."

Not without cause is it written in the Poets that *Bacchus* was twice born, for by him is denoted Christ, who was twice born, once before the worlds, and a second time humanly and carnally.

Semele also, who nursed *Bacchus*, is an image of the *Blessed Virgin*, of whom it is written in *Exodus*, "Take this child away and nurse it for me, and I will give thee thy wages."

Furthermore the story of *Pyramus* and *Thisbe* is to be allegorically and spiritually expounded thus :

Pyramus signifieth the Son of God, and *Thisbe*, the soul of man, which *Christ* loveth, and concerning which it is written in the Gospel, "A sword shall pierce through thy own soul also." And in like manner *Thisbe* slew herself with her lover's sword.

Concerning *Vulcan*, who was thrown down from heaven and was made lame, it is written in the *Psalms*: "They were cast down and could not stand."

All this, and much more, I have learnt out of that book. If you were but with me you should behold marvellous things.

And this is the way in which we ought to study Poetry.

Nevertheless you will forgive me if I seem, as it were, to be instructing your worthiness (for your learning is greater than mine), but it is in good faith that I have written.

I have arranged that one of the folk at *Tübingen* should keep me informed of Doctor *Reuchlin's* doings, so that I might warn you. But I have learnt nothing, or I would let you know.

And now, farewell, in love unfeigned.

HEIDELBERG.

XXIX

❦ *MAGISTER TILMANN LUMPLIN* to *Magister Ortwin Gratius, greeting*

"I AM more brutish than any man, and have no understanding; I neither learned wisdom, nor have the knowledge of the holy" (*Prov. xxx.*). Yet scorn me not if I make bold to give you counsel in your affairs, for I do this with good intent. I desire, moreover, to monish you according to my knowledge, and modestly to chide you, for "vexation giveth understanding." Now it is written in the *Wisdom* of the *Son of Sirach*, "He that toucheth pitch shall be defiled therewith." And thus it falleth out in your case, since you are fain to have me for a friend; wherefore you must take my chastenings in good part.

I have perceived, or understood, that you hold your peace in the matter of *Johann Reuchlin*, and make no rejoinder to his attacks. Therefore I have great wrath, for I love you, and it is written, " Whom I love, I chasten." Wherefore did you begin to retort to him if you meant not to persevere? Are you not man enough for him? By the Lord you are, and especially do you excel him in Theology, wherefore you should reply to him, and defend your reputation, and preach the Christian Faith, against which that heretic writeth. You should have respect unto no man, as saith *Solomon* in *Ecclus. xiii.*

Fear not the power of the Jurists—lest they should do you carnal hurt—for you must suffer such things for the faith and the truth. As saith *Christ*, in *St. Matthew's* Gospel, " If ye have faith as a grain of mustard seed, ye shall say unto this mountain, remove hence, and it shall remove, and nothing shall be impossible unto you." But it is impossible for Doctor *Reuchlin* to write what is true, for he hath not wholly kept the faith, since he defendeth the Jews, who are foes of the faith; and he holdeth not with the opinions of the Doctors; moreover he is a sinner, as Dr. *Johann Pfefferkorn* setteth forth in his book entitled " *The Tocsin.*" Now sinners should not meddle with Holy Writ, as it is written in the *xlixth Psalm*, " But unto the wicked God saith, What hast thou to do to declare my statutes, or that thou shouldest take my covenant in thy mouth?" Wherefore I exhort you, and I beseech you from my very midriff, to boldly defend yourself, that men may say, to your praise, that you have been a bulwark to the Church and to your own good name. Have respect unto no man—even though the Pope should inhibit you—for the Church is above the Pope.[48]

I pray thee have me excused for counselling you, for I love thee—lord, thou knowest that I love thee.

Fare thee well, in all stoutness of body and of soul.

XXX

❡ *JOHANN SCHNARRHOLTZ, licentiate, in posse, sendeth exuberant greetings, together with his humblest duty, to the most erudite and enlightened Magister Ortwin Gratius, Theologian, Poet and Orator, of Cologne, his most venerated master and preceptor*

MOST cordial and profound Herr Magister *Ortwin:* I, *Johann Schnarrholtz*, ere long licentiate in Theology in the University of *Tübingen*, greatly desire to seek counsel of your worthiness; but I fear lest this may savour of irreverence, seeing that you are of such learning, and of such high repute in *Cologne*, that no man dareth to draw near your worthiness without due forethought—as it is written, "Friend, how camest thou in hither, not having a wedding garment?"

Nevertheless you are lowly-minded, and can bemean yourself, as saith the Scripture, "Whoso humbleth himself shall be exalted, and he that exalteth himself shall be abased." Therefore will I put off diffidence, and confer boldly with your worthiness—yet so as with reverence meet.

I lately heard a certain Magister of *Paris* deliver a sermon here, before a great congregation on the Feast of the Ascension. He took for his text, "God is gone up with a shout"; and he preached a notable sermon, so that all who heard lauded it, and, with tears, were edified. The preacher in the second part of his discourse deduced two masterly and subtle inferences. First, that when the Lord ascended on high with uplifted hands, then the apostles with the *Blessed Virgin* stood and shouted until they were hoarse, that it might be fulfilled which was spoken by the prophet, "I am weary of crying, and my throat is dry." He proved, moreover, that this outcry was a shout of joy, and furthermore necessary for the Catholic faith, as saith the Lord in the Evangel, "Verily, verily I say unto you, if these should hold their peace, the stones would cry out."

61

They all shouted with rapture and great zeal—especially
St. Peter, who had a voice like a sackbut—as *David*
witnesseth, "This poor man cried." The *Blessed Virgin*
shouted not, but praised God in her heart, because she
knew that all these things should come to pass as the
Angel had foreshewn. And while the Apostles thus
shouted together with jubilation and devotion, an angel
came from heaven and said unto them, "Ye men of
Galilee, why stand ye here shouting, and gazing into
heaven? This same *Jesus* who is taken from you into
heaven, shall so come in like manner as you have seen,"
and this was done that the Scripture might be fulfilled
which saith, "They cried, and the Lord heard them."

The second conclusion was yet more profound, as
followeth: The Son of Man had his passion, his burial,
and his resurrection at *Jerusalem*, which is the centre
of the earth, that his resurrection should be manifest in
all regions, and that no heathen might make excuse for
his heresy, and say, "I knew not that the Lord was
risen from the dead." Now whatsoever is at the centre,
all men round about the centre can behold, but in order
that no unbeliever should find the least excuse for eva-
sion, in that place where the Lord ascended, in the
very core and centre of the earth, there hangeth a bell
that all the world can hear, and when it tolleth it
giveth forth dreadful voices concerning Doomsday and
the ascension of the Lord; and its tolling even the deaf
attend. And from this conclusion he deduced many
corollaries which he had learnt in *Paris*. And when
he had ended, a certain Magister from *Erfurt* would
fain cavil at the discourse, but he was discomfited. If
you will tell me of the books that deal with these
matters I will buy them.

BASLE (at the house of the *Beatus Rhenanus*, your friend).[49]

XXXI

❡ *WILLIBRORD NICETI, of the Order of Wilhel-mites, Cursor in Theology,*[50]*by authority of the most reverend the General of his Order, commendeth himself to Bartholomew Colp, qualified Bachelor in Theology, of the Order of Carmelites*

> *As many as drops in the midst of the sea,*
> *Or Beguins in holy Cologne that there be*[51]
> *As many as hairs on a jackass's hide ;*
> *So many my greetings—and many beside.*

VENERABLE Herr Carmelite *Colp,* your Order, I trow, is of the highest, and many the indulgences that you hold from the Apostolic See: no other Order may take precedence of your Order, and many are the cases you can absolve in confession when penitents are contrite and humble and would fain communicate.

I therefore desire to propound to your worship a theological question. This you are well qualified to determine, since you are an Artsman of parts, and can ably preach, and are full of zeal and of a good conscience ; moreover I have heard that you have a fine library in your Convent, in which are many books concerning Holy Scripture, and Philosophy, and Logic, and *Petrus Hispanus ;* the magistral syllabus, too, of the *Lawrence* Hostel, *Cologne,* where resideth acting regent Doctor *von Tongern*—a man right zealous, profoundly versed in speculative Theology, and enlightened in the Catholic Faith. Him a certain Doctor of Laws sought to vex, but—this fellow having no craft in formal disputation nor in the Book of Sentences—the Magisters heeded him not.

Now, above all, I hear that in the library aforesaid, where the Cursors in Theology study, there is confined by a chain of iron a most notable book, named *The Combibilations,*[52]*which* containeth authoritative opinions in Theology, and the first principles of Holy Scripture. This Book, I hear, a certain Divine of Paris bequeathed to you upon his death-bed—when he made confession and revealed certain secrets out of *Bonaventura*—and he ordained that no man should read therein save members of your Order, but to them so doing the Pope granteth certain indulgences and remissions.

Near this book lie *Henricus de Hassia*, and *Verneus*, and all the other commentators on the Book of Sentences, in the which you are versed, and are therefore a tower of strength in every disputation, whether of ancients or moderns, Scotists or Albertists, or even of those who are of the sect of Kuick Hostel in *Cologne*, and have a syllabus all their own.

Therefore I beseech you, heartily and in all charity, that you will take not amiss my petition, but will give me good counsel in my perplexity in so far as in you lies, and will quote to this end what the Doctors lay down thereon in replication and conclusion. Now the aforesaid question is as followeth: "Are the Lollards and Beguins in *Cologne* seculars or religious? Have they taken the vows? Can they wed?"

For a long while have I searched the *Discipulus* and the *Fasciculus Temporum* and other authorities in Holy Writ, but naught have I found thereon. 'Twas the same with a priest at *Fulda*, deeply read in the aforesaid writings, who hath found naught thereon in the *Catalogue* or in the books themselves: he is kinsman of the Pastor there, who is a poet—for he is a good latiniser and he can indite theses withal. Moreover, I am myself vicar at the monastery here and have the cure of many communicants—persons from whom I can make quest. Our Superior himself hath openly declare d that he cannot resolve this question, with ease to his conscience, notwithstanding that he hath attended the disputations of many Doctors at *Paris* and *Cologne*—for he is a qualified licentiate, and hath responded in due form and manner to that end.

If you are unable to decide this matter, I beg you to make enquiry of Magister *Ortwin*, and he will make all things clear—*Gratius* is he called by virtue of that divine grace within him which knoweth all things. I have put together an heroic ode concerning the book aforesaid; prithee read it and correct it, and make a mark where I have a foot too much or too little: learn,

too, what Magister *Ortwin* thinketh of it; and then I
will send it to the printer.　Followeth:—

> In pride presumptuous, who but a fool
> From *Bonaventure* pregnant truths by rule
> Would try to draw, or out of Holy Writ
> Would seek enlightenment, while not a whit
> He knoweth of the great *Combibilations*,
> By learned Doctors taught to all the nations?
> In every University professed,
> But first in *Paris*—dam of all the rest.
> *Cologne* divines, hamm'ring the question out,
> By proof seraphic shewed, without a doubt,
> *Combibilations* better 'tis to quote
> Than *Jerome* and *Augustine* cou by rote—
> (Although they scribbled Latin well enough.)
> *Combibilations* are the primest stuff!
> When Doctors in each Monast'ry contend,
> With word divine *Combibilations* end
> The brabble—and they rummage to the root
> Theology : some other things they moot.

XXXII

❧ *To Magister Ortwin Gratius, that man of un-
utterable learning, MAGISTER GINGOLF
HOLZHACKER offereth a thousand thousand
greetings in love unfeigned*

GLORIOUSEST of Magisters: I have loved thee
in my very midriff, with an innermost affection,
from the time when thou wert my very own teacher at
Deventer : and whatsoever goadeth thee in thy heart,
that goadeth me more, and whatsoever goadeth me,
that, I know, goadeth thee, and thy goad hath always
been my goad, and no man ever goaded thee who did
not goad me the more sharply, and my heart feeleth
the goad whensoever any one goadeth thee : believe
me faithfully that when *Hermann Buschius* goadeth thee
in that "*Prooemium*" of his he goadeth me more than
thee, and I have taken thought how I could goad in
turn that impudent brangler, who is of such presumptu-
ous arrogance as to dare to goad the Doctors of Divinity
of *Paris* and *Cologne!*　Yet he is himself not graduated

—though his comrades avow that he proceeded Bachelor of Laws at *Leipsic.* But this I credit not, for he even goadeth Magisters in *Leipsic,* to wit, *Hundt* senior and *Hundt* junior, and many others, who are much the apter to goad him than he is to goad them; but they desire to goad no man, on moral grounds, and according to the precept of the Apostle, "Kick not against the goads." Nevertheless it is meet for thee to goad him in return, for thou hast a fine intellect and art a cunning deviser, and in a single hour thou canst contrive metrical goads, and canst goad him concerning all his words and deeds. I have put together a tractate against him wherein I magistrally and poetically goad him; he can by no means evade my goad. And if he ventureth to goad me in return, I will goad him again the more sharply.

In haste, from STRASBURG, at the house of *Matthew Schürer.*[53]

XXXIII

❧ *MAMMOTRECT BUNTEMANTEL,*[54] *Magister in the Seven Liberal Arts, sendeth right hearty greeting to Magister Ortwin Gratius, Philosopher, Orator, Poet, Jurist, and Theologian, of discretionary Faculty*

RIGHT conscionable Herr Magister *Ortwin,* believe me in good sooth, you have been mine own dear heart from the days wherein I heard much discourse on Poetry from your worthiness at *Cologne,* where you overtop all others in that art, for you are a Poet much more excellent than *Buschius* or *Cæsarius*[55]—and can moreover expound *Pliny* and Greek Grammar.

In all confidence, therefore, I desire to disclose somewhat to your reverence under seal of confession.

Reverend Herr Magister, I have become enamoured of a damsel here, *Margaret* by name, the daughter of a bell-ringer. No long while ago she sat by your own side, to wit when the parson invited your worship to the feast, and treated you with deference due; when we drank and were merry, she too pledged you in great bumpers.

Her I love with such passion that I am beside myself. Believe me, because of her I can neither eat nor sleep. Folk say to me, "Herr Magister, why so pale? For the love of God quit your books; you study over much; you should now and again seek some diversion, and drink deep; you are yet in your youth, and are well able to proceed Doctor and become Magister Noster. You are a profound and able scholar, and are almost the equal of a Doctor."

But I am bashful, and cannot unfold my disorder. I have studied *Ovid*, "Of the Remedy of Love," which I annotated at *Cologne* under your worthiness, with many notabilia and moralisations in the margin—but it availeth not, for this love of mine waxeth from day to day.

Lately I danced with her thrice, at an evening junketing at the Mayor's house. The piper struck up the tune of "The Shepherds of Neustadt," and straightway all the dancers clasped their partners, as is the wont—so I also hugged mine right lovingly, with her bosom next my heart, and tightly did I squeeze her hand. Then she simpered, and said, "By my soul, Herr Magister, you are a sweet man, and you have softer hands than the others; you must not be a priest, you must take a wife!" Then she eyed me so amorously that I believe she loveth me—secretly. Her glance, in sooth, wounded my heart as though an arrow had pierced it, and straightway I went home with my servant, and flung myself upon my bed.

Then my mother fell a-weeping, because she thought I was sick of the plague, and she ran with my water to Dr. *Brunell*, crying out, "Herr Doctor, I beseech you by the Lord to heal my son; I will give you a fine shirt for a fee, because I made a vow that he should become a priest!" Then the leech cast the water, and said, "The patient is partly cholerical, and partly phlegmatical; there is danger of great intumescence in his reins, with tympanies and abdominal colics from ill concoctions. He must needs have recourse to a purgative There is a simple named Gyni, which groweth in moist places and hath a rank odour, as the *Herbarius* teacheth : the roots of this herb you must triturate with the juice thereof, and therewith you must make a great cataplasm, and cover his paunch with it at the accustomed time, and he must lie upon his belly a full hour, sweating profusely.   And thus without a doubt his colicky pains and tympanies will abate, for there is no other medicament so effectual as this for his distemper, as has been proved in the case of many patients.   But it will assuredly be proper for him first to take a cathartic of *Album Græcum*[56] and radish juice—four drachms of each—and all will be well."

Then came my mother, and gave me that concoction, sorely against my will, and I was purged five times ere dawn, and I slept not at all, but all the while I ceased not to think of how I had embraced the damsel at the dance, with her breast to mine, and how she looked at me.

Now I beseech you, by all your bowels of mercy, give me a remedy for Love out of that little book of yours wherein is written "I have tried this." You once showed it to me, saying, "See, with this book I can make any woman love me!"

And unless you do this, Herr Magister, I shall die, and for grief my mother will die too.

HEIDELBERG.

XXXIV

❧ *MAGISTER ORTWIN GRATIUS to his most learned friend, in friendship's loftiest rank, Magister Mammotrectus, sendeth salutations*

INASMUCH as the Scripture saith, "The Lord shall defend them who go simply," I greatly commend your worthiness, most argute Herr Magister, in that you have opened your inmost heart to me so frankly, and yet with a nice concinnity and a pretty trick in Latinising.   I, in like manner, will write to you congruously with the canons of Rhetoric, and not as a poet.

Most amicable Herr Magister, you have unfolded
to me your amours, but I marvel that you are not too
prudent to hanker after maidens; I warn you that in
this you do ill, and that you have a sinful end in view,
that may bring you to hell-fire.   I deemed you prudent,
and one that had no mind for such follies, for they ever
have an ill event.

Nevertheless I will give you the counsel that you
seek—as saith the Scripture, "Ask ye, and ye shall
take."   First, you must cast aside those vain imagin-
ings concerning that *Margaret* of yours, for they are
suggested to you by the Devil, who is the father of all
sin—as *Richard* allegeth, in his comment on the Fourth
Book.   Whensoever thoughts of her assail you, fail not
to cross yourself and say a paternoster, with that verse
of the Psalms, "The *Devil* stand at his right side."
Neglect not to eat consecrated salt on the Lord's Day,
and sprinkle yourself with holy water that the priest of
St. Rupert hath blessed.   Thus may you escape from
that devil who hath instilled in you so great fervour for
this *Margaret*—who, after all, is not so comely as you
think her; she hath a wart on her forehead, long red
shanks, and clumsy brown hands, and her breath
savoureth because of her foul teeth; moreover she
hath a heavy stern, in accordance with the common
saying that "*Ars Margaretæ* is a wonderful snare."
But you are so blinded by that devil-begotten passion
that you perceive not her faults.   She eateth and
drinketh over much, and when she sat by me at table
she made a bounce and said it was the foot-stool.   A
fairer wench than your *Margaret* was mine at *Cologne*,
nevertheless I sent her packing.   After she was wedded
she often used to send for me through an old crone—
yet I visited her but once, and then I was fuddled.   I
counsel you to fast twice on the Sabbath, and afterwards to make confession to a Doctor of the *Order of
Preachers*, who will set you on your legs again.   And
when you have made confession you must pray to *St.
Christopher* to bear you on his shoulders, that you
backslide not, nor be soused in that great and wide
sea wherein are creeping things innumerable—that is,
numberless sins, as saith the *Combibilator*—and, finally,

pray that you enter not into temptation. Arise betimes, wash your hands, comb your hair and be not
slothful; for the Scripture saith, "God my God,
to thee from light I wake." Avoid too, houses
of ill-fame, for we well know that places and op-
portunities oft lead men into sin, and especially into
lechery.

In that you desire to learn from me an experience
in fascination, I must tell you that my conscience
forbiddeth. When I expounded to you here *Ovid* in
his "Art of Love," I warned you that no man ought
to compass the love of women by the Black Art; and
whoso gainsayeth this is in sooth excommunicate, and
the Inquisitors of Heretical Pravity may hale him and
condemn him to the stake.

This former ensample, I pray you, bear in thy mind:
A certain Bachelor of *Leipsic* became enamoured of a
maiden—*Katherine* by name—the daughter of a miller,
and he tossed her a magical apple, which she caught
and placed in her bosom, between her breasts. Thereupon on a sudden she began to love that Bachelor like
a fury, so that when she was in church she could not
refrain her eyes from him, and when she should have
said, "Pater noster qui es in cælo," she cried, "Oh,
Bachelor, where art thou?" Even at home, when her
father or mother called to her, she would answer, "Yes,
Bachelor! What is your will?" Now the old folk
comprehended not the matter, until a certain Doctor
of Divinity, passing by the house, greeted the maiden,
saying, "Goodden, Mistress *Katherine!* Save you!
you have a fine comb!" Thereupon *Katherine* made
answer, "God be praised, dear Bachelor! Wilt join
with me in a draught of good ale?" And she held
out a tankard to him. Then was that divine mightily
wrath, and he made his complaint to her mother, and
said, "Mistress *Müller*, correct your daughter, for she
behaveth herself frowardly, and hath insulted our
University, in that she called me 'Bachelor,' whereas
I am Magister Noster! Verily, verily, I say unto you
that she hath committed a deadly sin; she hath robbed
me of my good fame; and this sin is not remitted
until she hath restored that which she hath filched.

Other Doctors, too, she hath called 'Bachelor'—take
heed therefore."

Thereupon her mother took a cudgel, and laid it
about her head and back till she beshamed herself;
and then she shut her up in her chamber for half a
year, and fed her on bread and water. In the meanwhile the Bachelor gained preferment, and celebrated
his first mass, and then received a cure of souls at
Pardau in *Saxony*. But when the maiden heard
thereof she leaped from a lofty window and came nigh
to breaking her arm, and fled to *Saxony*, to the aforesaid Bachelor. She dwelleth with him unto this day,
and hath borne him four sons. You know right well
that this is a grievous scandal in the Church. Take
heed, therefore, and shun that Black Art from which so
many evils flow. But by all means use that recipe of
Gyni that Dr. *Brunell* hath prescribed. 'Tis a sovran
remedy, and I have ofttimes tried it against such
colicky spasms.

Fare ye well—you and your mother.

From COLOGNE; at *Johann Pfefferkorn's* house.

XXXV

❦ *LYRA BUNTSCHUHMACHER,*[58]*Theologian,
of the Order of Preachers, to Wilhelm Hackinet,*[59]
Most Theological of Theologians, greeting

YOU have written me, from *London* in *England,* a
long letter excellently well Latinised, and in it
you adjure me to send you some tidings, whether good
or bad, since you are by nature inclined ever to be
hearkening to news—as are all men of a sanguine complexion, who delight to hear the concords of sweet
music, and are of joyful heart at the board.

I was greatly gladdened when I received your letter,
and was as one who findeth a precious pearl; and I
shewed it to Herren *John Grocyn*[60]and *Linacre,*[61]saying:
"See, my lords, see; is not this Doctor a paragon in
latinity, and composition, and the epistolary art?"

And they vowed that they could not themselves write such a letter in the Latin tongue, though poets, and possessed both of Greek and Latin.

They extolled you, indeed, above all writers in *England, France* and *Germany,* and in every other nation under heaven.

Small wonder then that you are General of your Order, and that in *France* the king loveth you; for you have no peer in Latinising, nor in disputation, nor in preaching; and right well do you know how to instruct the King and the Queen in the confessional.

The two poets aforesaid also lauded you, in that you were skilled in the art rhetorical; but there was a certain young man, *Richard Croke*[62]by name, who alleged against you that you did not write according to the Canons of the Art of Rhetoric: but when he made shift to prove his words he was put to confusion.

He is now at *Leipsic,* studying the Logic of *Peter of Spain:* I trow in future he will be more heedful.

But, to come to the news: The Swissers and the Landsknechts[63]have been mightily waging war,[64] and slaying one another in thousands; and it is to be feared that none of them will go to heaven, because they fight for pelf, and one Christian ought not to slay another. But these are matters that you heed not; the soldiers are but lewd folk, and they fight because they list.

Another piece of news is graver—God grant that it be not true—it is reported from *Rome* that *Johann Reuchlin's Augenspiegel*[65]hath been newly translated from the mother-tongue into Latin by the command of my lord the Pope, and that in more than two hundred passages it differeth in the Latin from the rendering made by the Doctors and Herr *Johann Pfefferkorn* at *Cologne;* they say too, for certain, that it is openly read in *Rome,* and is printed with the *Talmud* of the Jews. And they conclude from this that the Doctors are infamous falsifiers, because they have translated ill;[66] also that they are asses, ignorant of both Latin and German; and that as they burnt that book at *St. Andrew's* in *Cologne,* so ought they to burn their own Verdict, and the Verdict of *Paris,* or be themselves held as heretics.

I could weep tears of blood, so greatly do I grieve! Who that hears such things will study Theology any more, or show the Doctors of Divinity condign reverence? All folk will believe that Doctor *Reuchlin* hath more learning than the Divines : though this is impossible.

It is reported too, that after three months a final decree against the Doctors will issue ; and that the Pope will command, under pain of the severest censure, that the friars of the *Order of Preachers*, shall on account of their insolence, wear, in white, upon the back of their black mantles, a pair of spectacles, or barnacles, in perpetual memorial, to their shame, of their having wrought ill to the *Eyeglass* of Herr *Johann Reuchlin*, as they are also held to be disgraced on account of the poisoning of some Emperor or other during the celebration of mass.

But I hope the Pope will not be such a noddy as to do this; if he doth, we must everywhere throughout our Order, recite against him the Psalm " *Deus, laudem.*"

The Fathers and Doctors are pondering how to stave off this calamity. They purpose to seek from the Apostolic See plenary indulgences, and to collect great store of money in *Germany* and *France*, and by this means to hold out against that abettor of the Jews, until he die—for he is an old man. And then they will totally damn him.

Farewell, give counsel to the extent of your ability, and labour for the good of our Order.

XXXVI

¶ *EITELNARRABIANUS VON PESSE-NECK, Cursor in Theology, of the Order of St. Wilhelm, sendeth innumerable salutations to Mag. Ortwin Gratius*

" WE are by nature prone to sin," as we read in the *Authentica*. Hence it followeth that among men we hear more evil than good report. I lately held disputation at *Worms* with two Jews, and proved that

their Law was made by *Christ* of none effect, and that
their expectation of a *Messiah* was mere moonshine;
and on this matter I quoted Herr *Johann Pfefferkorn*
of *Cologne*. Then they laughed, and said, "That *Johann
Pfefferkorn* of yours is a vile braggart; he knoweth no
Hebrew, and he became a Christian to hide his naughti-
ness. When he was yet a Jew, in *Moravia*, seeing a
woman standing at a money-changer's counter, he smote
her in the face, so that she was blinded, and seizing
more than two hundred florins, he made off with them.
Elsewhere a gallows was set up that he might be hanged
thereon for theft, but by some means or other he escaped
scot-free; we have seen the gallows ourselves, and so
have many Christians, and some noblemen, whom we
can name. Call not to witness, therefore, a thief like
him." Then was I wrath, and made answer, "You lie
in your throats, vile Jews! Were you not privileged,
I would seize you by the weasand and roll you in the
mire! You speak thus out of hatred to Herr *Johann
Pfefferkorn;* he is as good and zealous a Christian as
any in *Cologne:* this I know from observation, for he
confesseth regularly to the *Dominicans*, together with
his wife; he rejoiceth to hear mass, and when the priest
elevateth the Host he regardeth it devoutly, and casteth
not his eyes down to the ground, as his revilers aver—
save when he hawketh, and this he doth because he is
rheumy and taketh pectorals of a morning. Think you
that the Doctors and Burgomasters of *Cologne* are fools,
who have set him over the *Revilien Hospital*, and made
him surveyor of salt? Assuredly they would not have
this done if he had not been a good Catholic. I warn
you that I shall relate all your words to him, for he can
well defend his honour, and trounce you to some purpose by writing about your own Confession. You say,
forsooth, that he is cockered by the Magisternosters and
Burgomasters because he hath a fair wife. But this is
not sooth, for the Burgomasters have fair wives themselves, and the Magisternosters pay no heed to woman-
kind; none ever heard tell of a Magisternoster who was
a gallant! The dame is as honest a matron as any in
Cologne; she would rather lose an eye than her good
fame. Moreover I have often heard that her mother

used to say that the circumcised are dearer to a woman's heart than the uncircumcised; wherefore she declareth that when her husband dieth, and she taketh another spouse, he must be one who hath been fitly trimmed. It is unbelievable, therefore, that she hankereth after Burgomasters, who have never been Jews, and are not circumcised as is Herr *Johann Pfefferkorn.* Wherefore leave him in peace, else he will launch against you a tractate which he will call *The Tocsin,* as he did against *Reuchlin.*" It would be well for you to show this letter of mine to Herr *Johann Pfefferkorn,* that he may stoutly defend himself against such Jews as these, and against *Hermann Busch,* for *Pfefferkorn* is mine own familiar friend, and lent me ten florins when I was admitted qualified Bachelor in Theology.

From BONN; where *Buschius* and his crony board together at "The Fatted Hen."

XXXVII

❧ *LUPOLD FEDERFUCHSER, Licentiate—in a little while—sendeth to Mag. Gratius greetings as many as are the blades of grass in a goose's supper*

HERR MAGISTER ORTWIN, among the quodlibets[67] at *Erfurt* a vengeance subtle question hath been mooted in the two Faculties of Theology and Natural Philosophy.

The one part hold that when a Jew becometh a Christian there ensueth a preputial regeneration, or retrieval of the virile deprivation inflicted in childhood under the Judaic law.

These disputants are of the Theological Faculty, and they allege for their part sundry weighty reasons, one whereof is that were it not so, Jews who had become Christians might be regarded as being yet Jews at the last Judgment—their virile deficiency being made manifest—and hence an injury would be done to them; but the Lord doth injury to no man.—Q.E.D.

And they find another argument in the words of the *Psalmist,* who saith: " He covereth me in the day of evils, in the secret place he covereth me ": but " the day of evils" meaneth the Day of Doom in the *Valley of Jehoshaphat*, when account of all sins must be rendered. Other arguments I omit for brevity's sake, for we at *Erfurt* are moderns, and the moderns ever delight in brevity, as you know. Moreover, in that my memory is weak, I cannot learn by rote a multitude of citations, as do the Jurists.

But there are others who contend that this argument holdeth not, and they quote *Plautus* on their side, who saith: "What is done cannot be undone." From this they prove that if a Jew in the days of his Judaism hath lost any portion of his corporality he will by no means recover it in Christian baptism. They argue, too, that their opponents' proof concludeth illogically; for, from their major premiss it would follow that Christians who had, through loose living, suffered some carnal deficiency—as happeneth many a time to both secular and spiritual persons—would also be held to be Jews at the Last Judgment.

But this is an heretical conclusion, and our Masters the Inquisitors of Heretical Pravity will by no means grant it, seeing that they themselves are now and then a trifle lacking thereabouts—a mishap which occurreth to them by no means from consorting with wantons, but from lack of care at the baths. Most humbly and devotedly I pray your worship, therefore, to determine the truth of this matter once for all by your decision, and to make enquiries of Herr *Pfefferkorn's* wife, seeing that you stand in her good graces, and she will not be backward in telling you whatsoever you ask in the name of the close friendship you have with her husband. Moreover, I hear that you are her confessor, and therefore you may compel her to due obedience under pain of penance.

Say to her: "Madam, be not bashful! I know you for as honest a lady as any in *Cologne:* and nothing dishonest do I ask from you. I do but seek to learn the truth from you: is your husband of the circumcision, or not? Speak boldly, without shame! Od's life! have you lost your tongue?" But I must not presume to instruct you, for you know much better than I how to deal with women. I write in haste.

From ERFURT: at the sign of the *Dragon*.

XXXVIII

❡ *PETERMANN KACHELOFEN, Licentiate,*
to Magister Ortwin Gratius most salutiferous
salutations

YOU wrote to me of late from *Cologne*, and chided
me for not writing to you, since, you averred,
you read my letters with more relish than any others,
inasmuch as their style is good, and they are artificially
composed according to the Epistolary Rules that I
learnt from your worthiness in *Cologne*. But I may
tell you that I have not always inspiration, and matter
withal, such as is now mine.

You must know that a public Disputation is being
held here, and the Magisters and Doctors exhibit their
craft and profundity in deciding, solving, and propound-
ing questions, arguments, and problems concerning all
things knowable. The Poets and Orators, too, prove
themselves highly skilled and learned, and amongst
them there standeth forth one who is woundily
magistral in that art above all the rest, and he
assumes a brave title in announcing his lectures—for
he alleges that he is the Poet of poets, and that
besides him there is none other poet.

He hath written a treatise all in verse, with a mighty
fine name—what it is called I have forgot, but I trow
it handleth wrath and choler—and in that treatise he
vexeth many of the Magisters, and the other poets
who hindered him from lecturing in the University, on
account of his licentious art. The Magisters, moreover, tell him to his face that he is not so fine a poet
as he boasteth himself to be, and they oppose him
stoutly, and prove their case by citing you, seeing that
you are more deeply immersed in the art poetical.
They prove too that he is not well grounded in the
quantities of syllables, as the Master of *Villedieu*
determines them in his Third Book (which the fellow
seemeth not to have duly studied), and they prove their

case by many arguments. *Imprimis*, by means of your name—and this in twofold fashion. First: this fellow would fain be a deeper poet than Magister *Ortwin*, and yet his very name will not suffer it.

Magister *Ortwin* manifestly hath the name *Gratius* from the grace given him from on high (which is called grace because it is given *gratis*), for you could not compose those profound poems without that gratuitous grace given you by the divine spirit that breatheth where it listeth. It is through your humility that you have obtained this, for " God withstandeth proud men, but to meek men he giveth grace." They who read your poetry, and understand such matters, vow that you have no peer, and marvel that this fellow can be so doltish and irreverent as to wish to excel you, when a child may see that you surpass him as doth the *Labyrinthus* the *Cornutus*.

The Magisters desire to collect your writings, and to print those that are scattered about in sundry tractates—as, for instance, in that book of Doctor *von Tongern*, High-master of *Lawrence Hostel*, against *Johann Reuchlin's* scandalous theses—in the " *Sentimentum Parisiense*"—and in many a treatise of Herr *Johann Pfefferkorn*, once a Jew but now best of Christians. They fear that otherwise your poetry will be lost, and they declare that it would be a disgrace to the age—nay, a mortal sin—if through neglect it should perish and not be printed. The Magisters pray that you will deign to send them your *Vindication* in reply to *Johann Reuchlin*, in which you soundly trounce that swaggering doctor who dares to contend with four universities : they would fain transcribe your work and restore it to you.

Among those who rely on the aforesaid arguments are Magister *Johann Kirchberg*, mine own particular friend and fellow-graduate—Magister *Johann Hungen*, my most loving friend—Magister *Jakob von Nürnberg*, Magister *Jodok Windsheim*, and many other Magisters, my own right worthy friends, and your undaunted well-wishers.

Some there are, nevertheless, who object, and say that albeit this mode of proof is indeed subtle, and the

conclusion regular, it accords not with your intention;
for it would sound vainglorious to say, "Sirs, I am
named *Gratius* after that grace from on high which
God hath given me in Poetry and all things knowable."
For this would seem to fit but ill with that lowliness
through which you received that grace, and argueth a
certain inconcinnity; for supernal grace and pride
cannot coexist, since grace is a virtue, and pride is a
vice, and these are incompatible; for "one of two
countraries expelleth the other, as heat drives out
cold": as saith the poet, according to *Petrus Hispanus*
in the "*Prædicamenta*," who showeth that virtue is the
opposite of vice.

Another solution is therefore much to be preferred,
to wit, that *Gratius* is so named after the Roman
Gracchi, a letter being dropped for euphony's sake.
Now concerning these *Gracchi* we read in Roman
History that they were very famous poets and orators,
and that in *Rome* in those days their equals were not
to be found, subtle and skilled as they in Poetry and
Rhetoric. It is related, too, that their voices were soft
and sweet, not strident and harsh, but dulcet as a flute.
And sometimes it was to the sound of a flute that they
opened their discourses, wherefore the people listened
to them with the liveliest delight, and lauded them
above all others in that art. Now it was from these
Gracchi that Magister *Ortwin* was surnamed *Gratius*.
For, in turn, no man is his equal in poetry, or in
dulcitude of voice. He surpasseth all, just as the
Gracchi overtopped all the poets of *Rome*. Therefore
the aforesaid poet of *Wittenberg* should keep silent and
humble himself: he is learned after a fashion, but compared to you he is a child.

This second proof is adopted by my familiar friends
Eoban Hessus, Magister *Heinrich Urbanus*, *Ritius
Euritius*, Magister *Georg Spalatin*,[68] *Ulrich Hutten*,
and especially Doctor *Ludwig Mistotheus*,[69] my honoured
friend and protector. Prithee, write and tell me which
are on the right track, and what is the truth of the
matter. And a mass shall be read for you that you
may get the better of Doctor *Reuchlin*, who un-
deservedly dubbed you a heretic in that you wrote

in your verse, "Jove's holy mother wept." Fare ye
well, in all holiness.

From WITTENBERG, at the Castle, with Magister *Spalatin,* who sends
you greetings as many as the Hallelujahs sung between Easter and
Whitsuntide. Farewell, once more, and be of joyous countenance.

XXXIX

❡ *NIKOLAUS LUMINATORIS sendeth to Herr
Magister Ortwin as many greetings as there be
fleas and midges begotten in a year*

MAGISTER *ORTWIN*, most learned preceptor,
I render you more thanks than I have hairs on
my body, for that you counselled me to trudge to
Cologne and study at *Lawrence Hostel.* My father
was well pleased thereat, and gave me ten florins;
furthermore he bought me a long gown with a black
hood. On the very day when I arrived at the University, and underwent initiation at the aforesaid hostel, I
learned a most noteworthy thing that I would not have
missed for ten silver pieces. A certain poet, one
Hermann Buschius, came to the hostel to confer with
the vice-regent on business. Thereupon the vice-
regent took him by the hand, and greeted him deferen-
tially, saying, "Whereof is this thing to me, that the
mother of the Lord cometh to me?" But *Buschius*
made answer, "If the Lord had a mother no fairer than
I am, of a truth she was not very comely!" Thus he
failed to comprehend the subtle rhetorical allegory that
the vice-regent had intended by his greeting!

I trust that I shall yet learn in this benign Univer-
sity many things as profitable as this notable topic.
To-day I bought the Statutes of the Hostel; to-morrow
I must argue in an academical disputation on this theme:
"Whether prime matter is an actual or potential entity."

LAWRENCE HOSTEL, COLOGNE.

XL

¶ HERBORD MISTLADER offereth to Magister Ortwin Gratius of learning incomparable, his own most sapient preceptor, salutations that no man may number

ALL-ENLIGHTENED Magister! When I parted from your worthiness at *Zwolle*, two years agone, you plighted your troth that you would write oft to me, and would provide for me in your writings patterns of fair diction. But, alas, you have gone from your word, and write not to tell me if you be quick or dead—and, whether you be alive or dead, you tell me not which, or what hath happed, or how the matter standeth. Dear Lord! how you rack me! I beseech you, by the Lord and *St. George*, free me from my solicitude; for I am in great dread lest you have a headache, or some infirmity in your bowels, with a flux such as you once had when you berayed your garments in the public street and perceived it not until a woman cried out, "Herr Magister! hast thou been sitting on a mixen? See! even thy skirts and shoes are slubbered!" And then you turned in to *Johann Pfefferkorn's* house, and his wife gave you a change of raiment. It behoveth you to eat hard-boiled eggs, and roasted chestnuts, and cooked beans sprinkled with poppy-seed, as is the wont in your country of *Westphalia*. I have dreamed a dream concerning you—that you have a grievous cough and much rheume withal; eat therefore sugar-plums, and peas mashed with thyme and pounded garlic; lay a roasted onion on your navel, and be continent for six days; wrap up your head and your loins, and you will be cured.

Or you may try the remedy that *Johann Pfefferkorn's* wife hath often given to the infirm, and the virtue whereof hath oft been proved.

From ZWOLLE.

XLI

❡ FILIPPAZZO OF ANTWERP, Bachelor, sendeth greetings numberless to his own particular friend, Magister Ortwin Gratius

THERE was a certain religious of the Order of Preachers, a disciple of Doctor *Jakob von Hoogstraten*, who came to me and saluted me. Straightway I asked him, "How doth my own particular friend, Magister *Ortwin Gratius*, from whom I have learnt much lore in Logic and Poetry?" Thereupon he replied that you were in ill-health, and immediately I fell upon the earth at his feet in dismay. Then that religious drenched me with cold water, and twitched my hairs, and with much ado revived me; then I cried, "Ah! how grievously you have terrified me: what is his malady?" And he told me that your right pap was swollen, and that you were galled, and hindered in your studies, by the anguish of that distemper. Then I came to my senses and cried, "Ha! is it no more than that? I can cure that ailment; I know the healing thereof by experience. But Herr Magister, learn first whence that infirmity proceedeth." And therewith I set forth the remedy: When wanton wenches see a proper man, like yourself, with auburn locks, to wit, and brown or hazel eyes, and ruddy lips, and a fine nose, and portly withal, straightway they hanker after him. But when he is virtuous, and a man of learning, like yourself, who pays no heed to their follies and wiles, then they resort to magic arts, and at night, mounted on besoms, they ride thereon to the comely man of their heart, and visit him in his sleep—but to him all is naught but a dream. And some assume the shapes of cats and birds, and suck the blood from their good man's breast, and at times make him so weak that he can scarce hobble with a staff.

It is, I trow, the devil who teacheth them these tricks. Nevertheless, this is the way to frustrate them, as I read in the Doctors' Library at *Rostock*, out of a very ancient book ; and afterwards I made trial of it, and it proved true.

Upon a Sunday take some consecrated salt, and with it make the sign of the cross upon the tongue, and eat it, as saith the Scripture, "Vos estis sal terrae," which is by interpretation, "Eat ye the salt of the earth." Afterwards make the sign of the cross upon the breast, and again on the back ; in like manner put some salt in each ear, not omitting the sign of the cross, and taking heed that none fall out. Finally recite the following devout prayer :—

> "Jesu Christe Domine,
> And Evangels four, do ye
> Fend me from ev'ry harlot's harm,
> And from the sorceress's charm—
> Lest she my blood shall suck, and wring
> My paps with anguish : I will bring
> If ye preserve me, as oblation,
> A pretty asperge for lustration."

And thus you will be delivered. And if the blood-suckers come again and gorge, they will fall sick themselves.

And, now, how standeth it with Doctor *Reuchlin?* The Magisters here say that he is too much for you ; but I cannot believe that he can overcome Magister-nosters. All the more do I wonder that you do not write somewhat against him.

Fare ye well, more than eternally. Greet for me Herr *Johann Pfefferkorn* and his wife : tell them that I wish them more good nights than the minutes that the astronomers reckon.

FRANKFORT-ON-ODER.

XLII

❡ *ANTON N., of the Art of Medicine almost Doctor—Licentiate, to wit, but shortly to be graduated—sendeth greeting to the inestimable Mag. Ortwin Gratius, his venerated teacher*

PRECEPTOR unparalleled ! Seeing that a little while ago you requested me to tell you the news, you must know that I have but now attained *Stras-*

burg, journeying from *Heidelberg,* to purchase certain drugs that, as I believe you know, we use in our medicaments. For it is the custom amongst your physicians, if aught be lacking in their stores, to proceed elsewhither to procure it for the practice of their Art. But let this pass. As soon as I arrived hither, there came to me a good friend, and one very well-disposed towards me ; you know him well, for he was for a long while under your ferule at *Cologne*—and he told me of a man named *Erasmus* of *Rotterdam,* of whom I had never heard, but who is profoundly skilled in all knowledge and in every branch of learning. This man, he told me, was even then at *Strasburg.* (I could not believe, and I yet cannot bring myself to believe, that a man so small as he is could know so much.) Thereupon I earnestly begged my friend to bring me to *Erasmus* that I might see him. I had with me a note-book that I call my medical *Vade-mecum*—for I always carry it with me when I walk abroad to visit patients, or to buy simples—and in this are jotted down sundry very subtle questions concerning the medical art. Out of this notebook, therefore, I culled me a question with all the comments thereon, and the arguments *pro* and *con,* and armed with these I purposed to beset this man whom they deem so learned, and make trial whether he knew somewhat of Medicine, or not. Now when I told my friend my intent, he made a great feast, and bade to it speculative Theologians, and Jurists of high renown, and myself as a representative, all unworthy, of the Art Medicinal.

Now, when we were set, for a long while there was a silence, and from modesty no man would break it ; then I nudged my neighbour, for of a sudden—heaven knoweth how—there rushed into my mind :—

"*Conticuere omnes, intentique ora tenebant.*"

This verse I still have fresh in my memory, for when you expounded to us *Virgil* in his Eneid, I limned beside it a man with a bolt on his mouth, to mark the passage, as you bade us.

At the last it was fairly brought to the proof, whether that wiseacre was indeed a poet, as the report

went.　For as we all sat in silence, he began to hold
forth in a mighty long preamble.

But of this—else am I no true-born man—I understood not a single word, by reason that he had such a
wee little voice; I think he did in some sort handle
theology, and this to engage a certain Magister Noster,
a man of vast profundity in matters theological, who
sat with us at board.

Thereupon, when *Erasmus* had concluded that pre-
lude, the Magister Noster began to argue with great
subtlety concerning entity and essence—but it skilleth
not that I should recall his words, for you are well
versed in such matters.　When he had finished,
Erasmus replied, but briefly, and once more we all sat
silent.　Our host, therefore, who is a humanist of parts,
fell to some discourse on Poetry, and greatly belauded
Julius Caesar, as touching both his writings and his
valorous deeds.　So soon as I heard this, I perceived
my opportunity, for I had studied much, and learned
much under you in the matter of Poetry, when I was
at *Cologne*, and I said, "Forasmuch as you have begun
to speak concerning Poetry, I can therefore no longer
hide my light under a bushel, and I roundly aver that I
believe not that *Caesar* wrote those *Commentaries*, and
I will prove my position with argument following,
which runneth thus: Whosoever hath business with
arms and is occupied in labour unceasing cannot learn
Latin; but *Caesar* was ever at War and in labours
manifold; therefore he could not become lettered and
get Latin.　In truth, therefore, I believe that it was
none other than *Suetonius* who wrote those *Commentaries*, for I have met with none who hath a style liker
to *Caesar's* than *Suetonius*."

After I had this spoken, and much else which
here, for brevity's sake, I set not down—since, as you
know from the ancient saw, "The moderns delight in
brevity"—*Erasmus* laughed, but said nothing, for I had
overthrown him by the subtilty of my argument.　And
so we made an end of the feast, and I propounded not
my question in the Art of Medicine, for I well knew
that he could not resolve it, since he could not answer
me that argument in Poetry.　He, a poet!　Pardy, I

declare that there is not so much in him as they say. In the way of Poetry I admit that he can speak fair Latin. But what of that? We can learn many such things as that in a year. But in respect of the philosophic sciences, such as Theology and Medicine, much more hath to be done if one would fain learn them. And yet would he be held a Theologian. But, my good Master, what kind of Theologian? A novice, forsooth, who dealeth with words alone, and tasteth not the inner meanings of things; as though—to make a fair comparison—one should desire to eat a nut, and yet only eat the outer husk, and come not at the kernel within. Thus it standeth with such triflers, according to my own dull understanding. But of this you know much more than I, for I hear that even now you are minded to assume the robes of the Doctorate of Theology—to which may God and the Holy Mother exalt you. Nevertheless, I will say this on my own behalf—that I be not more tedious than I had purposed—that I would gain more by my art—if God but grant that sick folk be multiplied—in a week, than *Erasmus* or any other Poet in a year. Let this, then, suffice for the present. Good luck to you! I have been greatly perturbed. Another time I will send you more news. May you live and prosper as long as doth a phœnix—this may all the Saints grant—and have affection for me as of yore.

From HEIDELBERG.

XLIII–XLIV

⟨ *GALLUS LEINEWEBER, of Gundelfingen, Singer among Good Fellows, sendeth greeting to Magister Ortwin Gratius, his well-beloved teacher*

REVEREND Herr Magister: seeing that you sent me a letter full of solace at *Eberburg*, in the which you consoled me, inasmuch as you had heard that I was sick, I render you sempiternal thanks. Nevertheless you wrote in that letter that you marvelled at my being sick, since I had no more labour to perform than the other do - nothings—the quality's lackeys, to wit. Ha, ha, ha! I must needs laugh— else I am no true-born man—that you can ask so foolish a question! Know you not that it is God's will to make a man sick when he pleaseth, and to cure him when he listeth? If sickness came by toil 'twould be a bad thing for me; although you say I have little to do. When of late I was at *Heidelberg* among boon-companions, I was compelled to labour so mightily with my throat, in the drinking of wine, that it would have been no marvel had I stretched my gullet thereby —and think you that no labour? But concerning that matter let this suffice. There followeth in your letter a request that I should procure for you a little book in which is set forth somewhat useful for the young, that you may use it for a primer. Since, therefore, I have ever held you in esteem by reason of the various branches of learning that you know by rote, I cannot refrain from sending you a letter culled from a fair volume intituled " *The Leipsic Magisters' Chaplet of Letters* " which the most accomplished Magisters in the benign University of *Leipsic* have devised. This I have done that, if this first letter please you, I may send you the whole book—but I do not willingly let it pass from my hands.

Here beginneth the aforesaid letter :—

MAGISTER HOFMAN, Senior Regent in Heinrich Hostel at Leipsic, sendeth greeting to Matthias Falkenberg, of noble family, for fifty years, and more, his friend inseparable

SINCE we have not met for a long while, it seemeth good to me to send you a letter, that our ancient friendship may not decay; I have heard from many that you still live, and are of good health, and are all the man you were in your youth: and this, by the Lord, I heard with vast pleasure—God, who is good, will pardon me for so round an oath. Would to God and Holy Mary that you might once in a way ride hither! But I hear that you take not the same joy in riding as was your wont when you were with me at *Erfurt* and in other parts of *Saxony*, and when I often marvelled at your ease on horseback. I had great fear, when I heard that the folk at *Worms* were at strife with a certain nobleman, lest you should be involved therein, for an ancient family, such as yours, readily joineth hands with its equals; and in your youth you ever rejoiced to drink and ride with such, of which I have ofttimes taxed you. But since all still goeth well, let us render thanks to *Christ* that we have so long remained in good health.

I marvel greatly that you have never written to me, notwithstanding that you have at your service many messengers to *Leipsic*, and you know well enough that I am ever to be found there. But I cannot be so slothful, wherefore I willingly write to you; I trow, forsooth, that in all those years in which we have never met I must have written as many as twenty letters to learned men, my contemporaries. I was mistaken in you; but let this pass with the rest.

Noble Sir, would that you had been here of late, when his Serenity the Prince of *Saxony* celebrated his nuptials with a splendid mask, at which many nobles were present. I was sent thither with our Rector, according to custom, to present a large bowl filled with florins, and there we abode two days, and were right well entertained and refreshed ourselves mightily with victuals and drink. My servant brought with him two jars, and learning where I should sit at table, he placed these under my stool: then we had wine of the best—you know what that is like, 'tis the sweetest of the sweet! and such I drink till my head goes round, and after supper I want to dance. Then I took and filled one jar with the liquor, and put it back under the table. This I did that we might have somewhat to drink by the way. Later on, among other dishes, we had a mighty fine ragout

full of chickens and other good things; thereupon
I took the other jar and popped a whole pullet
into it: this I did that his Magnificence the Rector
and I might have somewhat to eat by the way.
This done, I said to a nobleman near, "My Lord,
prithee summon my servant, I have an order for
him." This he did, and when my servant came,
I said, "Fellow, pick up my knife that I have let
fall beneath the board" (but I had dropped it on
purpose). Then he crept under the table, and
picked up the knife, and hid the jars beneath his
coat, and slipped away, so that no one saw him.

Saint *Dorothy!* if you had but fared with us
to *Leipsic!* With what jollity would we have
spent the time! I lived for two days on the orts,
for we could not eat the whole by the way.

I tell you all this, since I know that you also
gladly filch with sack and sieve, at least you did
—when you abode with me, and by my faith 'tis
a noble art! I would not lose it for a hundred
guldens. I learnt the other day that you have
a fair garden at your home, where you grow much
fruit—pears and apples and grapes; and when you
are at your Inn—for you keep no table at home
—you are wont to have a great satchel into which
you slip cakes, and roast chickens, and meat, and
so craftily do you make the pass, that no man
perceiveth it; whereat I marvel. This skill I
trow cometh from long use—for "practise maketh
perfect," as saith the Philosopher in the Ninth of
the *Physics.*

'Tis told me you have a doxy who is sand-
blind of one eye. I marvel that you are such a
man anights, being full of years. More wondrous
still, I have heard of that stubborn plight of yours
that persisted for six sennights. This you spake
of as your infirmity. Dio! if such an infirmity
were mine, what a good fellow I! But, believe
me, I am not the man I was. A month agone
I packed my cook out of the house. For many a
day I have been out of pocket.

There is one more thing I would fain say to

you before I make an end. If you have a son, or other kinsman—or a dear friend of yours hath one—who is destined to be a student, send him hither to me at *Leipsic*. We have many learned doctors amongst us, and rare good victuals in our hostels—seven courses twice every day, at noon and evening; the first is called *Ever*—that is, porridge; the second, *Always*—that is, Soup; the third, *Daily*—that is, greens; the fourth, *Again and again*—that is, meat; the fifth, *Sometimes*—that is, roast; the sixth, *Never*—that is, cheese; the seventh, *Now and then*—that is, apples and pears. We have good liquor withal, called *Conventum*. Behold now, and see! Is not this enough? We keep this order throughout the year, to the great content of all. Nevertheless in our chambers we keep not overmuch victuals to eat between whiles, for this would not be healthful, and would hinder the students in their work; wherefore I have sent round to all the scholars these verses:—

> "Within these walls let all observe
> The standing regulations:
> Be sure that he who sups with me
> Provides his proper rations."

You perceive that I too am a poet.—But enough, lest I should prove long-winded. Written at *Leipsic*, hastily, beneath the blue sky; and may you fare more joyfully than a bee among the thyme, or a fish in the waves. Once again, farewell.

See now, Herr Magister *Ortwin*, if this letter pleaseth you, and I will send you a whole book full of the like; and right excellent they are, according to my poor judgment. I have naught else to write to you.

Farewell, in Him who created all things.

Dated from EBERBURG, where I would that you were with me. Friday, between Easter and Pentecost.

XLV

❡ *ARNOLD VON TONGERN*, *Magister Noster of Holy Scripture, sendeth greeting to Magister Ortwin Gratius*

REVEREND Herr Magister! I am vexed beyond all vexation! Full well do I perceive that saying of the poets to be true: " Misfortunes never come singly"; and this I can prove as followeth: I am in poor health, and besides my distemper there falleth on me another heavy burden, namely this: Men flock to me daily, and write to me from various provinces, since I am known everywhere by reason of that tractate you wot of, which I wrote against *Johann Reuchlin's* " Vindication." These men declare that they marvel at our allowing *Johann Pfefferkorn*, a baptised Jew, to undertake the work of writing in our cause, to defend himself and all of us against *Reuchlin*, so that the fame is his, although we have written all the works published under his name—and all this, forsooth, is true enough. I tell you this under seal of confession. They say also that he hath now compiled a new book, the which in Latin is intituled, " *Defensorium Johannis Pfefferkorn contra Johannem Reuchlin*," in which he setteth forth the whole case from beginning to end—and this book he hath also translated into German. When I heard of this I swore that it was a lie—simply because I knew naught about the matter; but if he hath acted thus, then, pardy! it is disgraceful for him not to have informed me thereof, tho' previously he hath always consulted me. I trow that now he thinketh not of me because I am in ill health. If he had consulted me I should have told him that once was enough; for I am sure we shall gain nothing by writing, for *Reuchlin* is a devil incarnate, and ever hitteth back. If, however, the matter standeth thus, I desire earnestly that he refrain. You can hinder him as the corrector of his books.

Secondly, I have heard somewhat over which I do

not so greatly grieve; namely, that you have consorted with a handmaid of *Quentel's* the printer—I speak not as reproving you—and that by her you have had issue; I hear, too, that her master sent her packing, and would not suffer her to remain in his house—so she now liveth in her own home and maintaineth herself by tailoring.

I beseech you by the mutual friendship we have ever had, tell me whether this be sooth. For a long while have I had hankerings after her, but was afeared by reason of her maidenhood. If, however, you have done this, then, with your permission, we will maintain her in common: I to-day and you to-morrow—the worthiest first; I a Doctor, you a Magister. (I put it thus bluntly without intending any slight.) And thus, in secrecy, will we maintain her and the child at our common charge. She, I know, will be well content, and I trow that if I consorted with her for a while, I should be healed. I desire to purge my reins, and to become whole.

And now, farewell. If I had not been plagued with this flux I would have come to you, instead of writing. In haste, from our Hostel.

XLVI

℃ *JOHANN WAGNER VON AMBACH*
sendeth many greetings to Mag. Ortwin Gratius

SEEING that you lately wrote to me, asking how it fareth with me at *Heidelberg*, and what I think of the Doctors and Magisters here, I must tell you that so soon as I arrived at *Heidelberg* I was appointed cook at a hostel, where I receive my victuals and certain monies by way of guerdon, and am thus enabled to proceed Magister, in due course. *Harry the Poor*[70] did the like, who, having neither books nor paper, wrote all on his leathern jerkin. In like manner *Plautus* maintained himself, who carried sacks to the mill like an ass, and nevertheless became a very learned author, who wrote both verse and prose.

That you may know who are the learned here, I will speak first of the most worthy, and then of the rest in turn, since, as the Philosopher saith in the First Book of the *Physics*, "We must proceed from universals to particulars. *Porphirius* too descends from the most general genus to the most special species, where *Plato* calls a halt. Moreover, appellation should be based on the worthiest examples, as saith the heathen philosopher in his Second Book of *The Soul*. Among all the Doctors of Theology there is one here who is our Preacher, and he hath a mighty voice, albeit he is a little man. Folk hear his preaching right gladly, and think much of him—for, pardy, he is learned, nay, superlatively learned I can tell you, and folk throng to his sermons, for he is a delectable man and cracketh good jokes in the pulpit. I once heard him treat of that question out of the *Posterior Analytics*: Why? Wherefore? What? When? And he could discuss it all in German. Once too he preached concerning virginity, and said that virgins who had lost their virginity were wont to aver they had lost it by force. "'By force' is good," quoth he; "I ask you if one, having a drawn sword in one hand and its scabbard in the other, jounceth the scabbard—is it to impede the sword? And so it is with virgins."

Moreover, once when he was offering New Year's wishes to men of different ranks he turned to the students of the three Hostels—who here comprise both Nominalists and Realists—and to the former he allotted *Saturn*, reasoning thus: "*Saturn* is a cold planet, and he consorteth well with the moderns, for they are cold Artsmen, who follow not after the way of *St. Thomas*, and his *Copulata* and *Reparationes* according to the syllabus of *De Monte* Hostel at *Cologne*." But to the Thomists he allotted in the New Year the boy *Ganymede* who piggeth with *Jupiter*. *Ganymede* suiteth well with the Realists, for he poureth out wine and beer for *Jove*, and the sweet juice of liquorice—which story *Torrentius*[7] hath fairly expounded in the First Book of the *Æneid*—and in like manner do the Realists pour forth their Arts and Science; and thereon he argued much. And many other pleasant things said he, whereat I marvelled. I trow he lieth sleepless for many nights when he thinketh out these high and subtle matters. Howbeit there are many who say that he preacheth flapdoodle—and they call him *Quackulator*, and *Johnny Jolthead*, and *Goosecap*, for the reason that once he was found wanting in disputation, and he was sent packing with greater ignominy than had befallen a man for a hundred years : and a fellow waited for him near the chair, and doffed his cap—not by way of honour, but as those Jews did when they crowned *Christ*—and he bent the knee before him, and said, " Herr Doctor, by your favour, may God bless your bath !" Then quoth he, " *Deo Gratias*, Herr Bachelor," but he said no more, and went away—and I heard that the tears stood in his eyes, and that it was believed that he afterwards wept. And when I heard of these insults my bowels of compassion were moved, and had I but known who that rascal was, I would have fallen upon him tho' I had lost my head with a deal plank. He hath one pupil who is, believe me, a learned man—more than learned, as it were ; more learned than his teacher, perchance, albeit he is but a Bible Bachelor; he has already, a little while—a very little while—ago, put forward fully twenty questions and arguments, all against the realists; for instance, " Whether God is predicamental"; " Whether essence and existence are distinct"; " Whether Rollations are fundamentally distinct," and " Whether the ten predicaments are actually distinct."

Mercy on us ! what a crowd of respondents ! I never in my life saw more disputants in a lecture-room; yet he honourably defended his theses. A magister hath but to contend with one opponent. I wonder that the Dean admitted them—I believe he was mad by reason of the dog-days, for it is contrary to the statutes.

And when the disputation was over I straightway metrified these verses in his honour :—

> Liveth here a learned scholar,
> Who debated, twice or thrice,
> If the Being of Essentia
> Can be, by distinctions nice,

Sifted from its Existentia ?
　And about Rollations he
Argued, till the Categories
　Stood as stark as they could be.
Whether God within his heaven
　The Predicaments enfold,
He discusseth : none before him
　Matched him through the days of old !

But enough of this : I would fain say—or write—somewhat concerning the poets.

There is one here who lectures on *Valerius Maximus*, but he pleaseth me not half as well as you pleased me when you lectured on *Valerius Maximus* at Cologne, for he merely expoundeth the text—but when you treated of " The Neglect of Religion," or " Dreams," or " Auspices," you quoted Holy Scripture, that is to say, the *Catena Aurea* of *St. Thomas* which is called the *Continuum*, and *Durandus*, and other shining lights of Theology, and you bade us note down these passages from holy writ, and draw a hand beside them, and learn them by rote. You must know that not so many students matriculate here as at *Cologne*, for at *Cologne* the students can be as the beggars here—and there some students even steal their victuals, but this is not allowed here, where all must have their commons in a hostel, and be matriculated in the University.

But although they be few here, yet are they saucy—to the full as saucy as the many at *Cologne*. Lately they " staircased " a regent of the Hostel ; he was standing without a chamber, and listening to the merrymaking within, when one of those within came out, and finding him there threw him downstairs. They are, moreover, so bold here that they fight with the horse-patrol as they at *Cologne* do with the draymen, and they go about like patrols themselves with drawn swords, and ropes, and sabres, and pieces of lead attached to a cord, which they can throw and draw back again. A little while ago the patrol smote a student on the head so that he fell to the ground—but he jumped up and thwacked and belaboured them so that *St. Valentine* seized them and they all ran away.

There is still one other thing that you ought to know.

You must ask Magister *Arnold von Tongern*—who is no trifling Theologian—whether it is a sin to cast dice for indulgences. I know some overweening fellows—scoundrels that they are—who have played away all the indulgences that *Jakob van Hoogstraten* gave them when he had ended the business of *Reuchlin* at *Mainz*—the same three were there, and they declared that those indulgences were of none effect for men.

If it is a sin, as I think—for it is impossible for it not to be a sin—I know the fellows well enough, and I will inform the Dominicans, who will soon confound them; and I myself—for I am quite brave enough—will put a spoke in their wheel as well. I have no more to write, save that you may salute for me *Quentel's* handmaid, and fare ye well pancratically, athletically, pugilistically, regally, and magnificently, as saith *Erasmus* in his *Adages*.

From HEIDELBERG.

XLVII

❡ *WENDELIN TUCHSCHERER, Bachelor, and Quirister at Strasburg, sendeth many greetings to Magister Ortwin Gratius*

YOU laid blame on me in a former letter, in that my ink seemed precious balm—and my pen, byssus——and my paper, leaf of gold—so seldom did I write to you.

Henceforth, therefore, I will write to you oft—the more readily seeing that since you were my teacher in the fifth class at *Deventer*, and are, moreover, my godfather, I am in honour bound to write to you. But, inasmuch as I have at present no news to tell you, I must write to you on certain other matters, though I am sure they will please you not, seeing that you stand firmly on the side of the preachers. Lately we sat drinking together, and there was one there who spake such uncouth Latin, that I understood not all he said —yet a part I comprehended well enough, and amongst other things he declared that he would compile a book, to be brought out at next *Frankfort* fair, and to be intituled "A Catalogue of Prevaricators," that is, of Predicants—and that he would lay bare all their misdeeds, inasmuch as of all Orders they were the most iniquitous. In the first place he would relate how that at *Berne* the Prior and the Superiors introduced harlots into the Convent, and how they produced a new *St. Francis*, and how the Blessed Virgin and other Saints appeared to one *Nollharden*, and how afterwards the monks would fain have given the said *Nollharden* poison in Christ's body, and how that for all the follies and crimes that the monks had committed they went as they deserved to the stake.

Next, he would relate how that at *Mainz* a Dominican had knowledge of a trollop in the Cathedral, anear the altar—whence it came to pass that the other drabs had a spite against her, and called her "monkmort," and "quire-quean," and "altar-piece"—so that it came to folks' ears, and she is thus named unto this day.

He would relate, too, how that once at *Mainz*, at the sign of *The Crown*, when the Predicants from *Augsburg* lodged at that inn to sell their indulgences, one of their number would fain have forced a servingmaid who prepared his bed, and he pursued her and threw her to the ground, but she cried out, and men ran to her rescue, else would she have served his turn.

And, finally, he would relate how that here at *Strasburg* there were monks in the Monastery of the Preachers who brought women-folk to their cells by way of the river beneath their walls; and they trimmed their hair, so that for a long while they passed for monks, and went to market, and bought fish from their husbands the fishermen, but at the last they were unmasked. For in like manner the Predicants wrought evil among the vagrant scholars[72] and once when a Predicant went a-walking with a monkess, they came nigh unto the schools, and the scholars dragged them both into the school and set to work to chastise them soundly; but when they would have drubbed the monkess they uncovered her shame, and with laughter let them both depart in peace; but the whole town rang with tidings of these things.

Now when he had finished speaking, my wrath was greatly inflamed, and I cried, " You ought not to utter such words as these. Put case that they be true—nevertheless they should not be uttered, for it might well happen that destruction might come upon them in a single hour—as it did upon the Templars[73]—if men should learn of their iniquities ! "

Then quoth he, " I know further of matters that I could not write of on twenty sheets of paper."

Then said I, " Why would you write against all the Predicants ? All of them have not done such deeds : if those in *Mainz,* and *Augsburg,* and *Strasburg* are wicked, nevertheless others are upright." Said he, " Why darest thou to contradict me ? I verily believe that thou art the son of a Predicant, or hast been a Predicant thyself ! Show me a Monastery wherein there are upright Dominicans ! " Then said I, " What have those at *Frankfort* done ? " Said he, " Knowest thou not ? It is their Principal who is named *Wigand,* and he is the head and front of all their iniquities. He it was who started that heresy at *Berne,* and who wrote a book against *von Wesel,*[74] which he afterwards at *Heidelberg* recanted, annulled, and blotted out ; and he it was who afterwards wrote another book intituled ' The Tocsin,' and he was not courageous enough to issue it under his own name, but suborned *Johann Pfefferkorn* to set it forth under his name, for half of the profit—which would well content him, for he knew that *Pfefferkorn* was a reckless man, and, like all Jews, regarded not his own good fame so long as he could make money."

Now when I perceived that the more part were against me, I went my way, but I was sorely vexed that the fellow was not alone, for if he and I had been by ourselves, I would have played the devil with him. Farewell.

From STRASBURG : on Wednesday, after the Feast of *St. Bernard,* in the year one thousand five hundred and sixteen.

XLVIII

¶ *JAKOB VAN HOOGSTRAETEN, most humble
Professor of the Seven Free and Liberal Arts and
of All-holy Theology; in sundry parts of Germany
Master, that is Corrector, of Heretics, sendeth
greeting in the name of our Lord Jesus Christ, to
Ortwin Gratius of Deventer, who draggeth out
his life at Cologne*

NEVER was refreshing rain so grateful to the hus-
bandman after long drought, nor sunshine after
clouds, as was the letter you sent me hither at *Rome*.
When I read it I could have wept for very joy, for I
seemed to be back again at your house in *Cologne*—
where we were wont to drink a quart or two of wine or
beer, over a game at draughts—so glad was I.

But you desire me to do the like—to write to you,
namely, and tell you what I have for so long a time
been doing at *Rome*, and how I fare—and this will I
do right gladly. First, I must tell you that, by divine
inspiration, I am in good health. Yet although I am
well, I abide here against my will, for that Cause on
account of which I am here now goeth against me.
Would that I had never begun it! All men deride me
and plague me, and *Reuchlin* hath more friends here
than in *Germany*, and many Cardinals, and bishops, and
prelates and Curialists love him. Had I not entered
upon this business I should now be at *Cologne* enjoying
my victuals and drink, whereas here I have scarce a
crust. I trow that things go ill in *Germany*, too, now
that I am away; everybody is scribbling books about
Theology as he listeth. It is said that *Erasmus* of
Rotterdam hath composed many treatises on Theology;
I cannot believe he hath avoided error. He beginneth
by writing a tract to vex the theologians, and now he
writeth theologically himself—so that it passeth! If I
come back to *Germany* and read his scribblements, and
find in them the very smallest jot on which he hath
gone astray—or which I do not understand—let him

take heed to his skin! He hath also written in Greek; this is not well, for we are Latins and not Greeks. If he would fain write what no man can understand, why doth he not use Italian, or Bohemian, or Hungarian? For then none could understand him. In the name of a hundred devils let him conform to us Theologians, and dispute in his writings with *Utrum*, and *Contra*, and *Arguitur*, and *Replica*, and reach formal conclusions, as all Theologians are wont to do, and then we could read them.

I cannot tell you all now, nor describe the poverty into which I have fallen. When the Curialists see me they call me Apostate, and declare that I have deserted my Order, and they do the like to Doctor *Peter Meyer*, the Pastor, of *Frankfort*, whom they harass as greatly as myself, since he is of my part. Nevertheless he is better off than I, for he hath a good post, being Chaplain of the cemetery—and this, pardy, is a good post, though the Curialists aver that 'tis the meanest office in *Rome*. But this booteth not; they do but say it out of envy; at the least he earneth his bread and maintaineth himself by hook and by crook until he shall bring that case of his against the Frankfurdians to an end. Almost every day he and I go to take the air in the *Campo dei Fiori*, and look out for Germans, whom we would fain meet. But the Curialists come and point at us with their fingers, and laugh, and say: "There go the two who want to eat up *Reuchlin!* They eat him and then void him again!" And we have such tribulations as might move a stone. Then said the pastor: "Holy Mary! What doth it signify? We must endure this for God's sake. He suffered many things for us, and we are Theologians who needs must be lowly and despised in this world." And thus he maketh me of joyful heart once more, and, think I to myself, "Let them say what they will; yet they fail of their desire." If we were but back in the fatherland and a fellow did such things, we should know what to say and do to him, and I should have an easy task in proceeding against him. Just now we happened to be abroad together, behind two or three fellows who walked in front, and I lighted upon a paper that, I trow, one of them had dropped on purpose that we might find it ; and it contained these verses :—

EPITAPH ON HOCHSTRATUS.

Hochstratus dead—Craft, Fury, Spite, and Rage
With him die not, but still, with poison rife,
Infect the witless herd ; his monument,
Sprung from the hellish seed he sowed in life.

Another.

From out his bones let yew and hemlock grow ;
No crime he shrank from who lies here below.

Another.

Rejoice, ye righteous ! while the base complain—
For kindly Death hath made their loss your gain.

Another.

Herc Virtue's bane, Hochstratus, carrion lies,
In life the cynosure of scoundrels' eyes ;
Indignant fled his soul that she had run
Her earthly course—with evil left undone !

Now when the Pastor and I had found this paper, we went home and laid our heads together over it for a week or a fortnight but could not interpret it. It seems likely that the verses point at me, because the word "*Hochstratus*" occurreth in them. And yet mayhap the verses do not point at me, seeing that such is not my name in Latin, but *Jacobus de Alta-platea*, which is in German *Jakob Hoogstraeten*. And so I send you the paper that you may decide whether it pointeth at me or another. If it mean me—which I cannot believe, for I am not yet dead—I will hold an inquiry, and when I have caught the fellow I will make ready a bath for him that will be no laughing matter : that is easy. I have a good friend here, a countryman of mine, who is one of the grooms of the Cardinal of *S. Eusebius ;* and he can easily get the fellow sent to prison on bread and water—to die there of the pestil-ence. Wherefore I pray you use all diligence to write to me, that I may be certified of the matter.

I have heard that *Johann Pfefferkorn* hath once

more become a Jew—but I believe it not, for they said two or three years ago that he had been burned by the Margrave at *Halle*—though this was not true concerning him, but was true enough of another man of the same name. I cannot believe he hath become a renegade, for he hath written against the Jews; and it would be a disgrace to all the Doctors of Theology in *Cologne*, and all the Dominicans, for he hath been in high favour with them. Let them say what they will, I believe it not. And now farewell.

From ROME, at the sign of the *Bell*, in the *Campo dei Fiori*, August 21.

PART II

TO THE READER

Time was when Heraclitus smiled, and moved
*   To laughter, e'en grim Stoics shook their sides:*
Art sunk in doleful dumps?   Approach, and read—
*   Laughter is lord! and naught but Mirth abides.*

I

⁋ *JOHANN LABIA*, by the grace of God Apostolic Prothonotary, to the Reverend Herr Magister Ortwin Gratius of Deventer, as to a well-beloved brother, of Salutations a hundred thousand Sesterces, as the New Grammarians have it

I RECEIVED the day before yesterday, honoured Sir, a book that your worship will have sent me from *Germany*. This work was — or is — entitled "*Epistolae Obscurorum Virorum.*" Sonty! How rejoiced was I in mine heart when my eyes fell on that book—for it hath goodly contents, in prose and eke in verse. And I had great joy with dulcet jubilation when I perceived that you have many allies—Poets, and Rhetoricians and Theologians, who write to you and are your friends in opposition to *Johann Reuchlin.*

Yesterday there was a feast toward—and certain Curialists were present,—scholars and men of affairs— and I laid that book before them on the board. And after that they had dipped into it here and there, I mooted a logomachy, saying, "Masters, how think ye? Wherefore hath Magister *Ortwin* named this book of his, '*Epistolae Obscurorum Virorum*'—seeming thereby to call his friends and allies 'Obscure men'?"

Then answered a priest from *Münster*, a learned Jurist, and he declared that "Obscure" was a word of many meanings, as, following "*Lex Ita fidei sqq. de Jure Fisci,*" the first Solution hath it. He said, too, that it might be some family name. For it is recorded that the parents of *Diocletian* and some other kings were "Obscuri."

Then I nudged him, and said, "By your favour, Sir, this is beside the point." And next I put the question to a famous Theologian who drank with us. He is of the Carmelite Order and a native of *Brabant*. Full solemnly spake he his reasons: "Most eximious Herr Prothonotary, since, as *Aristotle* saith, it is profitable to make enquiry concerning each and all; therefore hath your Eximiousness proposed to me a question, to wit, for what cause did Magister *Ortwin*, in publishing a new Collection of Letters, entitle them '*Epistolae Obscurorum Virorum*.' By favour of these gentlemen, I pronounce my opinion that Magister *Ortwin*, who is a learned man and a philosopher, cognominated his friends 'Obscure Men' in a mystical sense: for I once read in an authority that truth lieth in obscurity. Wherefore also saith *Job*, 'He discovereth deep things out of darkness.' Also in the *Seventh of Micah* we read, 'When I sit in darkness, the Lord shall be a light unto me.' And, again, *Job xxviii.*: 'Trahitur autem Sapientia de Occultis.' Whence also, as I have heard tell, *Virgil* hath it: 'Truth is wrapped in obscurity.' And it may be presumed that Magister *Ortwin* and his friends are men who seek out the secrets of the Scriptures, and truth, and justice, and wisdom—which things are not to be understood of all men, but by those who are illuminated of the Lord.

"As it is written in *Kings cxxxviii.*: 'Yea, the darkness hideth not from thee, the night shineth as the day: the darkness and the light are both alike to thee.'" And after the aforesaid Theologian had made an end of speaking, all regarded me, to mark whether I was persuaded. But I pondered over these words.

There was present *Bernhard Gelff*, a Magister of *Paris*, a youth indeed, but, as I hear, of good parts, and one who studieth much, and maketh fair progress in the Arts, and moreover hath good grounding in Theology. And he, after his manner, shaking his head this way and that, spake thus with a grave countenance: "Learn, Gentlemen, the weighty and reasonable cause wherefore Magister Ortwin calleth his friends 'Obscure Men.' He doeth it for humility's sake. For, you may know, and even if you know not it may be presumed that you do know, how that three years ago *Johann Reuchlin*, when he published a Collection of Letters from his friends, entitled it '*Epistolae Clarorum Virorum*.' And Magister *Ortwin* chewing upon this,

and perpending much thereon, said within himself:
'Lo, *Reuchlin* believeth that none save he himself hath
any friends : what will he do if I prove that I too have
many friends—worthier far, and able to write better
metrifications and compositions than his friends?'
And so, to put him to shame he sent to the press those
Letters, and entitled them '*Epistolae Obscurorum Virorum.*' As saith the *Psalmist*, 'He sent darkness and made
it dark.' But this he did in lowliness, belittling and
humbling himself, that he might say with the *Psalmist*,
'Lord, my heart is not haughty, nor mine eyes lofty.'
Wherefore the Lord, beholding his humility, will in
due time give him grace to send abroad mighty works
and name them with exalted titles. As saith *Job*:
'And again after darkness I hope for the day.' But
it must not be supposed that that letter-book of the
friends of Magister *Ortwin* is not artistically composed
—for *Johann Reuchlin's* friends never in their lives
could compose anything better ; no, not to save their
necks—but, as I have declared, more excellent conceits
will ensue ; and, by God's help, I hope we may see
great things.

" Magister *Ortwin* layeth no store by swelling titles.
Wherefore he saith, 'The Lord is my light and my
salvation, whom then shall I fear?' For he knoweth
that in belittling himself he will hereafter be magnified.
As saith the Scripture, "Whoso exalteth himself will
be brought low.' And, as we read in the twentieth
of *Ecclesiasticus*, 'There is an abasement because of
glory, and there is that lifteth up his head from a low
estate.' These things the Prophet *Nahum* prophesied
when he said, 'And darkness shall pursue his enemies.' "

Then, desiring that the disputants should not be
out with one another, and that neither of them should
fall foul of me for saying, "this or that is the subtler
reasoning," I quoted that line of *Horace* in which he
saith, "The case is still before the judge." "When
next I write to Magister *Ortwin*," I added, "I will ask
him to tell me his motive. Forgive me, therefore, if I
have in any wise perplexed you."

So then they disputed no longer, though Magister
Bernhard muttered that he would contend to the stake

that he had rightly apprehended your motive. Therefore, Herr *Ortwin*, I adjure you in friendly wise that you reveal to me what you had in your mind when you entitled that fardel of Letters "*Epistolae Obscurorum Virorum.*"

And now farewell, in all health and honour.

The Court, at Rome.

II

⁝ *JOHANN GRAPP to Magister Ortwin Gratius*

EVER cordially wisheth welfare, with love unending, and commendeth himself as his humble servant. Brother and beloved preceptor, since you lately desired me to send you (that you might gather therefrom what I had learnt from you at *Cologne* and *Deventer*), a treatise, or an Epistle, or a poem in verse, in mockery of *Johann Reuchlin*, and the Reuchlinists who are your foes—behold, and see how that I have done diligence! Herewith I send you an odistic or metrified Epistle, like unto *Ovid* in his *Epistolæ;* for well I know that you would fain read verse rather than prose. Mend it, an you will; for the disciple is not above his master. Scan it, too, for I am not yet well-skilled in this art.

A Letter from Johann Grapp, *metrifying poetical tyro, to his teacher,* Magister Ortwin Gratius[1]

Grapp his greeting doth send, in this poetic Epistle,
Humble duty as well, to Magister *Ortwin* the kindly—
As is but meet for a youth who dearly loveth his master;
Therefore contemn not, I pray, my *Ortwin*, the metrification,
If it should harshly sound; for though thy resonant verses
Sweetly thunder indeed—yet all are not on a level,
Neither are all alike, whether teachers or diligent scholars;

One in logic is versed, another in poetry skilleth,
Natural Philosophy one acquireth, leechcraft another,
While yet another, through grace, hath competent learn-
　　ing in all things;
Thou the exemplar of such, who a peer doth hardly
　　acknowledge
At *Cologne*—or at *Rome*, in all the ranks of the *Rota*[2]—
Rome, where folk at the Court contend like so many
　　freshmen,
Brangling and wrangling at law, with an eye to possible
　　livings;
(I myself am embroiled, for lately in sharp litigation
I for a vicarage strove—nor yet hath peace been
　　attained to.)
But, in deep studies immersed, such vanities little thou
　　wottest,
All thy heart and mind intent on the pages of Scrip-
　　ture,
Heed not thou heathen men, of thee the bitter tor-
　　mentors—
Reuchlin with all his crew, and that maleficent junto
Secular Poets y-clept, and the crowd of jabbering Jurists
Who, with their quillets and quirks and screeds of flimsy
　　averments,
Seek to trip thee up, and scribble heretical verses.
Arnold von Tongern is with you, and *Pepericornus* the
　　Christian,
And that College in France that burnt the infamous
　　libel,
Augenspiegel to wit, by you triumphantly coped with.
Fain would I leave to you the defence of faith and
　　religion—
To you and *Hoogstraeten*—by far superior to *Plato*,
Who the philosophers tops in craft of subtle dis-
　　tinctions;
Therefore I bid you good-night—be all untroubled
　　your pillow,
　　　　　　　　　　　　　　　Deo Gratias.

　　Forgive me if there are faults in these verses, for,
as saith the Philosopher, "To err is human." Prithee,
send me some news.

This is written at *Rome*, where grow miraculous apples,
And in the hucksters' stalls it is by the pound that they
 sell them—
This I have seen with mine eyes, and I by experience
 know it.

    Amen.

III

⅏ *MAGISTER STEPHAN RUMELANT* to *Mag. Ortwin Gratius greeting*

FORTHWITH, and without preface, I would have
your worthiness to know that a Doctor of Theology hath just come hither, *Thomas Murner* by name.
He is of the Order of *S. Francis*, an Oberlander, and
he is vainglorious beyond belief. It is said that he
maketh certain cards, and whosoever playeth with these
cards learneth grammar and logic. He hath contrived
a game of checkers, too, which dealeth with the quantities of syllables. He boasteth that he knoweth Hebrew,
and he composeth verses in German. And the report
goeth that this Doctor wotteth somewhat of every art.

But when I heard this, I said, "Jack-of-all-trades,
and master of none!" and some that stood by laughed.
Now this Doctor is a great crony of *Johann Reuchlin's*
—devil take him! I fear that here he will so work
upon the Canons and other Clerks that they will side
with *Reuchlin*. He declared, before many who heard,
that a child could discern the folly, and the stupidity,
and the malice of the Theologians of *Cologne* and their
adherents. And he swore by the Holy of Holies that
unless the Pope took heed, and corrected them in their
perversity, a schism would spring up in the Church and
the Christian Faith ; for if the Pope permitted them to
act thus, it would come to pass that no man would
study, nor desire to gain knowledge. Moreover he said
that *Reuchlin* could in one day be of more profit to the
Church of God than could his enemies in a hundred
years. "And if," he went on, "they are upright men,

and have any just cause against *Reuchlin*, wherefore do they not act for themselves? Why do they need a baptized Jew to do their work for them, and why do they write scandalous books against the worthy doctor, and father them on that renegade? If they could have lighted upon a viler or more malicious man in all *Germany* they would have joined themselves to him! Yet this is nothing strange. 'Like draws to like.'" Thereupon I could no longer hold my peace, but said, "Herr Doctor, by your favour, *Johann Pfefferkorn* is an honourable man; he is the trusty counsellor of his Imperial Majesty, and he cometh of the tribe of *Naphtali*. That, be well assured, is a most ancient stock. He might, an he would, boast himself to be of noble birth—but doth not, for humility's sake." Then said the Doctor, "Take a spoon and bib your words!" Then said I, "Think you that I know naught of men? I am a Magister of *Paris*, and I have studied Theology at *Cologne* for two years. Be not so arrogant, Herr Doctor, ere you know to whom you speak." Doctor *Murner* made answer that he knew not that I was a Magister, and he added, "Of *Johann Pfefferkorn's* honour I have heard but little, but from what I have heard of him I can safely say that unless the Jews had sought to put him to death by reason of his crimes, he would never have become a Christian."

Said I, "Herr Doctor, hear me yet a little: the Jews do *Johann Pfefferkorn* an injury, for he never stole aught, nor did he commit any crime, even when he was a Jew—as is piously to be believed. And to prove that this is true, I may tell you that two Jews once sought to saddle him with the shame of theft—merely out of envy and execrable malice—whereupon he cited them before the Imperial Chamber, and they handed him thirty florins for costs, wherewith he was content. *Johann Pfefferkorn* was indeed born of a good stock, but when he was a Jew he did as other Jews. For, as the proverb runs, 'He who is among wolves, must howl with the wolves.' But now he eateth swine's flesh, and behaveth like a good Christian." Then answered Doctor *Murner*, "Doth *Pfefferkorn* also eat sausages?"

I answered, " I have not with mine eyes beheld him eating them, but it may be piously presumed that if he eateth pork, he also eateth such things as are made of pork." Quoth he, " You have made good apologies for *Johann Pfefferkorn*: hath he still two ears?"

I answered that he had them both when I was at Cologne, and that I believed he still had them, and will have them for ever. Then said he, " What opinion do you hold concerning *Johann Reuchlin?*" I replied that I knew him not, but that I was well aware that the Theologians and the Church for the most part regarded him as a heretic, because he hath assailed with undeserved calumnies *Johann Pfefforkorn* and other very eminent men. Then quoth he, " By the Lord, you do right well in defending *Johann Pfefferkorn* and the other very eminent men."

Then said I, " Hear yet more: this *Pfefferkorn* is very useful to the Church, for he hath won twelve souls for God, as he hath himself candidly confessed."[4]

Quoth Doctor *Murner*, " Where gave he those souls to God? In the *Bohmer Wald?* Maybe he, with other robbers, slew sundry folk whose souls passed to God."

I replied, " Not at all; but by converting them to the Christian Faith."

Said he, " And how do you know that these souls were added to God?"

I answered that this might be piously presumed. Then asked *Murner*, " And what doeth *Pfefferkorn* now?"

I answered that he perchance visiteth the church, and attendeth Masses and Sermons, and, while defending himself against *Johann Reuchlin*, awaiteth the Day of Judgment.

" Think you," saith he, " that *Pfefferkorn* will live so long?"

" Ay," said I, " with respect to his soul, but not with respect to his body."

Doctor *Murner* made answer, " Good! *Pfefferkorn* deserveth to have such a champion!" Thereupon he dismissed me, and all who stood around laughed, and said,

"Pardy, Herr *Stephan*, you have answered him stoutly!"

Then said I, "I will write every word of this to Magister *Ortwin*"—and this, as you see, I am now doing. Write to me in reply; I am yours to command.

From TRIER.

IV

❧ *MAGISTER JOHANN HUTER* sendeth *greeting to Magister Ortwin Gratius*

SINCE it is written in the Evangel: "In what measure ye meten it shall be meten again to you," it becometh me not, therefore, to write to you, seeing that you write not to me. Nevertheless I know of what moment it is that I should send you tidings from *Rome*, to wit, how it fareth with Doctor *Jakob van Hoogstraten* —that man of zeal unimpeachable, who defendeth the Catholic faith against those Jurists and secular Poets who have not the fear of God before their eyes, as have the Theologians in *Cologne* and *Paris* who burnt *Johann Reuchlin's Augenspiegel*. Though it would be but meet that I should do unto you even as you do unto me— and not write you a single drop; nevertheless this I will not do, but will yet this once favour you, on condition that you forthwith send me a reply.

You must know, then, that those Jurists and adversaries, with the help of the Devil, the enemy of the Christian Faith, have by their wiles—as is piously believed—suborned a swarm of allies, more especially curialists of high rank—who have no scruples of conscience; and they inflict grievous injuries on the aforesaid Doctor, baiting him like a very bejan, and declaring that he is himself a heretic, and the Theologians of *Cologne* mere jack-puddings. Sonty! What is to be said? Is it not marvellous that Sacred Theology should be thus vilified, and held as trash, and that the Theologians who are, as it were, the Lord's Apostles should be despised as so many fools? Mark my words! There will hence be much scathe to the Catholic Faith,

113

and, I fear me, confusion in the Church of God. The rumour goeth that the Pontiff holdeth with *Reuchlin*, being himself a poet and a favourer of the Jurists. Yet I trust that his Holiness will be enlightened by the grace of the Holy Spirit, and will not pronounce an unrighteous judgment—through the Lord who reigneth in heaven and on earth, and His Mother the *Virgin Mary*, and may she from all Poetry deliver us.

ROME.

V

ℂ *BROTHER JOHANN VON WERDAU*
to Mag. Ortwin Gratius

SUPPLICATIONS humble and devout, with greetings manifold.

You say, reverend Sir, that you have heard that your Cause goeth amiss, and that *Johann Reuchlin* hath obtained an apostolical Inhibition; you say, too, that you fear greatly lest he gain the victory against the Theologians and our most holy Order, and that thereafter scandal will befall the Church of God. Why are ye so fearful, O ye of little faith, that ye are incontinently dumpish? And yet when I abode with you at *Deventer* you were not thus timorous, but were of good courage. For I well remember how you smote those freshmen who fell upon you with swords, though you had neither weapon nor shield; yet by God's help you thwacked them so soundly and roundly that one of them beshamed himself for very anguish. This was seen of many folk, and they cried, " By the Lord, this Magister *Ortwin* is a doughty man!" You must know that here at the Court of *Rome* things are not as they are elsewhere, and accord not with expectations; one day a man prospereth, and the next he foundereth. It may hap that a man obtaineth two or three decrees in his favour and nevertheless loseth his case. Perchance you will say "The Pope hath permitted the *Augenspiegel* to be sold, read, and printed." But this skilleth not. What he hath permitted cannot

he in turn forbid? Yea, of a truth—for his Holiness
hath power to loose and to bind, and is not on that
account blameworthy. Hath he not plenary powers,
here and everywhere, as you know from the Evangel,
for you are wondrously versed in Holy Scripture?
Furthermore I can cite thereon the Canon Law: First,
the Pope hath sway over the whole world, *Quest*. IX.
Chap. 4, "Cuncta per mundum," &c. He can depose
the Emperor, alone, without a Council, as saith the
gloss on the Chapter, "Ad apostolicae, de sententia
et re judicata." Compare also *Quest*. VI. *Chap*. 100,
"De cetero." Moreover the Pope is not subject to the
Law, but is himself the living Law upon the Earth;
as saith the gloss on *Chap*. XI., "De officio Judic.
delegati." And since the Pope is the Law, he can do
whatsoever he listeth, and heedeth no man. If, therefore, he saith at one time "Yea," nevertheless he can
afterwards say "Nay." Be then of good courage, for
I lately heard from one of the judges of the *Rota*—a
notable man, and of wide experience—that it is not
possible that the Pope will pronounce sentence against
you, for yours is the best of Causes, the Cause of the
Faith.

Be ye therefore valiant in battle; and whatever
those noddies may say to you about the Inhibition,
credit it not, for it goeth for naught. I trust that I
may soon be able to send you good tidings, for Herr
Doctor *Jakob van Hoogstraten* is doing his uttermost. Lately he gave a banquet, and invited many
courtiers of years and experience, and an Apostolical
Secretary who is in high favour with his Holiness, and
sundry judges of the *Rota*. He plied them with par-
tridges, and pheasants, and hares, and fresh fish, and
the best Corsican and Greek wines. They all declared
that he had dealt with them most honourably, and said
among themselves, "By the Lord, we have here a
Theologian of consequence: We will be on his side."

Now therefore he taketh heart of grace. But I must
stay my hand, for the messenger will no longer wait.

Farewell, and salute for me all the Doctors and
Magisters, and *Johann Pfefferkorn*.

ROME.

VI

❦ *MAGISTER CORNELIUS STORATI*
sendeth abundant greetings to Magister Ortwin

CONFORMABLY to the request which you sent
me when I was at *Rome*, that I should let you
know to a tittle how matters stood in the Cause of
the Faith between you and the other Theologians,
on the one hand, and *Johann Reuchlin* on the other
hand—I would have you take note that I departed
thence in such haste that I was not able to write a
single word. I resolved, however, that I would write
to you as soon as I reached the fatherland, and this
I now do.

Know then, though I deeply lament it, that when
I left Rome matters were in a parlous state. Doctor
Jakob van Hoogstraten is in great poverty. Have
you Theologians no sense of shame, that you make
him no provision? You would fain accomplish great
results, and yet you will not loose the purse-strings!
Think you that this is the way to bring about your
ends? When the Doctor arrived at Rome with his
two or three horses, and gold in the bank, and when
he kept open house, then the courtiers rendered him
high honour. Quoth one to another, "Who is this?"
and the answer would come, "He is a Doctor from
Germany, none is more renowned : he is a philosopher,
and so excelleth in disputations that he hath no peer.
He is here to maintain the Cause of the Faith against
some secular Jurist." Then would the courtiers sing
his praises, and many a time has one said to me,
"Herr *Cornelius*, commend me to this renowned
Doctor!" Then his patrons abounded and his cause
flourished. But now you desert him, and stint his
supplies. Not long ago I was in his chamber, and
casting my eyes on his mantle that lay there, I saw
that it was full of vermin. And he, observing that
I saw this, cited the Scripture which saith, "Thy
congregation shall dwell therein, for thou, O God,

hast of thy goodness prepared for the poor;" and again, "My zeal hath even consumed me." And I for bitter ruth shed tears.

It behoves you to succour him, and see that the Friars Predicant send him money. If they plead that they have none, bid them take what is needed from the store they have amassed out of Indulgences: it is in the Cause of the Faith, and whatsoever is devoted to that cause is devoted to the Christian Faith. Farewell.

AUGSBURG.

VII

❦ FRIAR ALBERT NADLER to
Magister Ortwin Gratius

HONOURED Sir, a letter hath lately come hither, addressed from your worship to myself. With joy I opened it, for I recognised your seal. I have read it, and find that your worship desireth to know what folks say here of the Cause of the Faith between you Theologians and *Johann Reuchlin*. I will tell you—but you must not think scorn of me when you learn that they espouse not your cause. All men here say that the Theologians are treating *Reuchlin* as the scribes treated Christ, and that he hath ever been an upright man, and hath been the Counsellor of two Emperors. His skill in Jurisprudence, too, hath been of service to many burghers and princes, and all men have found him trusty and true. Yet because the Theologians have become envious of his fame, they seek to brand him as a heretic, by crooked devices and niggling quirks.

When I hear such things said, I raise my voice against them—but, as you well know, "many dogs can outbark one."

Two Magisters who have lately arrived from *Cologne* —one of them is a noble—declare that those who assail *Reuchlin* are for the most part bastards, cullions, and braggarts. And this saying seemeth to me very shameful. One of them even made an harangue, so that all

117

who stood near could hear, saying, "Gentlemen, that you may understand the true nature of this suit against *Johann Reuchlin*, let me tell you that the root of it all is *Johann Pfefferkorn*, who resembleth in name, and in all else, that *Johann Pfefferkorn* who was in this very place torn with red-hot pincers, and who in like manner had become a pervert from his faith, by reason of the wickedness that he had committed. If *Pfefferkorn* were safe here in gaol, and the executioners were to put the question to him as to what he had committed, he would make confession of not a whit less than his namesake. He hath egged on the Theologians at *Cologne*, and they have egged him on in turn, and they would fain have burned all the books of the Jews throughout *Germany*. And this, that the Jews might come privily to the Theologians and the aforesaid *Pfefferkorn* with large sums of money, beseeching them, and saying, 'Leave us, we pray you, our books—and lo, here are forty pieces of gold!' Some Jews, indeed, would have freely given a hundred, and some, a thousand pieces. Then came *Reuchlin* and baulked their scheme, and they were wrath with him. Hence they write books, and try to defame him, and declare him to be a heretic. Some books they write in Latin, and they publish them under *Pfefferkorn's* name, whereas he is ignorant even of the alphabet in Latin. This they do, since they know full well that no man will reply, for none will defile himself by touching such a scoundrel. It is plain that if they were true Theologians—or even honest men—they would do their own work, and not shield and hide themselves behind that braggart. Other books also they have published—some in the name of *Arnold von Tongern*, who hath been detected in forgery —this no man can deny, nor can he himself declare in his own defence that he is not a forger—it is known throughout *Germany* how he falsified the writings of *Johann Reuchlin*. Another writer on behalf of the Theologians is Magister *Ortwin Gratius*—the son of a priest, and one who keepeth concubines and hath been taken in advoutry. Then there is another scribe, of whom you have heard much, Doctor *Weigand Wirth* of the *Order of Preachers*, who is just as great a scoundrel. He wrote a book to prove that the *Blessed Virgin* was conceived in original sin, and he stirred up much sedition with his preaching. He was therefore compelled to recant and publicly to adjure his own preachments and writings at *Heidelberg* —as I myself heard and saw. And now you may judge what manner of men the foes of *Reuchlin* are."

Now when I heard these things I said, "Sir, it is not meet that you should utter such words as these before the people, even though they be true, for the whole Order hence cometh into ill odour, and folk are set a bad example thereby."

"Even you," he replied, "ought not to have acted as you have against *Reuchlin*, for you also have desired to defame him. And he now cannot clear himself without some hurt to you."

By the Lord, *Herr Ortwin*, I would that this Cause had come to an end, for it is mightily discommodious to us : folk will no longer give us alms. Last week I set out on a tramp for cheeses, and during ten days I collected no more than fifteen, for everybody said, " Get thee to *Johann Reuchlin*, and ask him for cheeses ! " May God grant a favourable issue ; and now farewell in the Lord.

From Halle, in Saxony.

VIII

❰ *MATTHÄUS FINK*, Bachelor, to *Mag. Ortwin Gratius*

GREETINGS indescribable, and love ineffable !
Honoured Sir, inasmuch as you know right well how it standeth with me here in *Rome*, how that I am of the Chancery, and, by God's mercy, am in good case; there is no need to tell you of such matters, for you suffer not tedious letters gladly. Nevertheless, seeing that I promised to send you news from *Rome* at least once a month, and, whenever the running or riding postmen set out, to avize

you how matters stand with regard to the war and so forth, and concerning the *King of France* and the *Emperor*, perchance you will say within yourself, " See, how haughty this fellow hath become ! He hath a fine post in *Rome*, and therefore he taketh not the trouble to write to me, forgetting that I was erstwhile his Teacher, and implanted in him Poetry, and the Arts, and a slice of Greek too, whence it cometh that he is no small Grecian." But I swear that it is not so, and may the Devil take me if I have you not ever in my thoughts and in my prayers to God. Saith not *Gregory* that ingratitude is the root of all evil? Wherefore he who committeth the sin of Ingratitude sinneth the sin of sins ; and if through pride I fail to write to you, then am I ungrateful to you my benefactor.

Howbeit I can show reasonable cause wherefore I have not sent letters to your worship, for I have been for a long while queasy, and I knew not what ailed me. The leech averred that I had certain ill-concocted baggage in my stomach. But the day before yesterday I took a cathartic, and, saving your honour's reverence, the peccant draff was as it were spoon-meat, and therewith passed a white gobbet of the size of a pear : " Lo ! " quoth the leech, " the crudity that caused the fever." And now I can eat heartily again, and have a good appetite, God be praised. If I abide in good health I will write to you oft. For the nonce it must suffice to say that *His Holiness* is at *Florence*, and the Curialists here are cursing him because he doth not come back, and their business is hindered. They should have patience, say I, and should by no means curse *His Holiness*, lest they should be excommunicated.

I quote the Law to them anent this matter—for I frequent the *Sapienza*, and study there, so that I am become an expert in both branches of the Law, in the one as much as in the other. It is said that *His Holiness* aileth in his eyes,[6] and cannot walk in the open air. You must know too that the *King of France* hath returned to his country, and is about to lead a greater host in array against the *Emperor*. The *Spaniards* will help the *Emperor*, and so you may be assured there will be a mighty war. We must not omit, therefore, to say in our prayers, "Give peace in our time, O Lord!" For war in those parts advantageth not the Curialists. If peace is maintained, prithee send me word concerning any vacant benefice —whether it be a cure of souls or not, and whether in a patron's gift or not.

I am now of ripe experience, and would fain be beneficed. If you have any suit toward, I will use my interest here on your behalf. With regard to *Johann Reuchlin's* case I may tell you that Doctor *Jakob van Hoogstraten* hath culled certain other paragraphs out of the *Augenspiegel*, and they are to the full as heretical as the rest. He is now at *Florence* with the Court, and worketh diligently. Doubt not that the victory will be yours. Send me the news in turn, and farewell, with glory.

From ROME.

IX

¶ *MAGISTER PHILIPP SCHLAURAFF* to
Mag. Ortwin Gratius sesquipedal greetings

VENERATED Magister! you must know that I have received your letter, written in mighty pretty poesy, as is your wont: and you date it "From *Cologne*,

> "Where we have good company—
> Living all in jollity!
> So, a fig for gravity!"

Whereby it hath come into my mind that you are well vinified—that is (to speak poetically) over-flowing with wine: and I trow that you were mellow when you penned those verses.

You bid me send you the poem that I composed concerning my peregrination throughout *Germany*— wherein I visited the Universities on behalf of the Theologians, to influence them, in their favour, against *Johann Reuchlin*—and concerning the tribulations I suffered at the hands of the Poets, who everywhere abound. I gladly comply, but you must send me in return an account of your own doings. I send my poem by the messenger who conveys this: You must know that I have composed it rhythmically, and not with observance of quantities and feet, for methinks it soundeth better so: besides, I have never learned the other kind of Poetry—but this irks me not. Farewell.

From BRUNECK, in Flanders.

❡ *MAGISTER PHILIPP SCHLAURAFF'S Rhythmical Poem that he composed and compiled when he was Cursor in Theology, and perambulated the whole of Upper Germany*

CHRIST omnipotent, the hope of every creature
        'neath the sun,
God of gods to everlasting, while the endless ages run—
Show thou me thy loving-kindness when, with buffetings, the foe
Unrelenting fall upon me: send a fiend from realms below
Charged all Poets—ay, and Jurists—to the gallows-tree to hale,
Who have wrought on me—all blameless—without ceasing, scathe and bale.
First in *Saxony*, a student of the dialectic art
I resided; 'twas *Sibutus* that its mystery did impart—
He of leech-craft was Professor, and was wedded to a crone,
But the beer she brewed and vended for all blemish might atone!
There a Poet, one *Balthasar*,[7] with his railing drove me mad,
And one *Philipp Engentinus*,[8] who was every whit as bad!
So I deemed it was but prudent, to escape another broil,
To direct my steps to *Rostock*, and to seek a distant soil.

Hermann Buschius there resideth, who to death a man
  be-rhymes—
But that there the plague was raging, luckily I heard
  betimes.
Fain at *Greifswald*[9] I'd have sojourned, but it meagre
  cheer supplied,
So by night I tramped to *Frankfort—Frankfort* on
  the *Oder's* tide:
There *Trebellius*,[10] with his verses blasphemous, reviled
  me sore,
And his pupils, the *van Osthens*,[11] at his bidding 'gan to
  pour
Bitter ridicule upon me with their fleers and jeers so
  pat,
Till folk cried whene'er they saw me, " *Seht das Köln-
  isch Kopulat !* "
To *Vienna* then I hied me—sure beneath a planet dire
I was born, for *Collimitius* there was Rector—may the
  fire
Of *St. Antony* consume him !"[12] For he proved a bitter
  foe,
Calling me a recreant rascal, vowing I to jail should go!
Heckmann timely me delivered: straightway *Vadian*
  a new
Quarrel fastened on me, guiltless of his hurt, (altho'
  'twas true
Pfefferkorn had soundly lashed him, rightly, in his
  own defence),
Shedding bitter tears of anguish, I proclaimed my
  innocence,
Praying that upon my journey I might scatheless go
  and free,
But the *Lily* Hostel's Rector whispered, " Let him
  prisoner be ! "
Then outspake *Cuspinianus*, who the Emperor's friend-
  ship wins,
" Masters," quoth he, " of the Arts are Doctors of the
  Deadly Sins ! "
Then t'wards *Ingoldstadt* I turned me, but one
  Philomusus there
Fulminates 'gainst Theologians—him to brave I did
  not dare;

So resolved, for peace and safety, on to *Nuremberg* to
fare.

There a wight named *Bilibaldus Pirckheimer* fell foul
of me,

Though no Master he of Arts is—it was told me privily

That, in league with many comrades, sojourners in
divers lands,

He the foes of *Johann Reuchlin* with his voice and pen
withstands,

And against us Theologians many a carping book
hath he

Written; and 'tis whispered, newly hath he censured
Usury—

Tho' the Doctors at *Bologna*, where the question late
was moved,

Have declared that Compound Interest may be by the
Church approved.

In a month I went to *Leipsic*—to the University—

There I met one *Richard Crocus* (Englishman he's said
to be),

When he met me straight he shouted, "That's the
beast I at *Cologne*

Lighted on!" But I the honour of his friendship would
not own.

Then he cried to his companion, "Lo, the ninny-
hammer! he

Johann Reuchlin fain would harass with his vain
Theology."

This to the Magister Nosters I reported, and they
swore

That for lectures *Richard Crocus* stipend should receive
no more.

Then spake *Mosellanus*—taking up his parable, Quoth
he,

"Straightway seize this meddling greenhorn—hang him
on the gallows-tree!"

So from thence they sent me packing, and I set my
face to go

On to *Erfurt*, where arriving, soon I found another foe!

Eberbach began to vex me—*Eobanus Hessus* too,

Ceased not to contrive my drubbing, egging on a
ribald crew

In the streets to basely swinge me, "Dash to bits the
  runnion's jowl!
Is he not the bane of *Reuchlin*, and a Theologian foul?"
"Whence doth come this callow bejan?" *Crotus*
  cried, "He is unknown!"
"I'm a graduate!" "Get thee gone then!" I was
  minded to *Cologne*,
Through the *Buchenwald* to journey, but a comrade
  cried, "Beware!"
Warning me of *Mutianus*, with his bludgeon, lurking
  there!
Through *Campanien* I evaded, and again to *Meissen* came,
But to *Aesticampianus* all too quickly spread the fame—
Straight he sent forth his disciples, and they dragged
  me by the hair,
And his neighbour *Spalatinus* came and threatened
  then and there
For a private grudge to swinge me—but my bruised
  and battered hide
Hardly saving, I escaped me to a forest dark and wide;
Did the Devil, or an angel of the Pit my footsteps
  lead
Then to *Sturnus?* When he saw me parlous was my
  plight indeed!
Mercy! How my lugs he basted! So I fled in evil
  case
To *Franconia's* river valley—and met *Hutten* face to
  face!
Solemn oath, with upraised fingers, made he that a
  scourging sore
He would give me if I lingered—so to save my skin,
  once more
On I hurried into *Swabia*, and to *Augsburg* won my
  way—
Peutinger, the foe of *Brulfer*, would not suffer me to
  stay
There in peace, so passing *Stuttgart*, knowing *Reuchlin*
  there did dwell,
Heretic by me suspected—ay! and dreaded, sooth to
  tell—
Thence to *Tübingen* I journeyed—many ribald fellows
  there

Write new-fangled nonsense, and they never Theo-
logians spare;
Of them *Schwarzerd* was the vilest—might his corse
rejoice mine eyne,
Gladly would I tramp, a footsore Pilgrim, to *St.*
James's shrine!
Bebel, Johann Brassicanus, with *Paul Vereander*,[13] swore
That, to save my back from bruises, I must go, and
come no more!
But by help of one *Franciscus*[14]—blessed be his saintly
name!
I, his prudent counsel heeding, safely from that
country came.
Eager then to leave those Poets far behind me, straight
I hied me
On to *Strasburg*, where *Gerbellius* with distracting
quibbles plied me:
Tangled in sophistic meshes, I was held to open scorn,
In the street before the vulgar—would that I had ne'er
been born!
Then *Sebastian Brandt* cried "Follow me!" and
took me by the neif,
"You're the man for *Narragonia*—welcome to the
Narrenschiff!"
Schurer too, gor-bellied glutton! grinning, wheezed "I
understand
You're the kind of lubbard losel that they want in
Lazyland!"
Girding up my loins, I scampered, and to *Schlettstadt*
took my flight—
In a greasy gown of leather, straightway *Wimpheling*
hove in sight;
Jakob Spiegel, too, who shouted, "Whence? thou
ninny-hammer, whence?"
Murmuring I came from *Swabia*, "Beast!" I got for
recompence!
Wrath was I, and one *Kirherus*[15] bade me off to *Athens*
pack,
Greek to learn—and *Johann Witz*, with all his scholars
at his back,
Thwacked me, till the Queen of Heaven I invoked;
then, "Down the stairs

Pitch him!" *Storckius* cried, but *Phrygio*,[16] softened
    maybe by my prayers,
Saved me: then *Rhenanus* asked me if from *Germany*
    I hailed,
" Ay, from *Flanders!* " but the answer, humbly spoken,
    naught availed !
Thumps upon my pate descended, Whack ! and Whack !
    on either ear,
And my staggered cerebellum buzzed till I could
    scarcely hear.
Then to *Hagenau* I hied me; out upon thee, *Wolfgang
    Angst !*[17]
For mine eyes thou foully smotest—but *Gott gebe dass
    du hangst !*
Comes a youth, one *Johann Letzer*,[18] with a folio thick
    and wide,
Knocks my breath from out my body, hurling it against
    my side !
" Hear, oh hear my last confession !" gaspingly the
    words I said,
" Shrive me in my deep contrition !"   But at midnight
    from my bed
Soft arising, off to *Friburg* I departed, seeking ruth—
There were nobles, clad in armour ! *Reuchlin's* fautors,
    and in truth
Terrible to see !   Their aspect threatened me with
    instant death !
But an old juristic gaffer, *Zazius* hight, with husky
    breath,
Coughed out " Art thou then a Scotist?"   With
    disdain I straight replied,
" Nay, but *Thomas*, Holy Doctor, of *Aquino* is my
    pride."
Up to scorn he held me, shamefaced, while *Amorbach*
    shouted " Thick
Tho' his pate be, something novel I'll implant there;
    fetch a stick !"
Born to sorrow, *Basle* I fled to, where *Erasmus* famed
    doth dwell,
I addressed him: " By your favour, will your ex-
    cellency tell
One who humbly asketh, are you candidate for a degree,

Or a postulant for licence?" "Oh, assuredly!" quoth
he.

There, within the house of *Froben*, many heretics abide,
Notably one *Glareanus*, who my aching back and side
Buffeted with thumps resounding, then to finish,
knocked me down,
Though I cried aloud for pity, "Mercy! by thy laurel
crown!"
Taking boat, to *Worms* I drifted; there I met within
an inn
Theobaldus, a physician—quickly did our strife begin!
How he raved 'gainst Theologians! "Thou'rt a
gowk!" I mildly said,
Scarcely had the words been uttered when a cheese
replaced my head!
Wounded, I to *Mainz* betook me, where with kindness,
in my need,
Good *Bartholomaeus Zehner* took me in, and gave me
rede:
"Go ye not to the *Corona!* Pardy! 'tis a dangerous
inn!
Certes, there the guests will shend you! Men of
violence and sin!"
Carbach there on *Livy* lectures: Woe is me! an
ancient foe,
One *Huttichius*, with a joint-stool, felled me at a single
blow!
For a bounce that all unwitting, slipped me, *Weydmann*,
standing there,
Smote me—while I vengeance threatened for the insult,
down the stair
Königstein propelled me headlong; but—the danger
'scaped, by flight—
As beside the *Rhine* I wandered, Doctor *Murner* met
my sight!
In a boat upon the river—Thomas *Murner*, Minorite!
" 'Tis my dignity that saves thee!" cried he, "or thou
straight should'st lie,
Underneath the rolling waters!" Shivering, I made
reply:
"Wherefore?" "Knave and fool!" he shouted,
"*Reuchlin's* wrongs will tell you why!"

But, at last, to *Köln* I drifted, where I found good
    company,
And I heeded not though *Buschius* and *Caesarius*
    flouted me,
With their Livy-reading pupils jeering; for with open
    arms
The Theologers received me faint from dangers and
    alarms.
There I dwelt in happy leisure, and I heeded not a hair
Tho' he boasts himself a Poet, *Hermann, Graf von
    Neuenar.*
Pfefferkorn hath somewhere written, that their rank
    doth not excuse
Nobles, who to duly answer for their deeds may not
    refuse :
Writing as *Obscuri Viri*, they must pay the penalty—
Ends my story : for the honour of the University.

X

❦ *DOCTOR BARTHEL GOWK to*
Magister Ortwin Gratius

GREETINGS innumerable, with the utmost respect,
reverend Magister!
    Without tedious preamble or ambagious circumlocu-
tion,—seeing that you lately sent me word that you
desired me to let you know how matters stand here
with regard to the Cause of the Faith, I would have
you know that it prospereth, but that the definitive
judgment hath not yet been promulgated.
    There is a Jurist here, one *Martin Gröning*,[19] a
Doctor of *Sinigaglia*—so he saith—and vengeance proud
and arrogant. He must needs translate the "*Augenspiegel*," and is mighty boastful, for he would cut a
figure. Some men praise him, and of such I lately demanded, "What more does this fellow know than
another?" They made answer that he had competent
knowledge of Greek. You see therefore that you need
not pay any regard to him, for Greek is not material
to Holy Scripture. I believe that he knows not a jot
of the "Book of Sentences." Neither can he frame me a

syllogism in Baroco or Celarent, for he is no logician. Not long ago he called me an ass, and I said, " Come now, if thou art so bold, dispute with me ! " for I made free to "thou" him. But he was silent. Then pressing my attack, I said " I will prove that thou art an ass. Thus : whatever bears a burden is an ass—thou bearest a burden—therefore thou art an ass. The minor premiss is evident, since thou bearest that book." Now this was true, for he was carrying a book, that *Jakob von Questenberg*[20]had given him to read, against Doctor *Jakob van Hoogstraten ;* and he was not shrewd enough to deny my major, although I could not have proved that—but I knew full well that he was unversed in logic. Then quoth I, " Herr Doctor, you wish to thrust your nose in Theologians' affairs, which pertain not to your Faculty ; I counsel you to hold aloof, seeing that you have no knowledge of the matter ; else you will surely come to grief, for the Theologians are not minded that Jurists should meddle with questions of Faith." Forthwith, fuming he cried, " I not only understand these things, but I can see that thou art a damned beast ! " Then I was enraged, and started up, and that day the strife was hot between us ! But Doctor *Peter Meyer*, parish priest of *Frankfort*, said to me, " Come now, let us go to the inn, and seek some victuals, for it is dinner-time ; and let this worthy gentleman be, for he doth not yet know his rudiments ; he must go to school and learn."

But, mark you, Magister *Ortwin*, we will roundly avenge that insult ; the fellow is a student of *Cologne*, and I know for certain that he resided at *De Monte* hostel ; if therefore you will prevail on the University to cite him, we will convict him of perjury ; for when he matriculated he made oath that he would work for the good of the University, whereas now he sideth with *Johann Reuchlin*, against it. Prithee, do this forthwith—and send me that treatise of *Johann Pfefferkorn's* entitled, " The Defence of J. P. against slanders." A student lately brought it hither, and my heart acheth to possess the book, for it containeth many subtle propositions. The Lord grant you welfare and peace.

Amen.

XI

⁊ *JODOCUS SCHNEIDER* to
Mag. Ortwin Gratius

SALUTATIONS unending, and a New Year full of
as good fortune as there is to be found on earth—
nay, more if possible—I wish your worship. You must
know that I am prospering, by the grace of God who
hath granted me His mercy, and, as the *Psalmist* saith,
"The Lord hath heard my petition; the Lord hath
received my prayers." Daily do I pray for my sins
and beseech our Lord to keep me in body and soul.
Especially the soul, for the body is but dust, and, as
Holy Scripture saith, "Dust thou art, and unto dust
shalt thou return." I hope, moreover, that it goeth
not ill with you, for he who by the grace of God always
repenteth of his sins, and devoutly telleth his beads,
even if he fasteth not oft—with him the Lord willeth
not that it should go ill.

I know that your conscience is good, and you are
ever studying how to forward the good of the Church.
I well know how that lately you wrote a book against
a certain heretic, *Johann Reuchlin* by name, and it was
composed so masterly that I was held in admiration
thereby. I said to a Cursor of the *Order of Preachers*
who was carrying that book, "I think the man must
have a pair of heads to handle a matter so canonically as that." Then the Cursor told me that you
were writing a commentary on that book of Doctor
Arnold von Tongern's that he composed, in the title
of "*Articles,*"²against the heretical propositions of the
"*Augenspiegel.*" Prithee, send me this Commentary
when it is completed. I trow that, without doubt, it
will be a miracle of art—expounding all the arguments,
and notabilia, and propositions, and conclusions, and
corollaries which few fully comprehend; for the Doctor
is exceeding subtle in his writings, as is the wont of
the School of the Albertists. You must not take it
ill if I praise the Albertists—you yourself being a

Thomist—for their diversity is not great, and on certain points they closely agree. Nevertheless the Holy Doctor is the more profound, and this by the special inspiration of the Holy Spirit; hence it is that he is called the Holy Doctor, although *Reuchlin* nameth him not thus in his writings—wherefore is he a heretic, and, in the devil's name, let him so abide. I was lately wrath against a Jurist who defended him, and I wrote an ode in verse against him. For I, too, am wont to poetise when I am alone, by aid of *Bebelius'* "Art of Versifying," which is very subtle.[22] The Ode runneth thus:—

> "Turn not away thine ear from the humble prayer of thy servant!
> Hearken, O Mother revered of the astripotent god!
> 'Tis for Theology's sake, O Mary, thy servant beseecheth;
> *Reuchlin* the wicked Jurist, holy Theology's foe
> Hath no light from above nor mental clarification,
> As there needeth to be in him who wisheth to please thee.
> To recite to your son our prayers therefore remember,
> That he may come to the aid of his own Faculty."

These are elegiacs, and they are scanned after the manner of the first metre in *Boethius*, beginning "Carmina qui quondam studio," &c.

If the messenger had not told me that he must make haste and be off, I would have sent you a pile of verses that I have written in defence of the Church and the Faith. Do not forget, then, to send me the commentary you have constructed, and I will send you further news in return.

Farewell—hurriedly, happily, fervidly.

From OLMÜTZ, in Moravia.

XII

❧ *WILHELM LAMP, Master of Arts, sendeth greeting to Mag. Ortwin Gratius*

REVEREND Sir, inasmuch as you bade me, and commanded me to write to you as soon as I reached Rome, and to tell you all that befell me on the way, and how I stood with regard to bodily health—you must know that by God's grace I am quite well, and I should rejoice to hear that you are quite well too. I hope that, please God, you are in good case.

Now you must know how that as soon as I arrived at the "*Crown*" at *Mainz*, I found certain folk there who were talking about the Cause of the Faith, and were of Doctor *Reuchlin's* part; and when they saw me to be of *Cologne*, they but talked the more, and treated me with disdain. They praised *Johann Reuchlin*, and disparaged the Magisternosters at *Cologne*, and called them bats that could do nothing in the light of day, but flew by night and busied themselves in the darkness. Then quoth I, "Hear the other side!" and I quoted to them the "*Flores Legum.*" Then they began to assail me with many words, till I said, "What have I to do with *Reuchlin?* Let me eat my money's worth." Perhaps you will say, "Herr *Wilhelm*, you ought to have maintained your ground and answered them boldly." But that was out of the question in such a place. I heard that in that Inn a man had just been basted with a joint-stool because he had said a word for Doctor *Jakob van Hoogstraten.* The men who come there for their victuals are very terrible rufflers, who wear swords and cutlasses, and one of them is a Count, who is a tall man and hath white hair. They say that he can take an armed man up in his hands and dash him to the ground. His sword is as long as a giant's. And when I set eyes on him, I held my peace and let them talk on. I intended to write to you forthwith, but there was no messenger at hand.

When I reached *Worms* we lodged at an Inn where there were many Doctors, assessors at the Supreme Court.[23] They said dreadful things about the Theologians, and I heard that they had indicted *Johann Pfefferkorn* on account of the "Tocsin." One of them said, "Mark my words; in a few years these Magisternosters will be swept away, and will be heard of no more." Then said I, "Who then will preach to you, and instruct you in the Catholic faith?" He replied, "That will be the work of learned Theologians who understand the Scriptures, such as *Erasmus* of *Rotterdam, Paul Ricius*,[24] *Johann Reuchlin*, and the like." Then I held my peace, and thought within myself, "Fools talk foolishness." There was one sitting at the board, *Theobald Fettich* by name, who is now Doctor of Medicine, and him I recognised, for he formerly resided at *Cologne* at *De Monte* Hostel; and he talked more than all the rest together. Then said I to him, " You ought to bear in mind the oath that you took to the Rector and University of *Cologne.*"

" To the jakes with the pack of you," quoth he. But let this pass.

Afterwards, when we had taken our departure from *Worms*, certain fearful men on horseback met us, with cross-bows in their hands, and made as though they would shoot us. Then my companion cried out " Jesus ! Jesus !" but I, being of good courage, bade him cry not out thus, and I said to the men, " Most noble Sirs, shoot us not ! We are not armed—we are no foes of yours— we are clerks who are on our way to *Rome* to seek benefices." Then cried one of them, " What are benefices to us ? Give us money that we may drink withal—or the Devil take you!" And so, to get out of their clutches, we had to give them two florins. And I whispered privily, " Drink ! and may the Devil give you his blessing !" After a while my companion asked, saying, "What think ye ? Shall we cite them before the Curia ?" But I told him that this could not be, inasmuch as we knew not their names.

Thereafter, through deep mire, we reached *Augsburg*, and meanwhile it rained and snowed so hard that we could scarce open our eyes. Then said my companion, " Good lack ! how cold I am ! If I were back at *Cologne*, I should never set out for *Rome !*" But I laughed. Now at the Inn there was a comely damsel, and in the evening there was a dance, and my companion joined the dancers. But I chided him for this, in that he was a Magister and ought not to partake of such frivolities. But he cared not a whit, and swore that he would eat a peck of dirt if only that damsel would join him for the night. But I would hearken to no more, and quoting from the *Preacher* " Vanity of vanities, all is vanity !" I went to bed. Next morning we reached *Landsberg*, and my comrade must needs lie with the serving-maid that night. In the morning when we quitted the Inn his horse fell lame. "More damsels abused?" quoth I.[25] But a smith came to the rescue.

Afterwards we came to *Schongau*, where we bought some fine glasses. Then we set forth for *Innsbruck*. But the ways were so foul that the horses could not make way, and sank up to their girths in the mud. And so after much tribulation we attained to *Innsbruck*, and there we found his *Majesty* the *Emperor*, with his vassals, and his courtiers, and his knights, and soldiers, and men-at-arms—having silken cloaks, and gold chains round their necks. And there were some who looked very fierce, with beards, and caps slashed soldier-wise; and I feared to sit at meat in the Inn, for I heard one of them say, "If I were Emperor, I would hang every one of these blood-suckers at the Court who come to *Rome* and learn wickedness. They cog and cozen one another for benefices, and seek to oust country parsons in *Germany*, and cause much money to flow from *Germany* to *Rome*." Hence I perceived that the Curialists heed neither God nor man, and therefore they will perish like dust before the wind.

Afterwards we passed over a mountain all covered with snow, and so high that I trow it reached half-way to heaven. And so bitter was the cold on the summit thereof that I feared lest it should give me a fever; and I thought of my stove at *Cologne*. And my comrade said to me, "Oh, if I but had my cloak!" Then said I to him, "You are for ever complaining of chills when you are abroad, and when you get to an Inn you desire revelry. Know you not that venery cooleth the blood?" But he replied that it seemed to him not to cool it, but warm it. I must tell you, Master *Ortwin*, that never in my life have I seen a man so given to lechery. Whenever we entered an Inn the first thing he did was to ask the drawer, "Is there aught within for my lap?"

Next we reached *Trient*; and your worthiness will forgive me, and take it not ill that I tell you the truth, that there for once I purged my reins in the stews by stealth. Nevertheless at night I read my *Hours* to the *Blessed Virgin* for my sin. At *Trient* were many soldiers preparing to advance against *Verona* and work

wonders there! And they made boast to us how that
the Emperor was going to capture *Venice*. We saw
bombards there, and many other engines that I had
never set eyes on in my life.

On a Sunday we reached *Verona*. This is a fair
city, with walls, and forts and bastions. We saw
there the house of *Dietrich von Bern*,[26] where he lived,
and where he overthrew and slew the many giants who
fought with him.

Afterwards, when we would fain have proceeded on
our way, for a long while we could not, for fear of the
Venetians, who, it was said, had taken the field. And
this was true, for afterwards at *Mantua* we heard the
sound of their bombards as they laid siege to *Brescia*.
At *Mantua* I said to my companion, "Here *Virgil* was
born." But said he, "What care I for that heathen?
Let us go to the Carmelites and see *Baptista Mantu-
anus*,[27] who is twice as good a poet as *Virgil*, so *Ortwin*
hath ten times told me." And I reminded him how
that you had once censured *Donatus* for saying that
Virgil was the most learned of poets and the greatest
of men. You said, "Would that *Donatus* were here,
that I might tell him to his face that he lied; for
Baptista the Mantuan is above *Virgil*." But when we
came to the Monastery of the Carmelites, it was told
us that *Baptista* was dead. "May he rest in peace!"
quoth I.

Thence we came to *Bologna*, where was his *Holiness*, and also the *King of France*.[28] There we heard a
Papal Mass, and gained many indulgences for all our
sins, both venial and mortal, and made confession.
The reverend Father *Jakob van Hoogstraten*, Magister-
noster, and Inquisitor of Heretical Pravity was there
too; and when I saw him, I said, "Reverend Father,
what doeth your Excellency here? I thought you had
been at *Rome*." Then I delivered to him your letter
and that of Doctor *Arnold von Tongern*, and he told
me that he was seeking by the help of the *King of
France* to bring it about that *Reuchlin* should be
declared a heretic, and that the "*Augenspiegel*" should
be burned. I asked him, saying, "Doth the King, then,
understand this matter?" He replied, "Of himself

doubtless, he doth not, but the Theologians of Paris have instructed him, and his Confessor *Guillaume Petit*, a very zealous man, hath told him, in confession, that he will not shrive him, unless he bring it about, through the Pope, that *Reuchlin* shall be declared a heretic." Then I rejoiced greatly, and cried, "May the Lord grant that it shall be according to your words!" I met many courtiers there who were known to me, and I invited them to the Inn.

Thence we proceeded to *Florence*, which is as fair a city as any upon earth.

Afterwards we came to *Sienna*, where there is a University, but the Theologians are few. Then we came to sundry small towns. One of these is called *Montefiascone*. There we drank of the best wine that I had ever tasted in my life, and I asked the taverner how it was named. "Lacrima Christi," said he.[29] Then said my companion, "Would that Christ shed tears in the Fatherland!" And there we had a roaring bowse.

Three days later we reached *Rome*. The Lord be praised, who hath delivered us from so many dangers by the way—not to speak of botched shoes. I have as yet heard no news at Court, except that I have seen a beast as big as four horses, and which hath a snout as long as I, and is a wondrous creature. When I saw it, I said, "God is wonderful in his works." I would give a florin for you to see that beast. And now, pardy, I trow I have acquitted myself well in writing. Do the like, or I will never write to you again. Farewell soundly.

From ROME; in haste.

XIII

℃ *THOMAS KLORBIUS*, of *Theology a humble Doctor, sendeth greeting to Magister Ortuinus*

SINCE, as it is written, "affliction giveth under-standing," take it not amiss if, in some measure, I censure you, seeing that I do it with all good will.

Lately, in a tractate, you described a certain theologian as being well-lettered, and a Doctor of long standing, and a profound Scotist, and deeply versed in the Book of the Sentences.

You also averred that he had conned by rote the whole book of the Holy Doctor[30] "Of Entity and Essence," and that he knew "The Fortress of Faith" like his paternoster, and that by memorative art he had impressed the Formalities of *Scotus* upon his mind like so much wax; and, finally, you alleged that he was "a member of ten universities."

You commit — pardon me — a solecism. One member cannot have many bodies; but, on the other hand, one body may rightly possess many members.

Thus, the human body hath a head, feet, hands, arms, belly, parts male and female; and a foot is a member of a man, and the head is a member of a man, and so forth.

Now, the whole body of a man consists of these members, and these members are comprised in the body, as species are comprised in a genus.

But none of these members consists of many bodies. On the other hand, if you were to aver that a certain Doctor was a body of ten Universities, I should still censure you. For any one might hence conclude that the ten Universities were members of that Doctor, and that he consisted of ten Universities. But if this were granted, it would be a scandal to those ten Universities, and they would be vilified if a single man—for even Doctors of Divinity, as you know, are men—was declared to be more worthy than so many Universities. It is an impossible case. For even the Holy Doctor himself is not greater than ten Universities.

How then shall we mend the matter? What should we rightly say?

Perpend; for the question is mightily intricate, and although it appertaineth to Grammar, yet many a Doctor knoweth not how to resolve it:—

A man who has been matriculated at ten Universities, who has studied therein for the appointed time— attending lectures and observing the statutes—when he has taken and kept the oaths, and has rendered honour to the Masters and Doctors, is entitled to say—"I am members of ten Universities"—not "a member."

This phrase is not solecistic, notwithstanding a certain lack of concord in the numbers.

It is a case of Apposition, as in *Virgil:*—

> "Formosum pastor Corydon ardebat Alexim,
>   Delicias domini,"

For here *Alexis*, who is but a single swain, is yet called "delights"—by Apposition.

Believe me, this is a most subtle and notable resolution. I learned it when I was at Louvain, and was not yet Bachelor: the question was debated for four days.

Take not this in dudgeon. I write to you with good intent. Farewell.

Coblenz.

XIV

❡ *MAGISTER OTTO HÄMMERLIN to Mag. Ortwin Gratius*

VAST store of salutations! Reverend Magister, your worship hath done me a great favour in sending me that notable book of *Johann Pfefferkorn's* intituled, "Johann Pfefferkorn's Defence." I cannot sufficiently admire how notably and excellently he reprehendeth *Johann Reuchlin*. When I read it I cried, "Would that that fellow *Reuchlin* were dead!" But a certain parish priest, who is a stiff Reuchlinist, always resisteth me—and favoureth the argument *a fortiori*. Yesterday, when before Vespers I walked with him, these words proceeded from his mouth, "If the Theologians have not overcome *Reuchlin* in Germany, much less will they overcome him in *Rome;* for in Italy there are very learned men, and they instantly recognise the stupidity and emptiness of the Theologians—for they pay no heed to such nonsense at *Rome*. What a testimony it is," quoth he, "against the Theologians that they do not dare to write against *Reuchlin* and his allies in their own names, but foist in a jack-pudding, who hath neither honour nor goods to lose, and ascribe their books to him." Then I made answer, "*Pfefferkorn* of a truth compiled the work, but Magister *Ortwin* afterwards Latinised it." Said the priest, "I know well enough that *Ortwin* composed the Latin, for I recognised his style at once. I know too that *Ortwin* is of a good stock—a priestly one, to wit. But tell me one thing : you must confess that *Pfefferkorn* knoweth not the Latin alphabet, much less can he read. And if he cannot read, much less can he understand. And if he cannot understand, much less can he write and compose. And if he can neither read, nor understand, nor write—much less can he discuss questions that none but a deeply learned man can deal with. Therefore, how is it possible that he put together that material, either in Latin, or German, or Hebrew?" I replied that I supposed that *Pfefferkorn* had such an enlightened intellect, and had heard so much of the subject-matter that, by God's help and the inspiration of the Holy Spirit, he was well able to dispute concerning it. "The matter is such an easy one that *Reuchlin* could be vanquished therein by *Pfefferkorn's* wife." Then said the priest, "That is very sooth. I trow that five sturdy young Westphalian boors could not vanquish *Johann Pfefferkorn's* wife, and much less could *Johann Reuchlin*, who is an old man and feeble, and impotent withal. But I marvel that his Holiness the Pope, and the Emperor as well, can allow such scandals to be perpetrated by that Jewish buffoon, and permit him to stand in a holy place, and preach to the people, and pronounce benediction, and do such things that if a layman who had always been a Christian were to do them, nevertheless we should have no good opinion of him—much less is it seemly in the case of a baptized Jew, who cannot be shewn to be a true Christian until he be dead.[31] And such things as this ought not to be suffered, much less should he be permitted to thrust himself into the disputations of learned men and thus be an offence to all honest folk. He ought to be hanged—with his books and his scandals—as he hath long deserved."

I made answer that his preaching was not pontifical, and was but simple instruction such as a layman might

give. And as for his books, it is evident that he doth
but defend himself against *Johann Reuchlin,* who disparaged him. And in his *Hand-spiegel* he chideth the
injustice of *Johann Reuchlin.* And that he is a good
Christian may be presumed from the fact that if he did
not intend always to remain a Christian he would not
be so wrathful against the Jews, and do them so much
hurt. The priest said, " To write, or compose, a book
is no small matter, and only great and learned men who
have taken high degrees are competent for this, not a
lewd fellow like *Johann Pfefferkorn:* and therefore the
Theologians of *Cologne* ought never to have thought
that they could persuade folk that *Pfefferkorn* wrote
the like. If I were Emperor, I would hang *Pfefferkorn* and *Hoogstraten* on the same gallows."

Quoth I, "What hath Doctor *Jakob van Hoogstraten* done? He is a good Imperialist, as I can
prove by his Letter to the Emperor, in the which he
saith ' May his Imperial Majesty prosper and rejoice for
ever; and may God preserve him for a thousand years.' "

Quoth the priest, "I have seen ten malefactors
suffer death, and none of them was so worthy of death
as *Hoogstraten,* who persecuteth so unjustly a good
and innocent man ; moreover he hath sought the aid of
the King of *France,* who is the Emperor's open foe,
against *Johann Reuchlin.* And this is the crime of
High Treason, over which he lamented at *Rome.*"

I replied that *Hoogstraten* had done this through
zeal for the faith; for the faith is greater than an
Emperor, and theologians pay no heed to secular rank.
Then departed the priest, crying, "Oh most innocent
Reuchlin! Why should you be harassed by these vile
and wicked persecutors? May God preserve you! If
there is any justice on Earth, you cannot be overthrown
in such a cause! Therefore can I say, 'the heathen
have raged, and have imagined a vain thing.'" I
answered, in my sleeve, "Let his days be few, and
his bishoprick may another take." Pardy, Master
Ortwin, our troubles are many. I would that our
cause made way. Write to me how matters stand
at *Rome.* Farewell—for as long as lived *Methusela.*

From BRESLAU.

XV

❦ *MAGISTER PETER STEINHART*
to Magister Ortwin Gratius greeting

I WAS minded, Domine Ortwin, to write to you at
large concerning all manner of news—about wars[32]
and battles, and about *Johann Reuchlin's* affair, and now
I am so beflustered that I cannot sit me down for
wrath ; and I cannot write about such things when
my heart is a-thumping me like a fist—because there
is a German here from *Meissen* or thereabouts, and
he promised to give me a Juristical Vocabulary, and
now he denieth it to me; I have often exhorted him
friendly, but it is of no avail. It is manifest that he
meaneth to insult me. And since, as you know, every
promise createth a debt, I thereupon summonsed him.
Then, to-day he sends me an abusive letter and gibeth
at me as if I were a dotterel. And so I am choleric
to such a degree that I know not what to be at. But
I shall to the magistrate, and apply for a warrant of
arrest, inasmuch as that fellow is by me suspect of
absconding himself. And if he sendeth me not that
book incontinent I shall set on the catchpoles to attach
him and put him in gaol—and then if he getteth a turn
or two of the strappado[33] he must e'en put up with it,
for I will learn him to fail a man, and not keep his
promises. Mark my word, I will set that fellow to
rights—my life else ! Because I must have that book,
since I am setting in order my studies, and I have
bought books about law and other things, going every
day for four hours to the *Sapienza* to hear the Institutes, and the Infortiatum, and the Canon Law[34] too,
and the Precepts of the Chancellery. And I have
found here a right useful book—it exceedeth ! I have
learnt many things from it—I doubt that you have it
in *Germany*—it is marvellous and mightily explicatory,
and it is intituled " Casus longi super Institutis,"[35] and
it treateth of the prettiest matters, and expoundeth the
Institutes so deeply that it often divideth one para-

graph into ten parts, and it runneth after the fashion of a dialogue—and as for its latinity, it is hugely elegant. I cannot tell you how useful it is to have a book like that.

But you must not blab to those Jurists in *Cologne* who are on *Johann Reuchlin's* side, for if they had that book they could practise the more subtilly.

I know very well that you commend not my studying Law, because you have often told me that I ought the rather to study Theology, which giveth a blessing, and is of higher desert than the Jurisprudence which maketh the crooked straight and the straight crooked— and you cited a passage in *Richardus*.[36] Nevertheless I say unto you that it is my duty, inasmuch as the science of Jurisprudence toucheth the earning of our bread, as it is written:—

> "Con well Justinian's code, if pelf you'ld gain,
> And Galen: chaff all else, but they the grain."

Moreover you know right well that I am a poor man; and my mother has written to tell me that I must bestir myself to get cheer and gear, because she will not send me another stiver—and, by the Lord, that's how it standeth.

And now again I bethink myself of that fellow who hath so mightily stirred my choler. From my heart, fare ye well.

Rome.

XVI

❡ *MAGISTER JOHANN HUTER* to
Mag. Ortwin Gratius

I SEND you more salutations than there are thieves in *Poland*—heretics in *Bohemia*—boors in *Switzerland*—scorpions in *Italy*—pimps in *Spain*—vermin in *Hungary*—Articles in *Paris*—topers in *Saxony*—chapmen in *Venice*—courtiers at *Rome*—chaplains in *Germany*—nags in *Friesland*—vassals in *France*—fishes in the *Marches*—swine in *Pomerania*—sheep in *England* —cattle in *Dacia*—harlots in *Bamberg*—artisans in

Nuremberg—Jews in *Prague*—Pharisees in *Cologne*—priests in *Würzburg*—ships at *Naples*—needle-makers at *Herzogenbusch*—furriers at *Frankfort*—nobles in *Franconia*—sailors in *Zealand*—children of *Sodom* at *Florence*—indulgences among the Dominicans—weavers at *Augsburg*—locusts in the summer—pigeons in *Wetterau*—cabbages in *Bavaria*—herrings in *Flanders*—sacks in *Thuringia!*

In a word, greetings infinite I offer you, reverend Magister, for you are beloved by me to the verge of possibility—with love unfeigned. But you may say that I pretend this affection, and that you do not believe it to be so heartfelt, therefore I will say but little about it. The saying goes, " Self-praise defileth the lips," or vulgarly, " Eigenlob stinkt." Nevertheless in token of my love I send you herewith two gifts; the first is a rosary made out of ox-horn, which hath touched the tomb of Saint *Peter* and Saint *Paul*, and many other relics at Rome. And over this I have read three masses. They say that it is sovran against robbers and all murderous assaults, if one telleth his beads with it. The second gift I send is something wrapped up in a piece of cloth which hath a virtue against serpents, and I have seen trial made thereof. And if ever a serpent bite you—which heaven forfend—it will do you no hurt. This I gave a Carlin for. There was a man here in the *Campo dei Fiori* who worked miracles by virtue of St. *Paul*, and he had a mort of serpents of terrible shapes, so that it was a marvel to behold. He touched them and they did him no hurt—but when they bit any one else, then he cured him by this talisman, giving him this kickshaw tied up; and they say that he is of that stock on which St. *Paul* conferred healing power. For when St. *Paul* walked the earth he was once entertained by a man who treated him with the greatest reverence, and played the good fellow, giving him victuals and drink and good lodging, and in the morning he asked him, saying, " Sir, take it not amiss—I see that you are a great man, and have especial grace from God, and I doubt not that you are a saint, for but yesterday I saw you work a miracle. Tell me,

I pray you, who you are." Then answered Saint *Paul*, " I am *Paul*, an apostle of Christ." Then the man fell on his knees, saying, " Forgive me, Saint *Paul*, in that I knew not who you were; I ask you to pray for my sins, and to give me by way of valediction a special grace from on high." Then said Saint *Paul*, " Thy faith hath preserved thee;" and he gave to him and all his posterity, the gift of healing men who had been stung by serpents. And the man who gave me this remedy is of his posterity, as hath been proved many a time. Accept it therefore with all good will. Write and send me tidings concerning the war; and tell me whether that Jurist *Johann Reuchlin* still composeth treatises against you—which mayhap he still doth out of mere hardihood and from no demerits in yourself. But I trust that you will fairly set him at nought, for Herr Doctor *Hochstrat* telleth me that his cause prospereth, and that I should avize you thereof. Farewell.

From ROME.

XVII

❦ *FRIEDRICH GLANTZ to* *Magister Ortwin Gratius*

A CONGLOMERATION of greetings. In case, Reverend Sir, you know it not already, let me forthwith tell you that I have been at odds with a certain quirister here who thinketh himself to be somebody, and yet is merely a poor student, like myself and the rest.

We were bowsing together, and he declared that he had pledged me in a full tankard of beer. I averred that he had not—for, by the Lord, I never saw him drink it. Then said I, " Master quirister, I did not see you drink; an I had seen you, right gladly would I have pledged you again, for I am not the man to be scared at a tankard of beer." Thereupon the fellow swore that he had in sooth pledged me, and argued that therefore I must needs drink to him. " Nay," quoth I, "drink to me, and I will hob and nob with you." Again he declared that he had pledged me, and that it behoved me to do my duty. I made answer that there was no statute to compel me to drink against my will. Said he, "Nay, but I can compel you." Said I, "Where find you that?" Said he, "In the Code: 'Vinum, etc., si certum putatur.'" Said I, "You cite the Code to me, but I am no Jurist; I will enquire further on this matter." Thereupon I paid my shot, and took myself off. The fellow cried that never, so long as he lived, would he drink with me again. "So be it!" said I. And thus the matter standeth, Herr *Ortwin*.

Send me now some news in return: and fare thee well, till a sparrow weigh a quintal.

MÜNSTER.

XVIII[37]

⊏ *BROTHER SIMON WURST, Doctor of Sacred Theology, to Mag. Ortwin Gratius greeting*

EVER since *Johann Pfefferkorn's* "Defence," which he composed in Latin, reached us here, daily there have been fresh rumours. One man saith this, another saith that. One man is on *Pfefferkorn's* side, another on *Reuchlin's;* whom one man upholdeth, another blameth. There is sore brangling, and folk would fain be at fisticuffs. If I were to relate all the squabbles that have arisen over that book, a whole Olympiad would fail me.

Briefly, however, I will glance at one or two matters. Many folk—especially the lay Magisters, and the priests and friars of the Franciscan Order—roundly declare it to be a thing impossible that *Pfefferkorn* composed that book, seeing that he never learned a word of Latin. I reply that this objection is futile, though it hath been for the undoing of great men even to this day, but with injustice—for *Johann Pfefferkorn,* who beareth with him a pen and an ink-horn, can jot down that which he heareth at public preachments, or at assemblies, or when students and Dominicans come to his house, or when he goeth to the baths. Sonty! how many sermons hath he not heard in twelve years! How many exhortations! How many opinions of the holy fathers! And these he could either lay up in his own mind, or dictate to his wife, or scratch upon the walls, or enter in his notebook. I added, moreover, that *Johann Pfefferkorn* avoweth of himself—without boasting—that he can apply, without help, everything contained in the Bible or in the Holy Gospel, to any purpose, good or evil, and that in German or in Hebrew. He knoweth too, by rote, all the gospels that are read throughout the year, and he can recite them to the letter—and this is more than the Jurists and Poets can do. He hath, moreover, a son named *Lorenz*—a right towardly youth—who studieth until he hath grown pale; I marvel however, that he is allowed to study those diabolical poets. He gathereth for his father saws from the Orators and poets—both personally and from the lips of his teachers—to be applied to any subject and any argument; moreover he can quote *Hugo*. *Johann Pfefferkorn*, forsooth, hath profited much from this sagacious youth, inasmuch as what he for lack of learning cannot attain to, his son despatcheth.

Let them therefore be put to shame who have falsely spread it abroad that *Johann Pfefferkorn* hath not composed his own books, but that they have been written by the Doctors and Magisters at *Cologne*: let *Johann Reuchlin*, too, blush, and groan to all eternity, in that he declared that Pfefferkorn composed not the *Handspiegel* himself — concerning which there hath been before now much discussion amongst the learned —since three men furnished him with the authorities he citeth therein. One asked me, saying, "What three men be they?" And I replied that I knew not, but that I deemed them to be the same three men who appeared unto *Abram*, of whom we read in the Book of Genesis. But when I said this they all made mouths at me, and mocked me as if I was a greenhorn. Would that the devil would smite them with heavy blows, as it is written in the book of *Job*, which just now in our monastery we are reading in the refectory. Exhort *Johann Pfefferkorn* to have patience, for I trust that the Lord will sooner or later work a miracle. Greet him, too, in my name. Prithee salute also his wife for me—you well know how: but privily. And now, farewell.

ANTWERP: written in hot haste, and without deliberation.

XIX

ℭ *KONRAD UNCKEBUNCK to*
Mag. Ortwin Gratius

I MARVEL greatly, reverend Herr Magister, that my parents have sent me no money, though they know that I have not a doit, and I have sent them twenty letters at the least. If they will send me no money, then, by the Lord, I have another plan in my head. Mark my word, I have been minded of late to bind myself under a bond to the Chamber and borrow two or three Rhenish florins, and come home and expound to them my opinion—in form thick enough for them to feel. The devil! Think they that I grow upon a tree—or that I can eat hay like a beast? Devil take me if I have had a Carlin these six months! and I never have any victuals save salad, and onions, and garlic, and once in a way a dish of beans or kail, or some spinach in Italian fashion. But well I know how my brethren at home guzzle fish and fowl and all manner of dainty dishes, and never give me a thought. But I will endure it no longer. Prithee tell them so, and then I will urge my master here to press forward your suit as you would have me do.

Moreover, I pray you, when my parents hand over the money, send it to me, and with it send me a piece of chalk, for there is no good chalk in *Rome*, if you were to give a florin for it. And, as you know, one must have chalk—for I am a logician, and when I want to make syllogisms there is not always ink at hand. Besides, it is irksome to make them with ink; send me, too, some German laces for my boots, for it is wonderful what bad laces they make in *Italy.*

Herewith I send you a vernicle[38]that hath touched the heads of *St. Peter* and *St. Paul* and many other relics—also I send an Agnus Dei. Greet for me the reverend Doctor Herr *Valentin von Geltersheim.* By the Lord, I could never have learnt logic so well had I not resided in his hostel, for he is mightily explicit, and his pupils gulch their facts when he lectureth.

Fare ye well—in all health of mind and body.

The COURT OF ROME.

XX

❡ *MAGISTER MARQUARD FOTZENHUT to Magister Ortwin Gratius tendereth greeting and friendly offices*

YOU ask me, Reverend Herr Magister, to tell you how it fareth with Doctor *Jakob van Hoogstraten.* You must know, then, that the Jurists withstand him sorely. Yet, as I hear, the devil will undo them; for many Cardinals are on your side, especially the Cardinal of *Santa Croce,*[39]who will be pope when the Pope dieth. I hear that he said, "I will defend that worthy Theologian *Jakob van Hoogstraten* against *Reuchlin,* though all the Jurists in the world should back him:" so he stood up formerly against *Peter* of *Ravenna*[40]in the matter of those theses, which were mightily heretical.

And you may take it for certain, Herr *Ortwin,* that the Cardinal will overthrow the Jurists, for he is on good terms with the Theologians. He is in the good graces, moreover, of the King of *France* and the University of *Paris,* and the old King of *France* would fain have made him Pope. Matters prosper, too, in other quarters. To that end Doctor *Jakob* a week ago gave a thumping bribe to the referendary of a certain Cardinal (whom here I name not), that he might work upon his Eminence as he well knoweth how to do. A rumour goes here that the Bishop of *Cologne* is dead, and that the Count *von Neuenar* has been elected the new Bishop. If this be true I must say that the Canons of *Cologne* are great fools, since Poet and Bishop are a pair of opposites. It is ill, too, for the cause of the Faith, for the Count is a stubborn ally of *Reuchlin*. A certain Curialist told me that when he left *Cologne* for *Italy* the Count gave him a letter to take to *Reuchlin;* and I have heard from others that he consorteth with many poets, and new-fangled Theologians like *Erasmus of Rotterdam*. When I was in *Würzburg*, there was a poet there, *Ulrich Hutten* by name, who was ever deriding and girding at the Theologians and Masters of Arts; and sitting at table in an Inn, he told another person of quality that he had that very day sent the Count a letter. Then quoth the noble, "What do you write about, when you write thus to one another?" And he made answer that he wrote to urge the Count to do good diligence in the Cause of the Faith, and to work for *Reuchlin* against the Theologians, so that they should not commit the *Augenspiegel* to the flames; and that he heartily commended *Reuchlin* to him; and he averred that he loved *Reuchlin* as his own father: but I held my peace, lest he should suspect that I was on your side. And for this reason it is not good for that man to be made Bishop. But I hope the rumour lieth. Tell me, then, the whole truth, and fare ye well from the soles of your feet to the crown of your head, as saith *Esaias*.

The CITY OF ROME.

XXI

❧ *JOHANN HOLKOT* to *Magister Ortwin Gratius*

GREETING, in all amity. Excellent Sir, I have received the letter which you drew up at *Cologne*. The said letter was dated on *St. Margaret's* Day, but it reached me on *St. Bartholomew's* Day; and when I received it I cried, "The devil! that letter was written a long time ago, and Herr *Ortwin* will be nettled with me, and will say, 'How haughty the fellow is! he deigns not to send me a reply.'"

Wherefore I beseech your Reverence to hold me blameless, and to know of a certainty that the matter standeth not thus.

You thought, forsooth, that I abode still at *Cassel*, but mine host there, when he received the letter, forwarded it to me at *Marburg*, and thus much time was spent. For I am at present at *Marburg*, and am grounding two young men of quality. When, therefore, you send me a letter, prithee address it hither. I gather that you are busy composing a notable treatise, and that you intend to send it to the printers, but deem it better to entitle it "Johann Pfefferkorn's Defence against Calumnies." You tell me that you shall not put your name to this, but shall attribute it to *J. P.*, inasmuch as *Pfefferkorn*, since he heeds not such things, has no fear of *Johann Reuchlin* and his complices, should they take it into their heads to concoct a rejoinder. But I would fain put this question to you: What an if *Reuchlin* should say, " Marry! *Pfefferkorn* hath no Latin, so he could not have written this: it is the Theologians of *Cologne* and that poet of theirs, *Ortwin* who compose these lampoons, and then say ' *Pfefferkorn* wrote them, not we!'"

I trust therefore that you will take much thought before you do this. If you were afterwards to deny the authorship, *Reuchlin* might recognize your style and prove that you wrote the book, and then you would be drawn into a scandal.

Forgive me, for I write but out of affection. Farewell.

Marburg.

XXII

❡ *JODOCUS KLYNGE, Bachelor of Arts, to Magister Ortwin Gratius*

REVEREND Sir, albeit in the flesh I am far from you, nevertheless I would have you know that in the spirit I am ever near you when I call to mind our

mutual amity when we abode at *Deventer*. But when
the freshman came hither, bearing with him your
treatise, he told me that you had said to him, "*Jodocus*
now dwelleth at home, and he leadeth a merry life, and
thinketh no more of me." I answer that this is not
true. I am not a man of that kidney, but I well remember how you used to scribble on the wall at
Deventer, "Out of sight, out of mind."

Yesterday, pardy, when we were at supper, and
were discussing some of those fish of my native country,
called *Amae*, that my father had brought me, I yearned
for you to be there, and I cried "Oh, if Magister *Ortwin*
were only here to guttle fish like these, how my heart
would rejoice!" Then said my father, "Who is this
Magister *Ortwin*?" Thereupon I told him that you
were an old crony of mine, my comrade at *Deventer*,
and when I abode with you, you were in the first class,
and afterwards at the University of *Cologne* you were
my inductor when I was initiated as freshman, because
you came to *Cologne* a year before me; and then we
kept terms together, till I took my Bachelor's degree,
and you proceeded Magister. But I, when by God's
grace, I had become Bachelor, migrated to the University of *Wittenberg*; and then I was a schoolmaster in
one place and another—and thus I lost sight of you.
The things I told him about you! And I described
how that once I made you laugh by quoting to you
this verse :—

"Veni Spandaw aggere, tunc inspexerunt me Amae!"

and telling you how the freshmen at *Spandau* had done
this verse into Latin out of German—for in the vulgar
tongue it runneth thus :—

"Ich kam gen Spandau auf den Damm,
Da schauten mich die plötzen an."

And then you told me that you never knew before that
that sort of fish, roach to wit, went by the name of
amae in Latin; and when I quoted the verse you
laughed consumedly—and I went on to tell you that
fish like that were very plentiful with us, and that one
as long as my arm scarcely costs a groschen. Then
you cried, "By Cocke, if we were but there!" And

this is why I longed for you to be with us yesterday. But my father said, "Thinkest thou that there are no fish at *Cologne?*" "Yea," said I, "but they are plaguy dear!"

You tell me that things go ill with you, and that your cause prospereth not at *Rome*, and that *Johann Reuchlin's* allies vex you sorely. Believe me, I grieve for you as though you were my mother. Yet I trust that the Lord will "give that which is good; and our land shall yield her increase"—that is to say that you Theologians at *Cologne*, now that you have burnt the heretical books, will yield your increase, by preaching, arguing, disputing, writing treatises on new subjects, and so forth. And may Christ, the Son of God, bring this to pass, and show you loving kindness. Amen.

The MARKET-PLACE, BERLIN—where there are prime fish.

XXIII

❦ *MAGISTER BERTHOLD HÄCKER-LING to Magister Ortwin Gratius*

BROTHERLY love, by way of salutation.

Honoured Sir, having in remembrance the promise I made you on parting, that I would tell you all the news, and how I fared, I would have you know that I have now been two months at *Rome*, but as yet have found no patron. An assessor of the Rota would fain have bespoken me, and I was well pleased, and said, "I am nothing loth, Sir ; but I pray your magnificence to apprize me what my charge will be." He replied, that my lodgment would be in the stable, to minister unto a mule, serve it with victuals and drink, curry-comb it, and keep it clean ; and that I must have a care that he was ready to carry his master, with bridle and saddle and so forth. And then it would be my office to run by his side to the court, and home again.

Thereupon I made answer that it was not meet for me, who am a Master of Arts of *Cologne*, to drudge thus. Quoth he, "If not, the loss is yours." I am resolved, therefore, to return to the fatherland. I, to curry-comb a mule and mundify a stable! The Devil run away with the stable and the mule! I verily believe it would be flying in the face of the Statutes of the University! For a Magister must needs comport himself as a Magister. It would be a scandalous thing for a Master of Arts of *Cologne* to do such drudgery. Nay, for the honour of the University I will return to the fatherland.

Rome moreover pleaseth me not in other ways. You would not believe how arrogant are the Clerks and Curialists. One of them said but yesterday that he would besquatter a *Cologne* Magister. "Besquatter the gallows!" quoth I. Then he made answer that he, too, was a Magister, to wit of the Curia, and that a Magister of the Curia took precedence of a Master of Arts of *Germany*. "That," said I, "is impossible. Would you fain make yourself out my equal, seeing that you have never offered yourself for examination, as did I when five Magisters sifted me with rigour? You are naught but a Magister by diploma."

Then began he to dispute with me, saying, " And what is a Magister?"

" A Magister," I answered, " is a person duly qualified, promoted, and graduated in the Seven Liberal Arts, having first undergone a magistral examination; he is privileged to wear a gold ring, and a silken lining to his cope, and he comporteth himself towards his pupils as doth a king towards his subjects. The name 'Magister' hath a fourfold derivation. First, from *magis* and *ter*, for a Magister knoweth three times as much as a lewd person. Secondly, from *magis* and *terreo*, for a Magister is terrible in the sight of his disciples. Thirdly, from *magis* and *theron* (that is, rank), for a Magister is of higher rank than his disciples. Fourthly, from *Magis* and *sedere*, for a magister ever sitteth in a higher room than any of his disciples."

Then quoth he, " What is your authority?" I answered that I had read all this in the *Vademecum*. Forthwith he began to carp at that book, and declared that it was in no way authentic. Then said I, " You find fault with the Ancients, because you know no better. But I never heard of any man at *Cologne* making light of that book. Have you no sense of shame?" And in high dudgeon I departed from him.

So, be well assured, I shall hie me back to *Germany;* for there Magisters are paramount; and rightly. I can prove it by the Gospel: Christ called himself Magister, and not Doctor, saying, "Ye call me Master and Lord, and ye say well, for so I am."

But I can now write no more, for paper faileth me, and it is a great way to the *Campo dei Fiori.* Farewell.

From the Court of Rome

XXIV

❡ *MAGISTER PHILIPP MESUE*[42] *to*
Mag. Ortwin Gratius

HUMBLE duty by way of greeting.

Reverend Herr Magister, inasmuch as I promised to impart to you all that I hear and see touching that cause of yours,—rightly called "The Cause of the Faith," seeing that it pertaineth to the Christian Faith universally—I must tell you that when I first came hither the Magisters all cried, "What news, what news, Magister *Philipp?* What news from *Cologne?*" Then I made answer that all the news I had knowledge of was, that lately my lords the Theologians, and the Inquisitor of Heretical Pravity, had burned an heretical book entitled "Johann Reuchlin's *Augenspiegel.*" Thereupon Magister *Egbert von Harlem*, a learned and upright man, and, believe me, indifferent withal, replied, "We know full well that they have burned that book, but we have also learned that they acted not well in that matter, but committed a scandalous deed, for we have read that book and have found naught that is heretical therein. What is worse—the Theologians have passed sentence while the cause is still pending before the Roman Curia, and his Holiness hath committed it to two Cardinals, and hath imposed silence on both parties to the suit. Yet in despite of this the Theologians have burned the book." Thereupon I answered that they acted thus at the instigation of the University of *Paris* and the four other Universities that withstood *Reuchlin.* Quoth Magister *Egbert,* " Though ten Universities opposed that Doctor, yet should they obey the supreme Pontiff, who is the head of the Church." I replied that it was taken for granted that so many universities could not err. " That postulate is baseless," he replied. " Mark my words, this business will have a bad ending." I was fain to make no further answer, but said, " 'Tis all one to me, whether it turn out A or B."

Now I tell you these things, Herr *Ortwin,* that you may be forewarned, for I fear me the decision will go against you, since the Pope is wrath ; and if you lose your case at *Rome,* the Devil will hold the candle.[43] The men of *Rostock* are bitter foes of the Parisians, for the Parisians have a statute by which they forbid the admission of the Magisters of *Rostock* to their Faculties. And in turn the Rostockians will not admit the men of *Paris.* But now you will know right well what you ought to do. I commend myself to you.

ROSTOCK.

XXV

ℂ *MAGISTER ADOLF KLINGESOR to Magister Ortwin Gratius*

SALUTATIONS, Magister *Ortwin,* so abundant that this letter cannot contain them, nor messenger bear them, nor can any man utter them nor pen them.

I trust, to boot, that you are of jocund heart, and are not in a taking concerning that Cause of the Faith. I counsel you never to be dumpish, but to give yourself repose.

Folk here often rail at me because I am of *Cologne.* But I snicker as though I heeded not ; yet now and again I make retort and give them a whirret in turn. For example, the other day a fellow who had resided

at *Cologne* ten years agone, told me that he believed
not that *Pfefferkorn* was yet a good Christian: for he
declared that he met him a year back and that he still
stank like any other Jew—and yet it is common proof
that when Jews are baptised they smell rank no longer.
He believes, therefore, that *Pfefferkorn* is still a knave
at the back of his head, and when the Theologians
think him the best of Christians he will turn Jew
again: "We should put no trust in him," quoth he,
"for all men have misgivings concerning baptised
Jews."

Then said I, "Sonty! Will you syllogise on a
suspicion? 'Men suspect baptised Jews to be
botched Christians—therefore *Pfefferkorn* is a botched
Christian!' It followeth not. I might be apt to
suspect Doctor *Arnold von Tongern* to be of the brood
of *Sodom*—yet would it not therefore be sooth, for all
the Colognese hold him to be an unspotted virgin.
Moreover, I will resolve that other objection of yours:
you say that *Pfefferkorn* savoureth: put case that he
doth—though I believe it not, neither have I ever
perceived it—then I maintain that there is another
cause of this emanation; for *Johann Pfefferkorn* when
he was a Jew was a flesher by trade, and fleshers are
commonly rank."

Then all they who stood near vowed that my
reasoning was just. So I conjure you that you dis-
quiet not yourself overmuch in this matter, for a broken
spirit drieth the bones. Farewell.

FRANKFORT-ON-ODER.

XXVI

⌐ *HEINRICH SCHAFMAUL* to *Magister*
***Ortuinus Gratius* many greetings**

INASMUCH as before I journeyed to Court you
charged me to write to you oft, and propose from
time to time knotty points in Theology, which you
would straightway resolve better than the Courticians
at *Rome*: therefore, I now write to ask your reverence

what opinion you hold concerning one who on a Friday, that is on the sixth day of the week—or on any other fast-day—should eat an egg with a chicken in it?

For you must know that we were lately sitting in an inn in the *Campo dei Fiori*,[44] having our supper, and were eating eggs, when on opening one I saw that there was a young chicken within.

This I showed to a comrade; whereupon quoth he to me, "Eat it up speedily, before the taverner sees it, for if he mark it, you will have to pay a Carline or a Julius for a fowl. For it is the rule of the house that once the landlord has put anything on the table you must pay for it—he won't take it back. And if he sees that there is a young fowl in that egg, he will say 'Pay me for that fowl!' Little or big, 'tis all one."

In a trice I gulped down the egg, chicken and all.

And then I remembered that it was Friday!

Whereupon I said to my crony, "You have made me commit a mortal sin, in eating flesh on the sixth day of the week!"

But he averred that it was not a mortal sin—nor even a venial one, seeing that such a chickling is accounted merely as an egg, until it is born.

He told me, too, that it is just the same in the case of cheese, in which there are sometimes grubs, as there are in cherries, peas, and new beans: yet all these may be eaten on Fridays, and even on Apostolic Vigils. But taverners are such rascals that they call them flesh, to get the more money.

Then I departed, and thought the matter over.

And by the Lord, Master *Ortwin*, I am in a mighty quandary, and know not what to do.

I would willingly seek counsel of one of the Courticians, but they are not devout men.

It seemeth to me that these young fowls in eggs are flesh, because their substance is formed and fashioned into the limbs and body of an animal, and possesseth a vital principle.

It is different in the case of grubs in cheese, and such-like, because grubs are accounted fish, as I learnt from a physician who is also skilled in Natural Philosophy.

Most earnestly do I entreat you to resolve the question that I have propounded. For if you hold that the sin is mortal, then, I would fain get shrift here, ere I return to *Germany*.

You must know, too, that Doctor *Jakob von Hochstraten* hath received a thousand florins[45] through the bankers, and I trow he will gain the day, and that the devil will overthrow *Johann Reuchlin* and the rest of the Poets and Jurists, because they would fain withstand the Church of God—that is, the Theologians, on whom the Church is founded, according to Christ's words—"Thou art *Peter*, and upon this rock I will build my Church."

And so I commend you to the Lord. Farewell.

ROME.

XXVII

❡ *MAGISTER WILHELM STORCH sendeth many salutations to Mag. Ortwin Gratius*

HOW cometh it that you write much to me concerning yourself, and nevertheless send me not the book that you have indited against *Johann Reuchlin?*

You tell me that you were full of inspiration when you wrote that book, and that you believe it will be a notable work, and that a publisher offered you twenty florins to entrust it to him. You tell me moreover that you will send me a copy to show to the Curialists and scribes here, and vex them thereby, since they will not believe that there are in *Germany* poets as good as there are in *Italy*. It is indeed most desirable that you should send it to me. And yet you send it not—although you are for ever promising it. I entreat you to send me that book, or tractate, for I would fain plague some clerks here who think that nobody else understandeth aught. They scoff at my odes, too, when I write them, declaring them to be faulty. You shall see for yourself whether this be true, for I send herewith a poem that I composed of late when Doctor

Hoogstraten arrived here, and I posted it on *Pasquin's* statue in his honour—for he is an eminent man, and defendeth the Catholic Faith against many a heretic. The ode runneth thus :—

AN ODE,

Upon the solemn entry of the Reverend Father Jakob van Hoogstraten, of the Order of Preachers, Magisternoster and Inquisitor of Heretical Pravity : By Magister Wilhelm Storch of Deventer.

Be it known to all—both young and old, by these presents,
That a grave Divine, immersed in learning profoundly,
Hath to the city come, and with great solemnity stalketh,
Jakob van Hoogstraten y-clept: this also his name is.
He from Germany came, where he abounded in cheeses
Which he collected in heaps—until at last at a Uni-
Versity he a degree Theological haply attained to ;
Craftily could he dispute, syllogisms subtly devising
In Baroco and Celarent, till all the world wondered.
This Theologians marked, and they in the Faith being zealous,
Made him Inquisitor 'gainst Heretical Pravity. If you
Ask, saying, "What doeth here this man so mighty in learning ?"
Lend me your ears awhile, and I will shew you the reason.
There is in Germany now another Doctor—a Jurist,
Johann Reuchlin his name, and him the Inquisitor cited
Here at Rome to appear, because he lately indited
A book of Theology void, but crammed with heresy hurtful ;
'Gainst the Faith it hath a heap of scandalous theses,
And—be it known to all—it likewise cockers the Hebrews ;
Therefore suspect it was, and, by th' Inquisitor tested,
It to the fire was doomed—to recantation, its author.
(Would you know its name ? The *Augenspiegel* its title.)
Now the Inquisitor grave hath hither come on the matter—
No delay nor rest would the Theologians allow him.
Swift to Rome must he fare, and rend that Jurist to tatters.
Therefore is honour his due, and reverent low salutations
When he walked abroad—for he is a disputant stalwart,
And in Logic few are worthy his latchet to loosen.

They say that this is not composed according to rule, and limpeth upon its feet. "What have I to do with feet?" say I. I am not a heathen poet, but a Theological, and I care not for such childishness; 'tis the sense I heed. Wherefore, Herr *Ortwin*, it behoveth you to answer this my composition, and deliver your letter at the bank.

But I have some news for you. Some men called

Spaniards have invaded *Lombardy ;* and it is said that the Emperor would fain drive out the King of *France,* and this would be a bad thing for Doctor *van Hoog-straten,* for it is through the King of *France* that he advanceth his cause before his Holiness, and the King of *France* doeth his utmost for him, for the honour of the University of *Paris,* which would be disgraced if the *Augenspiegel* were not burned. I know no more. Fare-well, in all happiness.

From ROME.

XXVIII

❧ *MAGISTER BERNHARD GELFF, one of the lowliest, to Mag. Ortwin Gratius greeting*

HONOURABLE, or excellent Sir ; notwithstand-ing that I have not personal acquaintance of you, I nevertheless know you by reputation, and for many a day I have had cognisance of that Cause of yours which is known as "The Cause of the Faith against *Johann Reuchlin,*" and I have the whole process in my possession.

Daily do I dispute with the Courtiers and the scribes who defend *Johann Reuchlin,* and when the Cursor who bears these presents told me that he was starting for *Germany* and would make his way through *Cologne,* I said, "Then will I, by the Lord, make acquaintance of Magister *Ortwin* and write somewhat to him." Then said he, "Ay, by the Lord, do so, and he will be right glad. When I left *Cologne* he charged me, saying, 'Bid all the Theologians, and Doctors, and Artsmen and Poets who are in *Rome* to write to me ; for gladly do I receive the missives that learned and well-skilled men send me, and then I collect the letters that they have written to me, and afterwards make a volume of them, and have them printed.'"

Thereupon I replied, "I know that full well, for I have seen a book entitled *Epistolae Obscurorum Virorum,* and it greatly delighted me when I read it, for it is mightily fine and containeth notable matters collected from all quarters !"

And therefore, Herr *Ortwin*, I beg that you will look upon me graciously, for I am an astonishing ally of yours and love you incredibly. Commend me also, I pray you, to *Johann Pfefferkorn*, once a Jew, but now happily baptized in Christ. His treatise entitled " The Defence of Johann Pfefferkorn against Calumnies " hath been brought to me from *Germany*, and I have read it through and have jotted down notabilia and summaries in the margin. I think very highly of the said book. But you must tell *Pfefferkorn* that one of the officers of the Curia[46] is a mighty upholder of *Johann Reuchlin*. He has collected sundry paragraphs out of *Pfefferkorn's* book, and seeks to prove that in these passages both Heresy and the crime of High Treason are to be found ; and he declares that he wishes proceedings might be taken against *Johann Pfefferkorn* on the grounds of Heresy and High Treason. I send you herewith a schedule in which these passages are copied out, and subjoined are the refutations which I have composed—for I held a disputation with that officer, and defended *Johann Pfefferkorn* to the utmost of my ability. And so, farewell, and look upon me as an acquaintance as well as a friend.

The COURT OF ROME.

(Enclosure.)

PASSAGES EXTRACTED FROM A BOOK BY JOHANN PFEFFERKORN AGAINST REUCHLIN AND THE REUCHLINISTS : THE WHICH BOOK IS ENTITLED "JOHANN PFEFFERKORN'S DEFENCE AGAINST CALUMNIES."

Following are the passages alleged by the Reuchlinists to be heretical, and to involve the crime of high treason—which, by God's help, is not, and hath not been, and never will be true.

ARTICLE I.

The Reuchlinist alleges, that Johann Pfefferkorn, in that book of his that is entitled " Johann Pfefferkorn's Defence against Calumnies," in his Letter to His

Sovereign Holiness Pope Leo, etc., utters blasphemy, and commits the crime of High Treason, in that he calls the Pope "the hand-maid of the Lord," as though he were a woman—as, indeed, we read that a woman was once Pope[47]—for he saith (A. ii. 1), "And thus your holiness as the Vicar of Christ on earth, and 'ministram.'" There is also heresy contained in this passage, for Pfefferkorn herein hints, not explicitly but nevertheless implicitly, that the universal church hath erred in making a woman a pope, which is the greatest of errors. But whosoever saith that the Church errs is necessarily a heretic. Q. E. D.

I reply, that Johann Pfefferkorn, who is not a good grammarian, and doth not understand Latin, thought that "Papa" was of the feminine gender, like "Musa": for he had heard from others that "nouns in *a* are of the feminine gender, with exceptions;" as Alexander puts it:

"Sit tibi nomen in *a* muliebre, sed excipe plura."

Whence it is manifest that Johann Pfefferkorn in the present tractate writeth like a Theologian, and Theologians pay no heed to grammar, for they belong to another Faculty.

ARTICLE II.

The Reuchlinists argue: Johann Pfefferkorn in many places, as for instance (A. i.) and (K. iv.), when he wishes to swear that something is true, says "mediusfidius," as though he should say "by my god Fidius." For "mediusfidius" is by interpretation "meus deus fidius:" whence it is manifest that Johann Pfefferkorn himself is an idolater, and hath for his Lord, not Christ, but Fidius, which was an idol among the pagans of old.

I reply, that Pfefferkorn in making oath "mediusfidius" did not think of this word "fidius"—which may be the name of some idol or other—but he used the term adverbially. And Donatus puts it thus, who is authoritative and is read in the schools, that "mediusfidius" means "assuredly" or "truly." Again, we may allege, as before, that Johann Pfefferkorn pays no heed to grammar: or again, that "mediusfidius" means "by my faith," as I heard from a Humanist.

Article III.

The Reuchlinist objects: " Whoso declares that he supports the Church is a heretic : but Johann Pfefferkorn declares that he supports the Church : ergo, he is a heretic. The major premiss is manifest, since he who boasteth that he supports the Church assumes that the whole Church is in error, and that unless he supported it, it would fall and be destroyed. Such an one would also appear to be Anti-Pope, that is, desirous of being Pope in opposition to that pope who has been chosen by the Catholic Church. For to support the Church is the duty of the Pope ; but Pfefferkorn arrogates this duty to himself—therefore he is Anti-Pope, and a heretic who implies that the Pope erreth and is not a good shepherd. The minor premiss is manifest from the words of Johann Pfefferkorn, who alleges in the aforesaid book that he is " a lowly member of the Church." Now in the body a lowly member is the foot, because the feet stand on the ground, that is upon the earth ; and if the feet were removed the body would fall : ergo, Pfefferkorn pretends that the Church stands on him, and that he supports the Church.

I reply, that Pfefferkorn does not use the words in such strictness, nor as in accordance with their primary signification. But he calls himself a member, that is a part, of the Church, in the sense that every good Christian man is a part of the Church—or even a member, to use the term in a wide meaning. " Lowly," too, is to be taken as signifying devout and simple ; as the same Johann Pfefferkorn saith in his Epistle to the Pope : " All unworthy though I be at thy most holy feet, etc." Therefore it must not be inferred that Pfefferkorn speaketh against the Pope.

Article IV.

The Reuchlinist objects: Pfefferkorn again commits the crime of High Treason, not once but many times. For he saith, (O. i.) that all the friends and upholders of Johann Reuchlin, both nobles and other learned and

unlearned men, sin in that they show favour to **Johann**
Reuchlin : but among these are to be numbered in
Germany full ten Princes, and his Highness the
Emperor himself, and at Rome many Cardinals and
Bishops, and his Holiness Pope Leo in person, who
lately, when he had read Johann Reuchlin's letter,
highly praised the writer, and said he would defend
him against all the Friars; and so said the Very
Reverend Cardinals of S. Marco, and S. Georgio, and
S. Chrysogono, and many more.[48]

I reply, that Pfefferkorn did this from the love of
truth, which is greater than Pope, and Emperor, and
all the Cardinals, and Bishops, and Princes.   And for
this cause in his final protest (O. 4) he excuseth himself,
saying, " I have defended myself, truth alone being my
guide, and without offence of any man.   For Jeremy
the prophet saith, " Cursed be he that keepeth back his
sword from blood : and, it is better to fall into the
hands of man, than into the hands of Almighty God."
And therefore he deems it better to offend Pope and
Emperor rather than Truth—that is God.   For God
is Truth.

Article VII.

The Reuchlinist objects : Pfefferkorn in that book
commits heresy and High Treason in one and the same
passage.   For he saith (O. i. col. ii.), " I fight not with
the sword, nor with violence, I march not into the field
with a spear like a soldier of the king, (for that would be
sinful pride), etc."   Here then he saith that it is sinful
pride to make war and take the field : but the Pope
and the Emperor do this, and always have done so, and
so have many who are in the Calendar of Saints.   If,
therefore, to take the field is sinful pride, then the
saints, and the reigning Emperor, and even the Pope
have committed deadly sin, and consequently the
Church, which regards them as holy, is in error.
Hence Pfefferkorn is in direct conflict with the Canon
and Civil Law, with the Emperor and the Pope, with
the Church and the Empire.

I reply, that these words are to be understood with
a reservation, namely that those who make war and

take the field are guilty of the sin of Pride only in so far that they do these things unjustly to the injury of others. But when the Emperor and the Pope wage war, it is to be assumed that they do so in defence of the Church and the Empire, and therefore Pfefferkorn's censure doth not apply to them.

ARTICLE VIII.

The Reuchlinist objects: Pfefferkorn accuseth the Emperor of falsehood, for he uses these words, (O. ii. col. i.), against Reuchlin, "I accuse him of being a betrayer of God and man and of his Imperial Majesty a faithless Counsellor." In these words he flatly contradicts the Emperor, and calls him a liar. For his Majesty the Emperor, in his Letter to the Pope, and in many mandates and commissions calls Johann Reuchlin his faithful counsellor and adviser. What greater slander can he utter than to call him a liar? Hence he is irremissibly deserving of the penalty of High Treason.

I reply, that this passage distinguishes, and should be punctuated with a comma after the word "Majesty." For Reuchlin is perchance a faithful counsellor of the Emperor in his affairs, but not faithful to Johann Pfefferkorn, as he has shewn by many proofs. And hence no man can suppose that Johann Pfefferkorn speaks against the Emperor, seeing that he is a good imperialist, as his writings everywhere show, whether German or Latin.

ARTICLE IX.

The Reuchlinist objects: that the chiefest and greatest, and most terrible, and most horrible, and most diabolical, and infernal charge of all is that Johann Pfefferkorn blames both the Pope and the Curia by accusing them of the sin of deceit. For he writes, (I. iv.), "But all these matters, his commission obtained, not justly, but with the greatest injustice, from Rome, the Master of Heretical Pravity heeded not, etc." Now it was the Pope who gave that commission; therefore Johann Pfefferkorn accuses the Pope of not rightly administering justice, and deserves to go thrice to the stake as a heretic.

I reply: Pfefferkorn does not say that the Pope or the Curia issued that Commission unjustly, but means that Reuchlin obtained it unjustly. Therefore it is Johann Reuchlin and not the Pope whom he calleth unjust.

ARTICLE X.

The Reuchlinist objects: Pfefferkorn once again commits the crime of High Treason, in that he lies manifestly concerning the Emperor and the Bishop of Cologne. For he alleges that a certain Inquisitor of Heretical Pravity, by the authority of His Majesty, and with the approval of the Bishop of Cologne, burnt the *Augenspiegel* at Cologne. This is utterly false. For neither did his Majesty authorise this, nor did the Bishop of Cologne approve of it : for if the Emperor had authorized this, he would not have laboured in Reuchlin's behalf by writing to the Pope, and desiring him to defend his Counsellor against the envy and craft of the Theologians. Therefore Pfefferkorn is plainly a forger, for he forges, or contrives, Imperial Commissions.

I reply, that it matters not about the Bishop of Cologne, for he is dead. But, as to the Emperor, Johann Pfefferkorn speaks deliberately with regard to what was implicitly the Emperor's intention. For at the first, when Pfefferkorn took up this laudable work in the Cause of the Faith, to wit, the condemnation of all Jewish books to the flames, the Emperor was minded, as it seemed, to burn all books that are contrary to the Christian faith. But Johann Reuchlin's book is one of these : therefore the Emperor was minded to burn that also. Hence Pfefferkorn declares what the Emperor intended—but implicitly, not explicitly and expressly. And he deems it to suffice that the Emperor once for all gave him authorization to deal with Jewish books, with which heretical books may be also included. For I have heard that if the Emperor had adhered to that laudable proposal, the Theologians would have made a visitation of all the libraries throughout Germany, and would have burnt all wicked books, and especially those works of the New Theologians which are not founded upon the Angelic Doctor, the Subtle Doctor, the Seraphic Doctor, or St. Thomas Aquinas. This would without doubt have been praiseworthy and highly profitable; and I believe the time will yet come—which may the Omnipotent grant who reigneth through all, and above all, and for ever. Amen.

XXIX

❦ *EGBERT THE NAMELESS to Magister Ortwin Gratius greeting*

VENERABLE Sir, who art mine own familiar friend! for a long while I have found no convenient messenger by whom I could transmit letters to your worship, or long ago I would have written to you.

Grant me forgiveness therefore, for gladly would I have written to you if I could but have found a messenger.

But since you have written to inform me that Doctor *Valentin von Geltersheim* asked you to let me know that I still owe him two florins, for lectures when I resided in his hostel, you may tell him I will not pay him a penny. For he promised me all manner of things, and told me he would give me a bouncing gratuity if I would go twice or thrice a day to the Rhine wharf, and scan the boats coming up or down the stream, see if any freshmen were in them, and persuade them to come and lodge at his hostel. And, by the Lord, I netted for him twenty yellow-beaks at the least, and I lost no end of time in running hither and thither, when I ought to have been studying.

But the Doctor never gave me anything, except what he gave us all—sorry commons, meagre meat, and sour drink. Bid him bear that in mind.

But fare ye well, in all affection.

Lo[UVAIN].

XXX

ℭ *BALTHASAR SCHLAUCH to Mag.* *Ortwin Gratius greeting*

UNTO you thanks be rendered—immeasurable, infinite, indescribable, incomparable, ineffable thanks —in that you have sent me Herr *Johann Pfefferkorn's* book which is intituled "Johann Pfefferkorn's Defence against Calumnies." I was so gladdened when I received that book that I skipped for very joy. I verily believe that *Johann Pfefferkorn* is he of whom *Ezekiel* prophesied, Chap. ix., saying, "And he called a man clothed in linen, with a writer's ink-horn by his side;" for *Johann Pfefferkorn* ever hath a writer's ink-horn with him, and jotteth down citations and postils at Sermons or in assemblies, and afterwards constructeth his tractates. You rejoice me greatly when you send me his books, for they are so craftily fabricated that I marvel thereat. I plume myself not a little at *Vienna* in that I am of his acquaintance; and when I mention him, I say, "*Johann Pfefferkorn*, my friend."

Nevertheless I have gathered from that book that the Theologians are at variance concerning the *Augenspiegel*—for some condemn it to the flames—for instance, the Parisians and Colognese; and others, to the rope— as did Doctor *Peter Meyer*, who when he set eyes on the *Augenspiegel*, cried with a loud voice, "To the gallows, to the gallows with such a book as this!" But you ought to be of one mind, and then would you gain the day against that heretic. I was greatly alarmed when I read of these things, and I said, "Now the Devil will hold the candle, if the Theologians fall out!" But I trust you will once more agree together. Nevertheless it seemeth to me that Doctor *Peter* and his friends are not judicious in holding that the *Augenspiegel* should be hung on a gallows. For the book is heretical, and being heretical, deserveth the stake. Heretics are burned—it is thieves that are hanged. Howbeit they may perchance contend that the *Augen-*

spiegel hath committed a theft, since *Johann Pfefferkorn* avers that through that book *Johann Reuchlin* hath stolen away his honour—which he would not part with for twenty florins; two Jews, forsooth, who in like manner robbed him of his good name, gave him thirty florins for it. However this may be, I would that you were all of a mind.

There is no news here to tell, save that the Poet *Joachim Vadianus*, who is one of the Reuchlinist faction, hath become Rector of the University. May the Lord smite the whole crew of Poets and Jurists, and leave not one of them of man's estate! I am minded to return home. What place is there for me in a University that hath a Poet for its Rector? There are here a host of Reuchlinists, such as are in no other University. There is *Joachim Vadianus* the Rector; *Georgius Collimitius Tanstetter*—now a Physician, formerly Mathematician; *Joannes Cuspinianus*, servant and counsellor of the Emperor; one *Thomas Resch; Simon Lasius*, a fellow-countryman of *Johann Reuchlin*, and many more. Yet Magister Noster *Heckmann* is with us, and he hath declared that he will cleave to the Theologians so long as he liveth. He saluteth heartily you and *Johann Pfefferkorn*. Farewell.

From VIENNA.

Once more, farewell—so long as *Pfefferkorn* abideth a Christian.

XXXI

❡ *ALBERT STRUNCK* to *Magister Ortwin Gratius of Deventer*

MY humble duty, by way of greeting, reverend Herr Magister! I earnestly crave your indulgence, in that I write not to you oft, because, pardy, the weather in *Rome* is so sultry that one can neither walk in the streets, nor sit at home: in sooth I can neither write nor compose a scantling, by reason of the fervid heat. And well you know what heavy

170

labour it is to frame theses, for you told me at *Cologne*
that you could scarce put together a seemly exercise in
a sennight.   You cited Horace to me—how that poet
hath laid it down that we ought to spend nine years in
the inditing a fair treatise.   And that, I trow, is the
manner fit.   For it behoves us to be wary, and to take
heed that there are no false concords.   Sometimes
congruity sufficeth not, for embellishments are needed—
according to the twenty precepts of the *Elegantiae,*
and the Art of Letter-writing of *Pontius,* or of *Paulus
Schneevogel,* who was Magister of *Leipsic.*   Those
Poets too, now-a-days, are vengeance captious, and
when one writes anything they straightway cry, " See,
in this place and that, there is sorry latinity!" and they
come here with their new-fangled whim-whams, and
subvert the good old grammar.   And so I cannot write
amidst such heat as this.   Therefore I pray thee hold
me excused.   Farewell.

ROME.

XXXII

❦ *MAGISTER HEINRICH SIEBMACHER*
with greetings to Mag. Ortwin Gratius

VENERABLE Master! First, and before all, be
it known to you that two judgments have gone
against me, and if I lose a third, the devil will be
Abbot! I am in great fear, for an Assessor just now
said to me, "If I were you, I would not appeal, for
you are in the wrong:" and therefore I know not
what to be at. I trow that this year is an ill-starred
one for Theologians; for even that eminent man,
Herr Magister-noster *Peter Meyer* prospereth not in
his cause against the Canons of *Frankfort,* and they
harry that pious and devoted father. It seemeth to
me that the Canons act thus on *Johann Reuchlin's*
behalf, whom they love for his poetry's sake. And
therefore, being minded to do him a pleasure, they bait
the good pastor, who is mightily at loggerheads with
Johann Reuchlin—and rightly, for he representeth his

Faculty. *Johann Reuchlin* is a foe to the Theologians;
Magister-noster *Peter* is a Theologian; therefore—etc.
And for a man to defend his Faculty is a thing most
permissible. Even Herr *Jakob van Hoogstraten*,
Magister-noster and Inquisitor of Heretical Pravity,
has met with no good fortune in the Cause of the
Faith. The Curialists now all desire to be thought
Poets, and hence they belittle the Theologians and
withstand them. And yet I trust it will profit them
but little; for the Lord will look upon his servants and
deliver them.

I lately heard that the Emperor hath sent a letter
to the Pope on *Johann Reuchlin's* behalf, and that
he wrote in the sense that if his Holiness doth not
speedily make an end of the business, and pronounce
judgment, he will himself take steps to defend his
Counsellor. But what boots it? If the Pope is on
the side of the Theologians, I have no fear. A man of
weight, an officer of the Curia, said to me, " What care
we for these letters? If *Reuchlin* hath any money,
let him send it hither. In the Curia one must have
money, or naught goeth forward."

Another officer hath told me privily that Magister-
noster *Jakob* hath again given donatives to certain
referendaries. Hence it cometh to pass that when
they meet him they greet him with respect, and con-
verse with him in friendly wise. Now therefore we are
the more hopeful. If I miss the benefice, then I shall
aim at the vicarage in *Neuss* that you wot of. My
proctor hath told me that my claim is good. I have
heard that news hath lately come hither that the
University of *Erfurt* intendeth to withdraw its judgment, or decision, against *Johann Reuchlin*. If this be
sooth, I declare all the Theologians there to be liars
and traitors, and I shall ever hold it a scandal that they
abide not by their own Faculty, and defend not that
most zealous man Herr *Jakob van Hoogstraten*, who
is the light of Theology, and shineth like a star by
reason of his doctrines and arguments on behalf of the
Catholic Faith. As a Theologian he hath no peer.
Lately he disputed here, very learnedly, in the *Sapienza*.
Whereupon a certain Italian said, " I knew not that

Germany possessed such Theologians ; " but another
averred that he was not well versed in the language of
the Bible, and understood not *Jerome* and *Augustine.*
Then said I, " O guter Gott! what sayest thou ?
The Doctor taketh such things for granted ; he himself
hath other things to attend to, and much more subtle
matters."

May the Lord grant that all turn out well ; then
cometh our triumph ; we will drive out Poetry from
the whole of *Germany,* and we will bring it about that
the Jurists shall not dare to utter a word when they
are in the presence of Theologians ; for they shall
fear lest the Inquisitor be set upon them, and they be
burned for heretics—as I hope will yet happen to
Johann Reuchlin, by God's aid, whose judges we are :
for as soldiers defend Justice upon Earth, so do we
defend the Church by our disputations and sermons.
Pardon my verbosity.　Farewell.

From the ROMAN CURIA.

XXXIII

❧ *PETER LAPP, Licentiate of the sacred page,
to Mag. Ortwin Gratius greeting*

INASMUCH as you once told me, Reverend Sir,
how great a marvel you hold it that there is now at
Cologne a host of illustrious Doctors—not to speak of
others not yet graduated but almost Magister-nosters—
and super-excellent Theologians in swarms, amongst
whom you name to me Magister-noster *Jakob van
Hoogstraten,* Magister-nosters *Arnold von Tongern,
Remigius,* and *Valentin von Geltersheim,* Magister-
noster *Peter,* who in my time presided over *Kuick*
Hostel, Herr *Roger* the Licentiate, and many others
now dwelling in *Cologne ; Johann Pfefferkorn* too, who,
although he is a layman, and unlearned in the Liberal
Arts, and hath never attended Christian schools nor
learnt Grammar or Logic, nevertheless hath, as you
say, a profound intellect and an enlightened heart.

(Even the Apostles were not men of learning, and

yet they knew all things; and so we may suppose that
the Holy Spirit can instil into the aforesaid *Johann
Pfefferkorn* all the knowledge of the Saints, as saith the
Scripture.)   You also name two Magister-nosters in
Mainz—Herr *Bartholomew Zehender*, preacher in the
Cathedral, and Herr *Peter Bertram* the pastor; as well
as, in *Frankfort*, Herr *Peter Meyer*, who excelleth in
his sermons, and maketh folk laugh or weep as he willeth,
and by his preaching worketh miracles.

Now therefore, having due regard to all these, I
would that you all put your shoulders to the wheel to
prevail over those Jurists and profane Poets—or impose
silence upon them, so that they should no longer venture to write books: or, at least, if they would fain be
at botching something together, let them first submit
it to the Magister-nosters to decide if it may be printed.
And if it meeteth not with the approval of the Magister-
nosters let it not be printed—or let it be burnt.   The
Magister-nosters ought also to issue a mandate that no
jurist or poet should write anything concerning Theology, nor drag this new Latin of theirs into holy Theology—as hath *Johann Reuchlin*, and, I am told, another
fellow, *Proverbia Erasmi* by name—for they are not
grounded in that Science, and 'tis likely that they have
never debated publickly, nor held syllogistic disputation
thereon, according to precedent.   They would ever be
putting their sickles into other men's corn—and this the
Theologians should by no means suffer.

I beseech you, therefore, to urge these mightily
learned men of whom you speak, to dispute against
these new-fangled Latinisers and dust their doublets
soundly.   If they make boast that they know Greek
and Hebrew, tell them that Theologians have naught
to do with such tongues.   Holy Scripture hath been
sufficiently translated, and we have no need of any
other renderings.   Furthermore, it is not meet that we
should learn such tongues, lest we bring upon us the
contempt of Jews and Greeks.   When the Jews see
that we learn their tongue, they say, " Lo, the Christians study our sciences, and without them they cannot
defend their own faith;" and thereby Christians are
deeply humiliated, and the Jews are strengthened in

their creed. The Greeks, moreover, have seceded from
the Church; they should, therefore, be regarded as our
enemies, and their learning should not be studied by
Christians.

Such is the course I earnestly counsel you to follow.
Write to me after a while, and tell me what cometh of
it. Farewell.

From HALBERSTADT.

XXXIV

❦ *MAGISTER JOHANN SCHNECK* to *Mag. Ortwin Gratius*

SALUTATION—pronounced with all simplicity,
and not with bombastic pomposity as is the wont
of the poetising Magisters who ambulate not in the
way of simplicity with the Theologians.

> Greeting in Christ—and in that Dreadful Day
> May He deliver us, we humbly pray,
> From all our tribulations—may He, too,
> Preserve us from the Jurist Capnion, who
> Is yet an infant in Theology;
> No skilled and subtle disputant is he—
> If with Theologers he should dispute,
> A word of Holy Writ would strike him mute:
> For Scripture is the weapon and the stay
> Of all who fain would hold the higher way,
> Or, like Hoogstraten, to condign confusion
> Condemn their foes, with logical conclusion—
> Hoogstraten, born to be the Faith's salvation,
> Dealing to poets and their crew damnation,
> Those erring souls, debile in disputation!

Zooks! I had no mind to send you poetry, and
yet I am sending it. All unawares I wrote it. The
metre followeth not the new-fangled secular poetry,
but is of that ancient kind that the Doctors at *Paris*,
and *Cologne* and elsewhere allow. In my time, when
I was a student at *Paris*, it was said that an old
Magister who dwelt at *Montmartre* Hostel turned the
whole Bible into verse after that metrification.

But I must tell you the news—for all goeth in
our favour. *Reuchlin* can no longer study as of
yore, since his eyes have become bleared; as saith the

Scripture in *Genesis*, "Their eyes were blinded, and they could not see."

A bachelor lately came hither from *Stuttgart*, who had been in his house, and I made as though I knew not of the strife you had with each other, and asked him, saying, "Prithee, Herr Bachelor, take it not amiss that I question you. In the first place, by your favour, I would inquire whether *Reuchlin* is in good health." "Yea," replied he, "but he cannot see very well without spectacles." Then said I, "And will you next tell me what he is now doing in the business of the Cause of the Faith? I have heard that he had some dispute with certain Theologians, and I trow they did him some injury;" (but I spake in irony), "what doeth he? I take it he is for ever composing somewhat against the Theologians." "I know not," he answered, "but I will tell you what I saw myself. When I entered his house, he said, 'Welcome, Herr Bachelor! Be seated!' He had spectacles upon his nose, and a book lay before him in strange characters, so that I could see at once that it was written neither in German nor in Bohemian, nor in Latin. And I said to him, 'Most excellent Herr Doctor, how name you this book?' He replied that it was called *Plutarch* in Greek, and dealt with Philosophy. Then said I, 'Read on, in the Lord's name.' And I verily believe he is skilled in magical arts. Then I espied a little book, newly imprinted, lying beneath his seat. And I said to him, 'Most excellent Herr Doctor, what is this book that lieth here?' He replied, 'It is a scurrilous work that a friend of mine lately sent me from *Cologne*; it is aimed at me, and the Theologians of *Cologne* compiled it, declaring it at the same time to be the work of *Johann Pfefferkorn*.' Then said I, 'What will you do concerning it? Will you not vindicate yourself?' 'By no means,' he replied, 'I am already vindicated. I pay no further heed to such folly, and my eyes scarcely suffice me for studying matters of use to me.' The book was intituled 'Johann Pfefferkorn's Defence against Calumnies, &c.' That is all I know of Doctor *Reuchlin*." And this is all that the aforesaid Bachelor told me. Therefore

Herr *Ortwin*, be of good cheer; for if his eyes grow so weak that he can neither read nor write, so much the worse for him. But you must not stay your hand, but assail him again and again. Farewell.

From ULM.

XXXV

❧ *MAGISTER WILHELM LAMP to*
Mag. Ortwin Gratius greeting

RIGHT distinguished and high-renowned Man, with the reverence meet to you my promoter![49]
You tell me that the letter in which I described my journey to *Rome* hath reached you—you tell me, too, that you thence learn of a surety that I love you dearly. These words are well said—for they are true. I love you verily in my heart of hearts. You bid me moreover to make known to you, or to apprize you, how it fareth with me now. You must know, then, that I reside with a Notary of the Rota, and it is my duty to prepare the board, and to go to market to procure pot-herbs, and beans, and bread, and meat and such like; and to put the house in order, that when my lord returneth from Court with his fellows, all things may be ready. Withal, I study. My lord told me lately that, God willing, if I abide with him for a year or two he will procure a benefice for me, as he hath for many others. This is easy of belief; for he hath much love for me.

To crown all—when of late he discovered me to be a poet, he declared that he would love me more and more. It thus fell out: One of those who sat at meat is a poet, after the new fashion, and he is ever talking at the board about Poetry, and he findeth much fault with the ancient fathers—*Alexander*, and the *Graecist*, and *Verba Deponentalia*, and *Remigius*, and the others. And not long ago he averred that any one who desired to write good verses must study *Diomedes;* and of *Diomedes* he spake much. Then quoth I, "It surpriseth me that you pay such heed to these new-fangled grammarians, when you may find all things concerning feet, and the quantities of syllables, set forth metrically in the third part of *Alexander*, not to speak of the Art of Scansion and the rest. Moreover that same *Diomedes* was no good Christian, for I once read that he kept horses that fed upon men, and he himself gave them men to eat."

Then the Curialist laughed loudly, jeering me, and asked me what I made the first syllable of "Abacuck?"

I replied, "We must distinguish. For, in so far as it is a proper name, the first syllable is indifferent, according to *Alexander :*—

'Ad placitum poni propriorum multa notavi;'

but in so far as it is asked what quantity the first hath conformably to the quiddity of common nouns, then it hath the first short; according to *Alexander*, who saith that in first syllables *a* before *b* is short—exceptions excepted."

Then he laughed me to scorn yet again, and said, "Get thee gone, thou Cologne abecedarian, with thine *Alexander*, who was but a Parisian ass—and there are plenty more." And thus, shamefully reviling the good *Alexander*, he went his way. "Ha!" quoth I, "to-morrow you shall see!" And in the morning I drew forth a poem that I had concocted in the night-time in praise of *Alexander*, and I send you a copy thereof. So soon as my lord set eyes on that poem, he applauded me, and cried,

"Oh *Wilhelm*, can you compose such verses as these? And I never knew it! In future I shall love you more than ever!" Therefore I trust I shall get good preferment, and when it pleases Heaven that I achieve somewhat, then shall I betake myself, as a priest, to mine own country once more.

From the ROMAN CURIA.

FOLLOWETH,

*An Epigrammatic Ode, confectionate by Wilhelm Lamp, Magister of the
Seven Liberal Arts at Cologne, in praise of Alexander Gallus.*

Who would of Grammar be an understander,
Must con with care the work of Alexander;
Parcelled it is into four diverse parts,
And disciplineth many useful Arts:
With milk and honey for the young it floweth,
As the Colognian Commentary sheweth.
Would you to metrifying skill attain?
Read Part the third—'twill make the pathway plain:
All ignorance 'twill purge away from you,
As well I know, who thereout wisdom drew!

XXXVI

❡ *JOHANN ARNOLDI sendeth many
greetings to M. Ortwin Gratius*

I SHOULD forsooth have been persuaded that at
any rate you might have heard, or that it might
promiscuously have reached your ears, how that I, in-
stigated by a certain righteous affection of the soul,
have very lately betaken myself, by ambulatory journeying, to the Urban Court of *Rome*, in contemplation
of remunerative emolument flowing from the acquisi-
tion of a trifling foolish benefice, or prebendicule, or
other cure of souls, whence, from time present to the
ultimate determination of my vital spark, sufficing
aliment and raiment be mine, by the divine grace of
God. Wherefore, by *Hercules* and *Mediusfidius*, it
would have been meet and right for you to have
addressed to me, and that not rarely, an epistolet
amicably concocted, or compacted, and therein to have
affectionately signified how you are situated with
respect to every corporeal and mental condition. And
how you have been fortuned by the fates, through that
divine predestination which was before the worlds, as
saith *Lactantius*—whom I have of late been earnestly

studying, since he hath been lectured upon in the *Sapienza* conformably with the regulations. Besides and furthermore, a juvenal hath come hither out of *Cologne* and the hyperborean regions of *Germany*, bearing epistolary missives to him addressed from all parts of the world, from which, forsooth, I have learned how that you have procured to be impressed by the typographical art an opuscule which is understood to be—or to have been intituled, or cognominated, "The Letters of Obscure Men to Magister Ortwin Gratius," in which booklet, or tractate, are comprehended—so I have been given to understand—all the letters addressed to your worthiness, lovingly and fraternally, by your friends and acquaintances throughout the world; and I have moreover heard that you have therein included my own epistolet, and thereby I have been very marvellously stupefied—to think that you should have glorified me with such sesquipedalian honour and promoted me to everlasting renown! And for this, believe me, I render you all the thanks in my power. I must tell you that I have been studying here to acquire incomparable virtuosity in the Poetic Art, and that consequently my diction differeth from its complexion of yore.

I bid thee a sesquipedal farewell.

From ROME.

XXXVII

❡ *FRIAR GEORG BLECK to*
Magister Ortwin Gratius

IN humility and with homage due, Herr Magister! You have sent me hither a book entitled "Johann Pfefferkorn's Defence." This I failed not, in accordance with your desire, to lay before the Divines throughout *Paris*, as well as before the Theologians of our Order, and they all cried with one voice, "See! what notable Theologians *Germany* possesseth! If an unlettered man can write thus, what cannot learned men and graduates put forth?" Then it was asked of me

whether the princes of *Germany* paid great honour to
Johann Pfefferkorn. I replied that some did, and some
did not; but that nevertheless he was the trusty and
well-beloved Counsellor of the Emperor in all that concerned Hebrew books and the increase of the Christian
Faith. I told him, moreover, how that the late Bishop
of *Mainz*, of pious memory, loved him dearly, and promised him aid in all things to the extent of his power
—and when *Pfefferkorn* journeyed hither and thither
on the business of the Faith he ·was wont to provide
him with large sums of money for his expenses. A
Theologian present said, " This *Johann Pfefferkorn*
doth great diligence, then, in the aforesaid business ? "

I told him, as you had informed me, that he had
indefatigably circumambulated the whole of *Germany*,
notwithstanding that it was discommodious for him at
that time to neglect his wife and children, whom it was
befitting for him to educate and maintain. Nevertheless during his absence, the Theologians ministered
not a little to his wife, affording her consolation, inasmuch as they knew that her husband was occupied
in the cause of the Faith. Sometimes, moreover, the
Friars from our Monastery come to her and say, " We
pity you in that you are so lonely." And she replieth
" Come then sometimes and visit me, for I am as it
were a widow, and afford me consolation." Howbeit
the new Bishop of *Mainz* favoureth not *Johann Pfefferkorn*, and the reason is that he hath other Counsellors
who strongly support *Johann Reuchlin* and hate the
Theologians.

This bishop, indeed, would not give audience to
Pfefferkorn when he desired to present him with his
" Defence,"—as I learnt from your letter. All this I
related. Then one asked, " And who is this *Pfefferkorn ?* " I replied that he was formerly a Jew—but is
now happily baptised into the Church—and that he is
without doubt a very upright man, and of the tribe of
Naphtali. And he said, " Of a truth the blessing conferred upon *Naphtali* is fulfilled in *Johann Pfefferkorn.*
For *Jacob* said to his son *Naphtali*, ' Naphtalym shall
be a hart sent out, and giving speeches of fairness,'
Gen. xlix." Thereafter many Divines, and Licentiates

and other Theologians read that book from beginning to end, page by page, word by word, paragraph by paragraph. But there is here a certain Oberlander who studieth Greek, and he everywhere bruiteth it about that it is not true either that *Pfefferkorn* is an Imperial Counsellor, or that he ever was—and he declareth that the Emperor hath written on *Reuchlin's* behalf to his Holiness, and desireth, without more ado, that the Theologians will henceforth let his upright and trusty counsellor alone. *Jakob Fabri von Estaples*,[50] too, of whom you have heard much, openly favoureth *Johann Reuchlin*, although the Theologians have told him that he ought to refrain. It is even said that in a letter he sent to *Germany* he declared that the Theologians of *Paris* have treated *Reuchlin* just as the Jews treated Christ. But let him say what he will, the fact remaineth that the more part in *Paris* are on our side, for the honour of the University and in despite of the Jurists. Be therefore, of good heart, and rejoice and be glad. Fare ye well for ever and ever.

PARIS.

XXXVIII

❡ *DEMETRIUS PHALERIUS* to *Magister Ortwin Gratius* greeting

YOU write to me asking how our University comporteth itself with regard to the Cause of the Faith—whether it taketh your part, or that of *Johann Reuchlin*. You must know, therefore, that throughout the whole of *Switzerland* the Brethren of the Order of Preachers are in ill odour and deep disgrace by reason of those innocent Friars who were burned at *Berne*— for I shall never believe that they did the deeds imputed to them. Therefore are their Monasteries deserted, while the Monasteries of the Franciscans flourish ; and where one man giveth alms to a Dominican, twenty give to Minorites, Augustinians and the rest. It is said that it hath been prophesied that the Order of Preachers will be wholly blotted out.

Moreover there is here a Theologian—as he calleth himself, but I should rather call him a Poet—*Erasmus* of *Rotterdam* by name, who is reverenced by many as if he were one of the wonders of the world. He it is who wrote the Book of Proverbs that you once shewed me at *Cologne*, saying, "What do we want with the Proverbs of *Erasmus* when we have the Proverbs of *Solomon?*" This *Erasmus* holdeth firmly by *Reuchlin*, and is for ever praising him; and lately he printed certain Letters which he sent to the Court of *Rome*, addressed to the Pope and some of the Cardinals. In these he lauded *Reuchlin* and slandered the theologians. When I saw them I cried, "If the Magisternosters do but cast their eyes on this, the Devil will nab him!"

It happeneth therefore that our University, which highly regardeth *Erasmus*, leaneth towards *Reuchlin*. The Poet *Glareanus*,[51] moreover, hath come hither—a very headstrong man, as you know—and he uttereth outrageous calumnies against you and other Theologians. He declareth that he is going to write a book about the iniquities of the Dominicans, and will relate from beginning to end all the doings that took place at *Berne*. I would gladly beg him, in friendly wise, to refrain from this, but he is a terrible man, and a choleric, for ever threatening buffets—and he must be possessed of a devil. I trust that judgment in favour of the Theologians will soon issue from *Rome*—and then all will go well. But, if it should prove in favour of *Reuchlin*, then the Devil will hold the candle! Farewell.

From Basle.

XXXIX

❦ *KONRAD STRILDRIOT to Mag. Ortwin offereth salutations; homage, and my affectuous duty toward your virtuousness, preventing*

I HAVE ofttimes told you that I abide not here of mine own free will. The Devil, I trow, carried me hither, and now I cannot get back. There is no good-fellowship here as there is in *Germany;* folk are not convivial, and if a man be but mellow once in a day, they take it amiss, and call him a swine. There is no wenching for me, either, for the bona-robas are woundily extortionate, and uncomely withal. I tell you of a truth that in *Italy* the women are as ill-made as is possible, notwithstanding their fine gowns of silks and velvets. For when they are scarce middle-aged they all grow crook-backed, and walk about as if they had the gripes. They eat garlic, moreover, and savour rankly. They are swarthy, too, and not fair like German lasses. Their cheeks are pallid as death—and though some be blowsy, it is plain that they have ruddled themselves with salves. Wherefore the women of *Rome* please me not. They have a saying that it is not physical to go a-wenching here in the dog-days. So, say I, let me get home to *Germany* again, where one can wench the year round.

Ofttimes I call to mind how we both had our doxies —you and I ; and how we held in contempt that young tuft who had a design on yours—but she would have beslubbered his visnomy !

I have lately heard that you must needs consort with *Johann Pfefferkorn's* wife for honesty's sake—for she is close-tongued, and—so to say—an honest woman. It is, forsooth, but seemly to possess your leman privily : but it hath been told me that *Pfefferkorn* once fell out with you, and said, " Herr *Ortwin!* would that you would eat from your own plate, and let me eat from mine ! " But you for a long time understood him not, for he is a very subtle man, and given to speaking mystically by tropes. But a friend of yours, as I have heard tell, expounded these riddling words, and interpreted them thus : " Would that you would eat from your own plate "—that is, lie with your own wife or mistress —" and let me eat from mine "—that is, lay not your hands on my wife, but leave her to me.

I asked a certain poet, here, to seek out this aphorism in the Adages of *Erasmus ;* but he told me that he could not find it therein. " Then," quoth I, " by the same token that Author is not complete but faulty ! "

Nevertheless, when I heard these things concerning

Johann Pfefferkorn, I declared him to be over-jealous if he acts thus. For there is a saying that friends have all things in common—though some hold that wives are to be excepted. Nevertheless, with thee he should not be angry, seeing that you have no wife of your own, and we ought to give to those who have not. I have heard, moreover, that you have lain with a maid-servant of *Quentel* the printer's, and that she hath borne you a child. It is not well that you should till fallow ground. I hold ever by the outworn, that beareth no crop. Howbeit, young or old, there are none here for me. Oh, that I were back, therefore, in *Germany*, where I fain would be !

Fare ye well, until that day when a laverock shall weigh a hundred talents.

From ROME.

XL

❡ *MAGISTER JOHANN KRAPP* to *Magister Ortwin Gratius greeting*

YOU tell me how mightily pleased your worship was with that my Metrical Epistle, of late composed ; you say indeed that you have scarce seen the like ; and I take it that you would fain have me ever write to you after that fashion. Yet I must warn you—though you know it well—that one cannot at all times be poetising. You well know in your own case, though you are vastly facund and can write verses in plenty, that neverthe-less "oil sometimes lacketh " as the saying goes ; some-times you are lickerish for verse, and sometimes for prose. I remember how that I once said to you at *Cologne*, " Herr *Ortwin*, devise me, I pray you, a metrical Ode ;" and you made answer, " *Apollo* is afar from me for the nonce." And you said that sometimes in ten whole days you would not make one good verse ; for the weather suffered it not, and you must needs wait the occasion, as saith *Ovid :*—

"Tempora labuntur tacitisque senescimus annis."

As soon, therefore, as *Apollo* is gracious to me, I will

indite somewhat and send it to you. You desire me likewise to send you some news; all I know is that there are here three eminent Theologians who are of high renown among the Germans, and cause us to be of good and laudable report throughout the Curia. Two of these you know well—the Reverend Father Herr Magister-noster *Jakob van Hoogstraten*, (in the Latin tongue, *de Alta platea*), and Herr Magister-noster *Peter Meyer*, of *Frankfort*, Pastor. The third is Herr *Kaspar*, Preacher at *Kempten*, Licentiate in Sacred Theology, and ere long to become Magister-noster.

They are here occupied with three notable Causes.

The first, Magister-noster *Jakob*, maintaineth the Cause of the Faith against *Johann Reuchlin*, who they say is a heretic; and they say well, for so he is. The second, Magister-noster *Peter*, instituteth a suit concerning competence against the Canons of *Frankfort*, inasmuch as they will not yield him his competence, and therefore he hath come hither to Court, and harrieth them woundily. The third, Herr *Kaspar*, maintaineth a suit concerning certain sacred oil, against certain monks who dwell without the walls of *Kempten*, and hoard this sacred oil; and when folk should be aneled the sacred oil is not forthcoming. Wherefore the aforesaid Licentiate desireth to correct those monks and compel them to yield the oil to the Burg for the common good of the inhabitants. I have no other news to relate; and from you I have heard naught. [I know not indeed the cause wherefore I have merited your reverence's neglect.] And now I commend you to the Lord—

> May he you in peril save,
> Make you as a lion brave,
> Wise as prudent Solomon,
> Fair of face as Absolon,
> Holy as the Baptist, John,
> Wealthy as Ahasuerus,
> And poetic as Homerus.
> Perish Reuchlin! and the crew
> Of ungodly poets, too—
> Humbly they might learn of you!

Lo! while I was not minded to write poetry, nevertheless I have dropped into verse. How this came to pass

I know not. Glory be to God! Farewell! Finis!
Telos! Tetragrammaton!

From the COURT OF ROME.

XLI

⁜ *MAGISTER SIMON POCOPORIUS to*
Magister Ortwin Gratius greeting

" SUCH knowledge is too wonderful for me; it is
high, I cannot attain unto it," saith the Psalmist.
These words I can apply directly to myself when I
consider your lordship's learning, which I lately became
aware of through that book of yours entitled "The
Orations of Magister *Ortwin*." Sonty! What a great
man you have become, though in days gone by you
were but a bungling pupil of mine? And now you
overtop your teacher, notwithstanding that Scripture:
"The disciple is not above his master." So then, as
I read that book, I cried in a loud voice, "Oh, *Ortwin*,
thy knowledge is too wonderful for me, it is high, I
cannot attain unto it!" "Wonderful" of a truth it
is, for I should never have believed that from my
teaching you could have indited compositions so fairly
and artificially; I glory greatly when I call to remembrance that by God's grace I was once your master
and teacher. "High" indeed it is, for though in days
gone by your knowledge was none of the loftiest, it
hath been heightened by the inspiration of the spirit
from above that hath enlightened you. Formerly—
pardon me—you had no mind to study: ofttimes I have
corrected you for knowing not the case of "mei" or
"sui," or the tense of "legat, legant," and I would say
to you this rime :—

> You must be a ninny-hammer
> If you cannot learn your grammar!

But now you can teach me, and I should feel it no
disgrace to learn of you. Nevertheless, I add, "I cannot attain unto it," since, as *Socrates* saith, "What is

187

above us toucheth us not." Persevere in compiling essays and you will become a notable man. Farewell.

Lübeck.

XLII

❦ MAGISTER ACHATIUS LAMPIRIUS to Magister Ortwinus Gratius with many greetings

I MARVEL greatly, honoured Sir, that you write to all your friends and adherents at *Rome*, and yet to me alone you write not, although you said that you would write to me oft.

I learn however, of a pilgrim from *Cologne*, that you would fain have knowledge of that art concerning which I once hinted to you—to wit, how a man may compass that a woman shall mightily love him. Now, albeit you have not written to me, yet will I impart this to you, that you may see how dearly I cherish you : for I will keep nothing secret from you, but will disclose matters

" Which the filosofes of olde,
Would not to their feres unfolde ; "

of such a kind is this subtle device. But you must reveal it to no man, for I keep it so covered that I would not whisper it to my brother—but you I love more than a brother. Therefore I am nothing loth to communicate the secret to you.

You must go about in this wise :—

When you are enamoured of a woman, you must first discover what her name is, and what her mother's name is.

Put the case that you are in love with a damsel named *Barbara*, whose mother's name is *Elsa*.

You must first procure a hair from *Barbara's* own head, and must thereupon be shriven as a penitent, or at the least make general confession.

Next, you must make an image of virgin wax, and over this Mass must thrice be read, the hair meanwhile being bound around its neck.

Afterwards, on a morning, having first heard Mass,

188

you must take a new glazed pot full of water, and
having kindled a fire in a room closed in all parts, you
must make fumigation with incense, and light a candle
made of new wax with which a morsel of a Paschal
candle has been mingled.   Then you must pronounce
this incantation over the image: "I conjure you, by
the virtue of the Almighty, by the Nine Choirs of
Angels, by the virtue of Cosdriel, Boldriach, Tornach,
Lissiel, Farnach, Pitrax, and Starniel, that you set
before me, in her proper substance and corporeality,
Barbara daughter of *Elsa*, to submit herself to me in
all things in accordance with my will."

Then you must write these names around the head
of the image with a silver style: Astrob + Arnod +
Bildron + Sydra +, and forthwith place it in the pot
of water, and set it by the fire, uttering this conjura-
tion: "I charge thee, *Barbara* daughter of *Elsa*, by
the power of the Almighty, by the nine Choirs of the
Angels, by the power of Cosdriel, Boldriach, Tornach,
Lissiel, Farnach, Pitrax, and Starniel, and by the power
of those names, Astrob, Arnod, Bildron, Sydra, that
thou instantly conceive such love for me, that without
tarrying thou wilt come to me, because I languish in
love."   Thereupon, so soon as the water becometh hot,
all is accomplished, for she will begin to love you to
such a degree, that when she sees you not—she knows
not where you are.

This has been proved oftentimes, and never fails.
Believe me, this is very precious lore.   I would not
unfold it to you were it not that I love you so fervently;
and, for once, you might in turn communicate a secret
to me.

May you abide sound in health.

The COURT OF ROME.

XLIII

❧ *BROTHER OTTO FLASCHENKLIRRER*
to Mag. Ortwin Gratius

MY pious prayers by way of greeting.
   Reverend Sir!   You tell me that all we Theologians should render thanks to Almighty God for that

Theology is now in blossom, and that there is a cloud
of learned Divines in all parts of *Germany*. Moreover
all men, masters or servants, nobles or churls, do them
high honour, calling them Magisternosters by reason of
their pre-eminence, and doffing their hats and caps when
they meet one, saying, "Commend me to your egre-
giousness, eximious Herr Magisternoster!" And
when a Magisternoster passeth along the street all
folk salute him as though a prince passed by. And
this is well—for Magisternosters are as the Apostles
of God. So then in your letter you tell me great
things. Nevertheless must I hold myself opposed, and
say that this doubtless is true enough for *Cologne*,
but not elsewhere. Here, especially, in my own
country, Magisternosters who are Regulars are paid
no honours, but the Canons and nobles shamefully
belittle them. Yet the secular priests are accorded
honour, and held in respect. Now this seemeth to
me unbecoming, for Regulars should ever take the
first place, inasmuch as they are the more spiritual,
and a Regular with respect to celestiality standeth
above a Secular. For Regulars are naturally fitted
for chanting lauds to the glory of God, and of his
Holy Mother, the ever-blessed Virgin Mary, and of
all the Saints and Martyrs, and Confessors, and the
rest. Therefore it seemeth to me a great error for
men to honour Seculars rather than Regulars. Moreover the secular Theologians in high places begin to
wax proud, and are, as it were, opposed to the Regulars,
while they themselves grow more worldly, and further
removed from the Kingdom of Heaven. You know
how that Christ hath said, "Ye who follow me shall
sit upon thrones, judging the twelve tribes of Israel."
Now Regulars have left their goods and chattels, and
are despised in this world, therefore are they nighest
to the Kingdom of Heaven. Forgive me in that I
write such things concerning secular Theologians, seeing
that you are one. But it is otherwise at *Cologne*, for
there folk are humble and reverent towards Regulars.
Nay, even you may be yourself deemed a Regular,
as far as zeal goeth, and you once said to me at
Cologne, "Herr *Otto*, I trow that one day I shall

become a monk of your Order, for I have a strong
hankering thereafter." Hence I write to you from
my heart. But it irketh me mightily that Secular
Theologians should now-a-days be so over-weening—
as is Doctor *Johann Reiss,* who is a preacher at the
Cathedral in this Burg. He is held in high esteem,
and all the Canons and nobles make much of him;
for he knoweth how to gloze them with fair words.
Yet this Doctor seemeth to be mightily prejudiced
against the Regulars. One told me, who often sat
with him at board, that he altogether holdeth a way
of his own, and is neither an Albertist, nor a Scotist,
nor an Occamist, nor a Thomist. And if any one
asketh him, "Most excellent Herr Doctor, of what
way are you?" he answereth, "The way of Christ."
He laugheth when the Doctors of Theology call themselves Magisternosters.

Moreover he holdeth not greatly with the Regulars,
saying that it is not needful for us to put on a cowl,
but that we can be saved by other means. He declareth
that God hath no respect for vesture. In this he
seemeth to me to be heretical, for he lacketh reverence
towards the Regulars and the Holy Father. He useth
moreover an uncouth method of preaching—for he doth
not, as do others, propound subtle questions and construct arguments *contra,* and afterwards solve them
and deduce Corollaries, but he proceedeth without art
or rule. I marvel, therefore, that folks listen his
sermons gladly, for he preacheth not canonically. I
have by two instances been convinced that he is ill-
disposed towards Regulars. Once when you at *Cologne*
instituted, with the aid of our Order universally, that
laudable strife against *Johann Reuchlin,* I brought
him a paper containing the decree concerning *Johann
Reuchlin,* that his book should be burned and he
himself be forced to recant. I said to him, as I had
been instructed by our Provincial, "Excellent Herr
Magisternoster, your excellence here hath a decree
that *Reuchlin* is a heretic and that his book is to be
burned. Be pleased, therefore, to publish it from the
pulpit; and at the same time we request you to join
us in withstanding the aforesaid heretic."

Thereupon he read the mandate, and said :

" I cannot see that aught is decreed herein save that the *Augenspiegel* is not to be sold publicly until the charge is heard and decided. It doth not appear that *Reuchlin* is pronounced a heretic." I answered that this might be piously presumed from the fact that the sale of his book was banned, and I asked him to espouse our Cause from the pulpit. He made answer, " I pray thee leave me in peace : I am here to spread the word of God, and to offend no man. For it is written, ' But whoso slandereth one of these small,' etc. ; " and so I could not bring it about that he should aid the Cause of the Faith.

On another occasion I observed that when Brother *Jakob* of our Order was here, and distributed the indulgences that we had procured at *Rome* for the Monastery at *Augsburg*, he also asked the aforesaid Doctor *Reiss* to extol the Indulgences in the pulpit, and exhort women, and others, so that money might flow into the chest, for it would be well spent. But he neglected to say what was required, and would not even utter a single word concerning Indulgences. Thereupon Brother *Jakob* said to him, " Lo, you grudge our collecting money ; yet collect it we will, if it should break your heart ; " and from the pulpit he cried, " Lo, here you have indulgences, and letters of indulgence, and that which is written in them is as true and credible as the Gospel ; and when you receive these indulgences, you are as surely shriven as though Christ had come hither and shriven you himself." Then Doctor *Reiss* argued to the contrary, and said :

" Naught can be evened with the Gospel ; and it will go well with him who doeth well. If a man receiveth those indulgences a hundred times over, and yet liveth not uprightly, he shall perish ; nor shall the Indulgence profit him. But, on the other hand, if a man liveth righteously, or, after sinning repenteth and amendeth his ways, I tell you that he will be an inheritor of the Kingdom of Heaven, and will need no other helper." And hence it hath entered my mind that this Doctor *Reiss* is an enemy of the Regulars :

and it seemeth to me that he favoureth *Johann Reuchlin;* but I cannot tell. You will perceive there-fore how matters stand. I allow that the Theologians in *Cologne* are held in high reverence, and that the Secular Theologians and lay folk are in close bonds with the Regulars—but here it is not so. Yet I trust that when *Reuchlin* is overthrown, then the Theologians will rejoice in their turn; which may our only-begotten Saviour grant. Amen.

From WÜRZBURG.

XLIV

ℂ *PETER OF WORMS* to *Mag.* Ortwinus *Gratius sendeth many greetings*

EXIMIOUS Sir; Inasmuch as you are by nature well-disposed towards me, and have shewn me much favour, I too will do on your behoof what lieth in my power.

Now you said to me, "O *Peter*, when you attain to *Rome*, mark whether there be any new books, and send me some." Receive, then, with this, a new book that has been printed here.

I trow, indeed, seeing that you are a Poet, you will learn from it for the perfecting of your art.

For I heard, at a session of the Court here, from a Notary, who was doubtless proficient in that mystery, that this book is the well-spring of Poesy, and that its author, one *Homer*, is the father of all the Poets.

He told me moreover, that there is another *Homer*, in Greek.

"Nay," quoth I, "what care I about Greek? The Latin one is better, for I want it to send to *Germany*, to Magister *Ortwin*, who pays no heed to those Greek fantasticalities."

Then I sounded him concerning the theme of this book. And he told me that it treated of certain folk called Greeks, who made war on some other folk called Trojans, whom I had heard tell of before. These same Trojans had a great city, and the Greeks pitched before it and lay there for more than ten years. And anon the Trojans sallied forth and laid about them mightily, and they slew one another so wondrously that all the ground was bloodied, and there was a certain river there, and that was all dyed with blood and made quite red, so that it flowed like so much gore—and the noise was heard in heaven; and a wight threw a stone that twelve men could not lift, and a horse began to speak, and prophesied.

But I do not believe such things as these, for they seem to me impossible, and yet I suppose that this book may be very authentic. Write to me, I beg you, concerning it, and let me know your opinion. And now, farewell.

ROME.

XLV

❡ *JOHANN GERLAMB* to *Magister* *Ortwin Gratius*

AS the saying goes, "A friend in need is a friend indeed," and I desire to make proof whether you still hold me in remembrance, and this I shall put to the test in manner following: The bearer of this letter is my kinsman, he is a youth of good parts, and desireth to study the liberal Arts; his father was minded to send him hither to this University, but I dissuaded him, because I would fain have him study after the methods of the Ancients, as I myself had been taught. I pray you, therefore, receive him as your charge. Although I am an Albertist, I should disapprove not of your sending him to *De Monte* Hostel, where they cleave to the methods of *Thomas*. The Rector there is an Oberlander, and, after all, there is no great difference between Thomists and Albertists — except that the Albertists hold that adjectives are appellative, and that the mobile body is in nature the object, while the Thomists hold that adjectives are not appellative, and that the mobile Ens is in nature the object. The Albertists assert, too, that logic proceedeth from terms of the second intentions to first intentions, while the Thomists assert that it proceedeth from first to second intentions. Again, the Albertists hold that a mobile body *in vacuo* moveth continuously, but the Thomists hold that a mobile body *in vacuo* moveth instantly. Again, the Albertists say that the Milky Way is celestial in its nature, but the Thomists say that it is elemental. Yet it matters not much with which side a man holdeth, so long as he followeth the ancient ways. I desire that this young man should have his commons in the hostel, and that he should be kept under strict control and not permitted to run wild wheresoever he willeth. And when he transgresseth, chastise him. For it is written in the Book of Proverbs, Chap. xxii.: "Withhold not correction from the child; for if thou beatest him with the rod he shall not die. Thou shalt beat him with the rod and deliver his soul from hell." Induce in him the habit of joining in the disputations of the hostel, and take heed that he attendeth not the lectures of *Caesarius,* or other poets. I rejoiced when you told me that *Buschius* no longer abideth at *Cologne,* for he was a stumbling-block to the University, enticing students away with that poetry of his. There are two Poets here—*Eoban Hesse* and *Peter Aperbach,* who are enemies of mine, but I pay no heed to them. Whenever they see me they fall to talking about *Johann Reuchlin's* case, making him out to be in the right, and defaming the Theologians. But I hold my tongue—though a little while ago I did say, "*Johann Pfefferkorn* knows right well what to call him," and I shewed them that book of his called "J. P.'s Defence against Slanders," and with that I took myself off. God grant that the judgment may go in your favour, or else these poets will laugh us to scorn. And now I commend the young man to your charge. Farewell.

ERFURT.

XLVI

¶ *MAGISTER KONRAD UNCKEBUNCK sendeth to Magister Ortwin Gratius abundant greetings*

"MOUTHS have they and they speak not; eyes have they and they see not; ears have they and they hear not," saith the Psalmist: and these words will serve as preamble and text of my discourse:—

Magister *Ortwin* hath a mouth and speaketh not—else would he have said to some Curialist setting out for Rome, "Salute Herr *Konrad Unckebunck* for me:" Eyes hath he and he seeth not—for I have written him many letters and he replieth not, as though he could neither read nor see them: and, in the third place, ears hath he and he heareth not—for I have commissioned many a comrade departing hence for the provinces to greet him, but he cannot have heard my salutations, inasmuch as he reciprocateth them not.

In this you sorely err, for I love you, and you therefore ought to love me in return. Howbeit you do not — for you write naught to me. It would gladden me exceedingly were you to write to me very oft, for when I read your letters they inwardly rejoice the cockles of my heart.

Nevertheless I have learnt that you have of pupils but a few, and complain that *Buschius* and *Caesarius* lure the students from you — notwithstanding that they lack your skill to expound the poets allegorically and to cite thereanent the Scriptures. The Devil, I trow, is in those Poets. They are the bane of the universities.

An old Magister of *Leipsic*, who hath been Master for these thirty years, told me that when he was a lad, then did the University greatly prosper: those were the days when there was not a Poet within twenty miles. He told me, too, how that the students then diligently attended lectures—whether public or bursarial; it was deemed a great scandal that a student should walk in the street without having *Peter of Spain* or the *Parva Logicalia* under his arm; or, if they were grammarians, then they would carry with them Alexander's *Doctrinale*, or his *Opus Minus*, or the *Vade Mecum*, or the *Exercitium Puerorum*, or Johann Sinthen's *Dicta*. Then were there zealous students in the Schools, who held the Masters of Arts in honour, and if they spied a Magister they fell to trembling as if they had seen a devil. He told me that in those days there were four promotions of bachelors each year, and many a time fifty or sixty graduated at once. In those days the University was in full bloom; and when a student had resided for a year and a half he was made Bachelor, and after three years, or two and a half years, in all, a Magister. Thus it came to pass that his parents were well pleased, and freely sent him money when they saw that their son had attained a place of honour. But now-a-days all the students must needs attend lectures on *Virgil* and *Pliny* and the rest of the new-fangled authors—what is more, they may listen to them for five years and yet get no degree: and so, when they return home, their parents ask them, saying, "What art thou?" And they reply that they are naught, but that they have been reading Poetry! And then the parents are perplexed—but they see that their sons are not grammarians, and therefore they are disgruntled at the University, and begrudge sorely the money they have spent. Then they say to others, "Send not your sons to the University—they'll learn naught, but go trapesing in the streets anights; money given for such a bringing-up is but thrown away."

The old Magister furthermore told me that in his time there were full two thousand students at *Leipsic*, and a like number at *Erfurt;* four thousand at *Vienna* and as many at *Cologne*—and so with the rest. Now-a-days there are not as many students at all the Universities put together as there were then in one or two. The Magisters at *Leipsic* bitterly lament the scarcity of scholars. It is the Poets that do them this hurt. Even when students are sent by their parents to hostels and colleges they will not stay there, but are off to the Poets to learn stuff and nonsense. He told me that at *Leipsic* he used to have two score pupils, and when he went to the Church, or to the market, or to stroll in the Rosengarten, they would all follow after him. In those days it was a grave offence to study poetry. If a penitent admitted in the confessional that he had privily listened to a Bachelor lecturing upon *Virgil*, the priest would impose upon him a thumping penance—to wit, to fast every Friday, or to rehearse daily the seven penitential Psalms. He swore to me, on his conscience, that he saw a candidate rejected because he had once been detected by one of the Examiners reading *Terence* on a feast-day. Would that it were thus in the Universities now; then I should not have to drudge here at the Curia. For what work is there for us at the Universities? We cannot make a living. Students no longer will dwell in Hostels under Magisters. Among twenty students you will scarce find one with a mind to graduate. Yet all of them are eager to study the Humanities. When a Magister lectureth he findeth no audience; but, as for the Poets, when they discourse it is a marvel to behold the crowd of listeners. And thus the Universities throughout all *Germany* are minished and brought low. Let us pray God, then, that all the Poets may perish, for "it is expedient that one man should die—" that is that the Poets, of whom there are but a handful in any one University, should perish, rather than so many Universities should come to naught.

And now you will surely send me a letter—or long will be my lamentations over your neglect. Farewell.

From ROME.

198

XLVII

☙ *FRIAR BENEDICT the SCOT to*
Magister Ortwin Gratius

SENDETH brotherly and heartfelt love by way of salutation.

Let me tell you, in reply to your question, that your letter reached me on Michaelmas Day, and I will now answer it categorically.

First, you ask why we Predicant Friars chant with a louder voice than any others. I answer that I trow it is for no other reason save that it is written in Isaiah lix., "We shall roar all of us like bears, and shall lament as mournful doves;" and that I believe *St. Dominic* desired to fulfil this prophecy.

Secondly, you ask whether I hold *St. Thomas* or *St. Dominic* to be the holier? I answer that it is a moot point, and that Doctors of our Order dispute with one another concerning the matter. Some hold *St. Dominic* to be the holier as touching his life, but not as touching his doctrine; and, on the other hand, *St. Thomas* to be the holier as touching his doctrine, but not as touching his life. Others contend that *St. Dominic* is absolutely the holier, and this they maintain for two reasons: The first is that *St. Dominic* was the founder of our Order, and therefore that *St. Thomas*, who was a member of the Order, was his disciple: and the disciple is not above his master: Q.E.D. The second is that learning hath no preeminence over life and conduct, and that therefore, perchance, *St. Thomas* was more learned than *St. Dominic* and yet not necessarily holier. Others again will have it that *St. Thomas* is absolutely the holier, inasmuch as no other Doctor among all the saints is called the Holy Doctor except *St. Thomas*. Hence, just as *Aristotle* is called "The Philosopher," and *Paul*, "The Apostle," so *St. Thomas* is called par excellence "The Saint"; therefore, not only in learning but also in sanctity doth he excel *St. Dominic*.

To this it is objected that *St. Thomas* is called "Holy," not as being absolutely holier than all other saints, but merely as being the holiest of the canonized Doctors. Hence he is not holier than *St. Dominic.* But an aged member of our Order hath told me that he will show me a very ancient book in which disputation concerning the relative sanctity of these two saints is prohibited. Wherefore I dismiss this question, and pronounce not my judgment thereon.

You ask me, in the third place, whether I think *Johann Pfefferkorn* will persevere in the Christian Faith. I answer that, by the Lord, I know not what to say. It is a mighty ticklish point. You will call to mind that precedent at St. Andrew's in *Cologne*[52]— how a Dean of that Church, who was a baptized Jew, abided long in the Christian Faith, and lived an upright life. But upon his death-bed he ordered a hare and a hound to be brought to him and enlarged, whereupon the hound in a trice seized the hare. Then he ordered a cat and a mouse to be brought—and the cat pounced on the mouse. Then said he to many who were standing around, "You see how that these animals cannot cast off their natures; and a Jew can never cast off his faith. Wherefore to-day I would fain die a true Israelite," and so speaking he died. Thereupon the citizens of *Cologne* in memory of this event set up the brazen images which still stand on the wall before the cemetery. I have heard, too, of another Jew who in like manner upon his death-bed commanded a large stone to be brought, and to be placed in a pot full of water beside the fire. After it had stood there quite three days he asked whether it was yet cooked. They answered, "Nay," for it was not possible that a stone should be cooked. Then said he, "As that stone can never be sodden by the heat, so can Jews never be turned into true Christians. But they are baptized for gain's sake, or through fear, or to work some treachery. And to-day I will die a faithful Jew." And therefore, by the Lord, there is much to be feared concerning *Johann Pfefferkorn*, though I trust that God will grant him especial grace and keep him in the faith, and at any rate it behoves us—on account of *Johann Reuchlin* and his allies—always to maintain that for a certainty he will continue a Christian.

In the fourth place you ask me my opinion about Proper Nouns; whether they are wanting in a plural, as the ancient grammarians, *Alexander* and the rest, hold—or, have a plural, as the modern and new-fangled writers, such as *Diomedes* and *Priscian*, contend. I answer that we should say that Proper Nouns, in so far as they are proper, have no plural. Nevertheless sometimes they are declined in the plural, and can then be classed with common nouns : as " two Jameses," that is, the two Apostles named *James*—" two Catos," that is, two Kings or wise Roman Senators so named—" three Maries," that is, three women named *Mary*.

I have now answered you to the best of my ability ; if I knew more I would answer you better. Take, then, my words in good part. Greet for me with right good will Dr. *Arnold von Tongern*, mine own esteemed preceptor. Farewell.

ZWOLLE (?)

XLVIII

€ *JOHANN KALB to Magister Ortwin Gratius amicable greeting*

HONOURABLE and Reverend Herr Magister, I would have you know that I marvel greatly how it cometh that you importune me in continually bidding me to send you " some news." You are endlessly craving for news, notwithstanding that I have other business to attend to, and therefore cannot occupy myself with gossip; for I must needs run hither and thither in canvassing, lest I miscarry in my candidature, and come not at the benefice.

Nevertheless, I will write to you this once, to satisfy you, so that, after, you may leave me in peace with your " news ! "

You have doubtless heard that the Pope had a huge great beast called *Elephant*, and held it in great honour, and mightily loved it. And now I would have you know that this beast is dead. When it was ill the Pope fell into great grief, and he summoned a host of physicians, and said, "If it be possible, cure *Elephant* for me." Thereupon they bestirred themselves, and cast its water, and gave it a cathartic that cost five hundred golden crowns—yet were not the bowels of *Elephant* moved thereby, and so it died. Sorely doth the Pope grieve for *Elephant*, for whom, they say, he'd give a thousand ducats.

In sooth it was a marvellous brute, and it had a great abundance of long snout; and when it saw the Pope it would kneel to him, and cry in a terrible voice, "Bar, bar, bar!" There is, I trow, not the like beast in the whole world.

The rumour goes that the King of *France* and King *Charles* have made a treaty of peace for many years, and have exchanged oaths. But some think this peace is but politic, and will not long endure. I know not if this be so—nor do I greatly care. For when I come home to *Germany*, then I shall betake me to my parsonage, and spend happy days. There shall I keep flocks of geese and hens and ducks, and I shall have in my byre five or six cows to yield me milk for the making of cheese and butter. And I shall keep a cook who can turn her hand to such work. She must be of ripe years, for if she were young she might sorely tempt me, and I might fall into sin. She will spin for me, and I will buy the flax for her. I shall keep two or three pigs, and fatten them to furnish me with good bacon. Before all things I shall keep in my house great store of victuals. Once a year I shall kill an ox and sell half to the country-folk, and cure the rest in the reek. And behind the house there is a garden where I shall sow garlic, and onions and parsley—with pot-herbs, turnips, and the like. Then in the winter I shall sit in my chamber and study how to hold forth to my flock, out of the Paratus, or the Simple Sermons, or even out of the Bible, so that I may become practised in preaching. But in the summer I shall go a-fishing, or dig in my garden; and I shall take no heed of wars, for I shall live my own life, and preach sermons and read mass, heeding not those worldly concerns that bring damnation to the soul.   Farewell.

The Court of Rome.

XLIX

❦ *PHILIPP SCHNEIDER VON ERFURT* *to Magister Ortwin Gratius*

REVERENTIAL Salutations to your Reverence. Venerated Herr Magister, you lately wrote to inform me that a certain Poet in *Germany, Erasmus* by name, of *Rotterdam,* inditeth many books, and that in particular he hath drawn up a letter to the Pope in the which he commendeth *Johann Reuchlin.* I must tell you that I have read that letter. I have moreover seen another book of his, a big one, intituled " The New Testament," which he hath sent to the Pope, and I understand that he would fain obtain the Pope's approval of it.[53] I trust that he will not get it. For the Master of the Sacred Palace, a man of consequence and of high repute, declared that he could manifestly prove *Erasmus* to be heretic, inasmuch as in certain passages he reprehendeth the Holy Doctor, and maketh light of the Theologians. Besides this he hath written a treatise called " Moria Erasmi," which containeth many scandalous and irreverent passages, and, here and there, open blasphemies. Wherefore the Parisians are desirous to burn that volume. I trow, therefore, that the Pope will not grant his approval to the big book. The hopes of Doctor *Jakob van Hoogstraten* run high. Yesterday he invited me to his board and told me of a truth that a Cardinal had assured him that judgment would go in his favour. But *Johann Wick,*[54] who is *Johann Reuchlin's* Proctor, withstandeth him sorely : Doctor *Jakob* once said to him, in my presence, " You, forsooth, are now my adversary, but, mark my words, if I gain the day, I will harass you so that you will not find a place of safety in the whole of *Germany.*" And another time he said to him, " I know that *Reuchlin* hath no money to give you, and are you so foolhardy

as to wish to make enemies of the whole Order?" And
then there is another man, Dr. *Martin Gröning* by
name, who must needs translate the *Augenspiegel*. I
hear that Doctor *Jakob* will privily give him a hundred
ducats if he will falsify that book—and if this be done,
the victory is yours. I trust Dr. *Martin* will consent.
Write, and tell me all the news you hear. Farewell.

Rome.

L

¶ *MAGISTER ADOLFUS CLINGESOR*
sendeth much greeting to Magister Ortwin
Gratius

NOT long ago I sent you word that folk here were
wont to dispute with me concerning *Johann
Reuchlin* and the Cause of the Faith. I would have
you know, therefore, that after you sent me that book
of *Johann Pfefferkorn's* intituled "J. P.'s defence against
Slanders, &c.," I took it to a certain man who held an
opposite opinion, and shewed him how that it was
written in that book, at the end of O. ii.: "Twenty
years ago, if I remember right, this was prophesied
to us at *Cologne* by *Johann Lichtenberger*, otherwise
Ruth the outlandish eremite (whose prophecies have
been printed at *Mainz* in Latin and German). In them
it is written, fol. 16, 'Take heed, O ye Philosophers of
Cologne, lest ravening wolves break into your sheepfold! For in your days strange and unheard of things
shall arise in your churches, which may the All-bountiful
avert.'" Now when he had read this, he stood for
a while in thought. Then quoth he, "I marvel at
the folly of the Theologians! Think you all men to
be children, that you practise upon them with such
fustian? But since the Theologians of *Cologne* thus
desire to appear subtle, I will show you a prophecy
concerning *Johann Reuchlin* which will be much more
to the point: and afterwards I will prove that the prophecy which they have cited tendeth in *Reuchlin's* favour
and not against him. Turn, therefore, to the first

Chapter of the Book of *Zephaniah*, where saith the prophet, ' And it shall come to pass at that time, that I will
search Jerusalem with candles, and will punish the men
that are settled on their lees, that say in their heart, &c.'
Now since you men of *Cologne* make bold to wrest the
scriptures after your own good pleasure, hearken how I
interpret those words of the prophet.   The Lord saith,
by the mouth of the prophet, ' And it shall come to
pass at that time that I will search Jerusalem,' that is
to say, I will visit my Church, to the end that I may
reform her, and remove whatsoever errors may be within
her; and I will do this ' with candles '—that is, by the
mediation of enlightened men, such as are *Erasmus* of
Rotterdam, Johann Reuchlin, and *Mutianus Rufus*,[55] and
others in *Germany;* and ' I will punish the men '—that
is, the Theologians; ' settled '—that is, obstinately
bigoted; ' on their lees '—that is in a sorry, misty, and
bootless Theology, which a few centuries ago they took
to their bosoms, deserting the ancient and learned
Theologians who walked in the true light of the Holy
Writ.   Knowing neither the Latin, the Greek, nor the
Hebrew tongue, they cannot understand the Scriptures.
Therefore, casting aside the veracious and primitive
Theology, they do naught but dispute, and wrangle,
and moot unprofitable questions.   And in so doing they
declare that they are defending the Catholic Faith, notwithstanding that there are none among the disputants
who attack the Faith.   And thus to no purpose do they
spend their days, and do not advantage the Church of
God.   If, indeed, their disputations were of any profit,
they could turn them to account in the service of the
faith of the Catholic Church, by journeying throughout
the world and preaching God's Word, as did the
Apostles, and convincing the Greeks that they should
come again into union with the Church of *Rome*.   Or,
if they wish not to wander far from home, at least let
them go amongst the Bohemians and put that folk to
silence with their Arguments and Syllogisms.   Nevertheless they do none of these things, but wrangle concerning unprofitable matters.   Therefore will the Lord
punish them, and will send among them Doctors learned
in Greek, and in Latin, and in Hebrew, who, purging

those 'lees'—that is, sweeping away the sophistries, and the false and darkening commentaries of Theology, shall bring their 'candles' and cast light upon the Scriptures, and give us once more the primitive and true Theology; in like manner as the aforesaid *Erasmus*, for example, hath lately emended the works of *St. Jerome* and caused them to be imprinted. He hath emended the New Testament also, and this, I take it, is of more profit than if twenty thousand Scotists and Thomists were to wrangle for a hundred years concerning Entity and Essence." Now, when he had made an end of speaking, I cried, "God preserve me! What do I hear? You are *de facto* excommunicate!" and I would fain have left him. But he detained me, saying, "Hear yet the conclusion of the matter." "I will not hear the conclusion," said I. "At least listen while I expound your prophecy," said he. Then I thought within myself that I would listen, for it is not a sin to listen to excommunicates so long as we do not eat or drink with them. Straightway he began, "Hearken, oh ye Philosophers of *Cologne*—the prophet saith not 'Theologians' but 'Philosophers,' inasmuch as the theology of the men of *Cologne* is rather to be termed philosophy, that is, the Art of Sophistry, than truly Theology, for it consisteth of naught but diabolical garrulity and fatuous loquacity. 'Lest ravening wolves,' namely *Jacob von Hoogstraten, Arnold von Tongern*, and the like, who, by their lying and frauds, with rage and violence ravish the innocent sheep—such as are *Peter of Ravenna* and *Johann Reuchlin*—desiring to brand them as heretics by reason of their learning and their renown which they envy. And since they perceive that they cannot do such mighty works as those most learned men, they would fain destroy them. These then are the 'ravening wolves' who lie in wait against the repute and the very lives of the innocent. And now for seven years have they on all sides harassed and maltreated *Johann Reuchlin*, that poor old man, and unless the Almighty had averted their wickedness, they would have altogether destroyed him. It cannot be alleged that *Reuchlin* himself is a ravening wolf, for in all his life he hath ravaged no one, that is he hath

accused no man falsely, nor has he attacked the life or
reputation of any man by word or deed.　Hearken
once more—what mean the words that follow, ' Break
into your sheepfold ' ?　*Reuchlin*, good man, never
entered the University of *Cologne*—never, indeed, did
he pay any heed to the Theologians or the Church at
Cologne, for he was occupied with more useful matters.
Therefore it is impossible to reckon him as one of the
ravening wolves of whom *Lichtenberger* speaketh ; for
such must be found in the Colognese sheepfold.　Then
followeth, ' For in your days strange and unheard of
things shall arise.' ' Strange and unheard of' is good.
For neither hath eye seen nor ear heard, nor hath it
entered into the heart of man, that so learned and upright a man, who hath profited so many and done hurt
to none, should, in his old age, be so cruelly and so
treacherously harassed and tormented and persecuted.
Then, too, the words that follow, ' in your churches'
cannot by any possibility be applied to *Reuchlin*, for,
most fortunately, he hath lived outside the jurisdiction
of the Church of *Cologne*—namely, within the diocese
of *Constance*.　' And so I hope that the dogs will
come,' that is, the faithful warders of the flock, who,
without envy and malice, will humbly and faithfully
feed Christ's sheep—that is, all Christian folk—' and
will tear those wolves that lay waste God's fold, and
will purge the Church of God '—that is, drive out those
base and lewd theologians who know nothing and boast
to know all things."　Now when he had done speaking
I departed from him, and swore by all that is holy that
I would write to *Cologne*.　I therefore humbly entreat
you to report these things to the Magisternosters, and
to *Johann Pfefferkorn*, who is, as it were, the mouthpiece of the Colognese, and wondrously skilled in composition—and let him trounce the fellow soundly with
his pen.　The man who said these things is a native of
Berlin.　If you wish to learn his name, send me word,
and I will tell you.　He once resided at *Bonn*, where
he was strictly disciplined, nevertheless he continues to
speak against the Theologians and is no good Christian
—he abideth in wickedness, and will therefore perish in
hell—from which may God preserve you, and the Theo-

logians and the Friars Predicant, world without end.
Amen.

FRANKFORT-ON-ODER.

LI

❧ *JOHANN HELFERICH* (*latine Juppiter*) *to
Magister Ortwin sendeth greeting and humbly
commendeth himself*

REVEREND Herr Magister, you tell me that you
marvel how it cometh to pass that I dub myself
Juppiter. You must know, then, that when I resided
at *Vienna* I attended lectures on poetry, and there was
a certain young poet there—*George Sibutus* by name—
who had been a pupil of *Conrad Celtis*. He was my
companion, and we were ever together, and he said,
"You ought to be named *Juppiter*, for *Juppiter* hath
in Latin the same meaning as *Helferich* in German."
So *Juppiter* is my cognomen. *Sibutus* now dwells at
Wittenberg, and he has taken to himself an old trot
seventy-eight years old and more. I visited his house
a while ago when I was making my way out of
Prussia—and there sat the crone behind the stove.
"Is that your mother?" I asked. "No," said he,
"that is my spouse and wedded wife." "Why did
you marry such an old woman?" quoth I. He made
answer that she was still not so over-ripe as to have
lost all sapor, and had good store of pelf; moreover she
could brew rare stingo, which she sold and turned to
profit. Then said I, "Thou hast done well; and how
call you your wife?"

"My *Corinna*," he replied, "my *Lesbia*, and my
Cynthia." But let this pass.

You tell me that it seemeth to you that the Day of
Judgment is at hand: for the world hath become so
depraved that it cannot by any means grow worse, and
men walk in such evil ways that the times are portentous. The young are fain to put themselves on a
level with their elders, scholars with their teachers,
and Jurists with Theologians. All things are out of
joint, and heretics and mock Christians are springing

208

up—*Johann Reuchlin, Erasmus* of *Rotterdam,* one
Wilibald [56]—something or other—with *Ulrich Hutten,
Hermann Busch,* and *Jakob Wimpheling,* [57] who wrote
against the Augustinians, and *Sebastian Brant,* [58] who
wrote against the Dominicans—the pity of it! and
wantonly rails at them. Thereby many scandals arise
within the Faith, and I can well share your belief, for
I have read that such happenings will immediately
precede the Last Judgment. Moreover I will declare
to you somewhat else, to wit that I have heard (it was
told me as truth by a Father Superior) that Anti-
Christ hath been born, but is as yet a child. He told
me, too, that a revelation had been made to a certain
Carthusian Monk, who, as he was sleeping in his cell,
heard a voice from heaven crying, "The world shall
perish! The world shall perish! The world shall
perish!" Then the monk feared, and would fain have
spoken, but silently made supplication against the wiles
of the Devil. Then once more began the voice to cry
out—and yet again a third time. Then perceiving in
his heart that it was the voice of the Lord, he cried,
"Why, Lord?" and the voice answered, "By reason
of its sins." Then cried the Monk, "When, Lord?"
and the voice answered, "There are yet ten years."

Wherefore I go in great dread. When I passed
through *Bologna* I heard that there was a citizen
there who had a familiar Spirit called *Rilla:* and that
wondrous spirit speaketh to him concerning the King
of *France,* and the Emperor, and the Pope, and the
end of the world. I have read his prophecies. And
now, I have told you what I know, and commend you
to the Lord.

THE ROMAN CURIA.

LII

❦ *HEINRICH SCHLUNTZ* to
Magister Ortwin Gratius

ALL amity and humble duty to your excellence, first
and foremost, with my uttermost service to your
excellence, here and everywhere—in all honest places.

Reverend Herr Magister, herewith I send your excellence a notable and right profitable book. It seemeth to me that this book is most skilfully composed; it containeth very masterly propositions, and is named "Rationale Divinorum."[59] I bought it here, at the fair, for I said to myself, "That is the book for Magister *Ortwin!* The Lord be praised that I have lighted upon it! Now will I send it to him, just as he lately sent me *Johann Pfefferkorn's* work entitled 'Johann Pfefferkorn's Defence against Calumnies,' which he compiled in the intent that it should be a bulwark of the Holy Catholic Faith against *Johann Reuchlin* and his followers, and wherein he flouted them with many a shrewd gibe." But you may say, "Why doth this fellow send the book to me? Doth he think that I have not plenty of books myself?" I answer that such was far from my mind. If indeed you think that I was for this reason moved to send you this book, you do me an injustice, for I do but send it with fair intent. You must not believe that I disparage you in that you possess but few books, for I know that you have many. Indeed, when I was in your study at *Cologne* I could see well enough that you had a multitude of volumes, both great and small. Some were clad in wooden boards, and some in parchment bindings,—some were covered all over with leather, red and green and black, while some were half-bound. And there you sat, with a whisk in your hand, to flap away the dust from the bindings. "Pardy!" said I, "Magister *Ortwin*, you have full many a fair volume, and you hold them in high esteem." Then you replied that in this we might know whether a man were learned or not; for he that honoureth books, honoureth knowledge; and he that honoureth not books, honoureth not knowledge. And that saying I have laid up in my heart, and I will keep it there world without end. Amen.

NAUMBURG.

LIII

❦ *JOHANN SCHLUNTZIG to*
Mag. Ortwin Gratius

YOU have lately sent me a most vituperative letter, and you lay it to my charge that I tell you not how standeth the controversy, concerning the Faith, with *Johann Reuchlin*. When I read the letter I was very wrath, and said, "Wherefore writeth he to me in this fashion? Have I not sent him two letters in less than half a year! Is it my fault that the messengers have not delivered them?"

Believe steadfastly that I have related to you, precisely and word for word, all that hath come to my knowledge. But peradventure the messengers have not given you my letters. In particular did I inform you that when I was riding from *Florence* to *Rome* I overtook upon the road the reverend Father *Jakob van Hoogstraten*, Magister-noster, and Inquisitor of Heretical Pravity, coming from *Florence*, where he had been on business concerning your cause to the King of *France*. Thereupon taking off my hat, I said, "Reverend Father—are you, or are you not?" and he replied, "I am that I am." Then said I, "You are Herr Doctor *Jakob van Hoogstraten*, Inquisitor of Heretical Pravity." Quoth he, "Of the truth, I am." Thereupon I gave him my hand, saying, "Mein Gott! how cometh it that you walk afoot? It is a shame that such a man as you should walk on his feet through the mire and clay!" He made answer, "Some with chariots, and some with horses; but we come in the name of the Lord." Quoth I, "Yea, but now it raineth sorely, and it is bitter cold." Then lifted he up his hands towards heaven, saying, "Drop down, ye heavens, from above, and let the skies pour down righteousness!"

Then thought I within myself, "Pardy, is it not right pitiful that such a Magister-noster should be in these parlous straits? Two years ago I saw him enter

Rome with three horses, and now he goeth afoot."
Then said I to him, " Would you fain have my horse ? "
And he answered, riming :—

> " ' Willest thou have ? ' he need not say
> Who fain would freely give away."

Then said I, " Pardy ! Excellent Sir, there is a
vacant benefice awaiting me, and I must needs make
haste—else would I yield thee my steed," and thereupon I left him. So now you see how matters stand.
It is manifest that the Doctor is in great straits : procure money for him, therefore, or it will go ill with
the Cause.

Reuchlin's proctor—*Johann von der Wick*—worketh
zealously for him, and runneth hither and thither.
Lately he laid before the Court certain libels against
Magister-noster *Jakob*, so scandalous that I marvel the
Lord did not then and there smite him with plagues ;
moreover, he abused the aforesaid Magister-noster to
his face, saying, " I will bring it about, by the help of
the truth, that thou shalt perish in infamy, misery, and
sorrow, and *Johann Reuchlin* shall triumph : and this
all the Theologians shall behold, even though they
burst." It is manifest, therefore, that the aforesaid
Johann von der Wick putteth himself forward as the
enemy of all Theologians ; he is a woundily daring
man—and foolhardy beyond belief. I have heard that
Master *Jakob* said, " If it had not been for that fellow
I should have obtained judgment in my favour as soon
as I arrived at *Rome*."

And this is sooth ; for I have heard from others
that when Doctor *Jakob* first came to Court he was
so overbearing that all the Curialists were in dread of
him ; and none of the proctors would act for *Johann
Reuchlin*, for they all feared the Doctor ; and *Jakob
von Questenberg* sought in vain for a proctor throughout all *Rome*, and could find none—for they said that
in all else they would gladly serve him, but in a matter
of Faith they feared lest the Inquisitor *Jakob* might
inquisite them to the stake. In these circumstances
this Doctor—if he deserve such a title—*Johann von
der Wick*, came to *Jakob von Questenberg* and said,

"I am ready to oppose myself to this monk's fury."
Then Doctor *van Hoogstraten* openly threatened him,
saying, "I will make you repent ever having said one
word on *Reuchlin's* behalf." And I heard him declare,
with his own lips, at the time, that when he had
obtained judgment against *Reuchlin* he would instantly
proceed against Doctor *von der Wick*, and denounce
him as a heretic, inasmuch as he had collected certain
heretical propositions out of his words. But now all
is changed! Believe me, the business fareth but ill—
and you may now find anywhere ten upholders of
Reuchlin and not one of the Theologians.

Moreover upon a division after a disputation by
Theologians, eighteen were found to vote for *Reuchlin*,
and only seven for his accusers: nay, even those seven
did not declare that the *Augenspiegel* ought to be
burned, but spake with limitations.

Therefore I can hold out but little hope. You
must do all in your power to bring about *Johann
von der Wick's* death, for he it is that is the cause
of *Reuchlin's* ascendency, and the Theologians' decline.
Had it not been for him such things would never have
happened.

And now I trow I have acquitted myself so well
in letter-writing, that never again will you have grounds
for vituperating me. And so, farewell.

From the COURT OF ROME.

LIV

❦ *WILHELM BRIKOT to*
Mag. Ortwin Gratius

YOU entreat me for news without ceasing, and
albeit I write to you oft it availeth not: I will
therefore write to you yet once again, and pray that
this may suffice.

I have received a letter from the Roman Court
wherein it is related that your especial supporter,
Matthew Finck, is dead; and certain Curialists, his

compatriots, have desired me to write his epitaph. This I have done in manner following :—

> " Old Finck is dead — His cloak was red
> For him be said — A prayer, for he
> Full joyously — Right Corsic swilled,
> His belly filled — and piously
> Lived in true faith and charity."

There is one thing concerning which I would fain seek instruction from you, and that is in what manner I am to understand the Parisians in setting forth their opinion concerning the *Augenspiegel* to use these words, "Without reproach, however, to the writer himself, whom, by reason of his humble submission, and his other laudable writings, we regard as a true Catholic." I know not how this might be—that the *Augenspiegel* can be burned as a heretical work without shame to *Johann Reuchlin* who composed it, and still defendeth it. It is manifest that the workman, as the efficient cause, is more blameworthy than the work that he produceth. Moreover I would that the Doctors of *Louvain* had not boasted, in their letter to the Pope, that the opinion of the Parisians, and their condemnation of the *Augenspiegel*, brought them much spiritual delight; for his Holiness the Pope may think to himself; "Lo, I now perceive that all this is mere envy on the part of these Theologians; if they were true Theologians, nay, if they were Christians, they would have compassion over the misdeeds of a fellow-Christian rather than rejoice and exult over them." Mark me, this will greatly further *Johann Reuchlin's* cause, and folk will believe that out of envy he is persecuted: which however admitteth of no proof. For that adversary of ours—friend, I should say, in Christ—and the Philocapnions, that is "Sons of Johann Reuchlin," have done much hurt to *Johann Pfefferkorn*, who defendeth himself, and hath written but the truth; he desireth indeed, that he may die if he hath lied in the smallest particular. Nevertheless, as the Psalmist saith, "All men are liars." Nor should it be objected that *Johann Pfefferkorn* was habituated to villainy and crime from his youth—alas!—as he himself admitteth in his "Defence." For even though for a long time a man may be wicked and abandoned, nevertheless he may full well be rendered righteous again; and this is piously to be believed in the case of *Johann Pfefferkorn* who was regenerate by the grace of the Holy Spirit, by the mediation of baptism, and therefore now is upright—as I doubt not, and he will remain a Christian till the end of the world. It has likewise come to my knowledge that an infamous rumour everywhere spreadeth abroad concerning you; to wit, that you are the son of a priest, and are illegitimate. I marvel that those ribalds have no sense of shame, and are so bold. Have you not letters of legitimisation? I should cite the fellows who say such things. I pray you to have great diligence in the Cause of the Faith, so that that heretic may go to the gallows; and so farewell.

From WORMS.

LV

❧ *MAGISTER SYLVESTER GRICIUS to Mag. Ortwin Gratius*

INASMUCH as I have sworn an oath to defend my Faculty, and by all means to further its interests, I will therefore set down for you, in order, the names of all those who here stand by the Theologians and by *Johann Reuchlin*, respectively; so that you may lay them before the Theologians, and they may act accordingly.

First, there are certain fellows who sojourn at the sign of "The Crown," and who are ever deriding the Magister-nosters and brethren of the Order of Preachers, and have thus brought it about that no one at that inn giveth alms to a Dominican. I know the names of some of them. There is Magister *Philipp Keilbach*, who is continually singing *Reuchlin's* praises— and once Pastor *Peter Meyer* of *Frankfort* put him down finely; then there is one *Ulrich von Hutten*, an arrant brute, who once declared that if the Preach-

ing Friars insulted him as they have *Johann Reuchlin*
he would be their foe to some tune, and wherever he
came across a monk of that order he would lop off
his nose and his ears. The fellow hath many friends
at the Bishop's Court, who also take *Johann Reuchlin's* part. But now he hath departed for a year—
God be thanked—to be made Doctor. The Devil
fly away with him!

Then there are two brothers—sprigs of nobility—
Otto and *Philipp von Bock* — who gird at all the
Theologians. Once, during the solemn Act which
the Magister-nosters celebrated against the *Augenspiegel*, Magister *Jakob van Hoogstraten* by virtue
of his office granted indulgences to all those who
were present at the rite; and these same brothers
with other scoffers, in the presence of the Theologians
who were sitting in the Inn, cast dice for the indulgences.

Then there is a fellow, *Johann Huttich* by name,
who also is your enemy; and another, lately made
Doctor of Law, one *Conrad Weydmann*, who always
sideth with those who withstand you. There is a
Doctor, too, who was once an Artist—in the way of
the Moderns—who calleth himself *Eucharius*. Then
there are *Nikolaus Carbach*, who lectureth on Poetry;
and *Heinrich Brumann* who is Vicar at the Cathedral,
and a good organist: I am ever telling him to mind
his organ, and leave the Theologians in peace. But,
worst of all, the Canons are almost to a man on
Reuchlin's side — as well as many other Magisters
who hanker after Poetry but whose names I have
forgot.

And now I will tell you of your own friends and
supporters. You have here an ally who is a very
eminent man—Herr *Adular Schwann* by name; he
is of noble birth, and beareth a cup on his scutcheon:
his father was a bell-founder. He is a very subtle
disputant, after the school of the Scotists, and he
argueth profoundly, and averreth that he would put
down *Johann Reuchlin* in a crack if he might but
dispute with him. There is another very peculiar
prop of yours, named *Heinrich Han*—otherwise *Glock-*

enheintz, since he taketh great pleasure in bell-ringing.
He is a most skilful man, and hath a marvellous intellect; you would scarcely credit the profundity of
his genius.　He is ever ready for a disputation, and
when he argueth, he laugheth; and by his laughter
he putteth down his adversary.　When he saw *Johann
Reuchlin's* heretical theses he declared that on the
score of a single one of them *Reuchlin* ought to be
burned.

Next you can reckon amongst your company a
young nobleman and soldier, *Matthias von Falkenberg*
by name: he is a very warlike man, and goeth ever
armed as becometh a knight; he always sitteth on
the hither side of the board, and never behind it—
for, as he saith, it is not possible for one sitting behind
the table to leap up on a sudden and smite one's foes
if war should break out.　He is moreover a very subtle
disputant after the school of the ancients, and he declareth that if *Reuchlin* doth not yield, he will come
to your aid with a hundred horse.　Then there is a
burgher of *Mainz* named *Wigand von Solms*.　He is
but a youth, yet so learned that he is the equal of a
Magister-noster, and he saith that he would fain dispute with *Reuchlin* for ten florins.　A little while
ago he out-argued *Johann Huttich* so that he was
undone and could answer nothing.

Besides these there is also on your side *Herr
Wernher*, who is prodigiously well up in the
"Summa Thomae contra Gentiles" and knoweth
the "Formalitates" of *Duns Scotus* by rote—and
he saith that if Magister *van Hoogstraten* were not
already at the Curia he would go there himself and
settle *Johann Reuchlin.*　These allies of yours that
I have named, meet together once a week at the
house of the eminent Herr Magister-noster *Bartholomew*, who is chiefest of all your friends, and there
they discuss matters of mighty abstruseness.　They
oppose one another in turn, and one holdeth the
opinion of *Johann Reuchlin* while the rest argue
against him, and their disputes are very notable.

Of the others here who are on your side I have
no knowledge, for they are not of my acquaintance.

When I have knowledge, I will let you know. And now I commend you to God.

From MAINZ.

LVI

❦ *GILBERT PORRETONIUS, Master of Arts and Bachelor of Laws, to Magister Ortwin Gratius*

GREETING, and good-day to you, Reverend Sir. I have read the letter which you have sent me here at *Ingoldstadt*, and I wholly understand your meaning. You tell me that you rejoice that I, though a Theologian to begin with, now study the Law, for it is meet that some Theologians should be learned in the Law, that they may be able to dispute with the Jurists. Furthermore, you consult me concerning certain technical terms—as desiring to know what they signify, and you suspect that they appertain to matters juridical. You are right: they do.

I subjoin their significations, gathered from the glosses, and from *Accursius*.[60] You will hence perceive that I have laid a firm foundation in the study of Law. A *laticlave* is a title of dignity: or, it is a wand of metal that the tribune used to throw into the thickest of the enemy, and then all the other soldiers would fight furiously to recover the said wand. *Episto-graphum* is a wooden tablet on which debts are inscribed, as is done unto this day: it is so named from *opibus* and *graphia*—that is writing—as being a record of wealth. *Abaces* meaneth precious vessels. *Corinthia* meaneth vessels of common material, such as straw or reeds, which are sold at *Bologna*. *Balnea* is a shining vessel, or—so to say—"bajulans lucem, vel lancem." *Prothyrum* cometh from *thyros*—that is, master—but what it meaneth I know not: or, it is "quod procul trahitur," that which is brought from afar—as water to wit, or anything else, as the hydraulic engine in *Accursius'* own house. *Obsonatores* are they who guard their master when he is abed; or, those who are sonorous, and sing to their master at table. *Hypo-*

caustum is a place where sick folk stand when they need the fire. *Gallus gallinaceus* is a caponed cock, impotent, yet the more courageous in combat with the serpent. Or, he is named *Gallus gallinaceus* as being a lover of hens—as we call a man uxorious who is a lover of wives, witness *Horace* in his Odes. *Dieta* is a place at Court where the gentlemen stand by the fire. A *Chorus* is a multitude of slaves, singing to a certain instrument of music named a chorus.

Centumviri are senators, one hundred in number.

Patritius signifieth *pater principis*, the father of a prince: witness that place of *Sallust*, "O patres conscripti," for their names were inscribed either on their headgear, or elsewhere. Whenever you entertain a doubt in matters pertaining to Canon or Civil Law unfold them to me, and I will resolve them as fairly as *Johann Reuchlin*, or any other Jurist that is in the world.

And now—farewell.

INGOLSTADT.

LVII

❦ *GALEN OF PADERBORN* to *Mag.* *Ortwin Gratius greeting*

REVEREND Sir, a direful rumour hath reached me, and hath made the hairs of my head to stand upright. It is this: Almost all the clerics and students who have come hither from *Cologne* declare that there is a report that the Preaching Friars, rather than suffer *Johann Reuchlin* to get the better of them in the Cause of the Faith, will preach another religion. And it hath even been said that it is quite possible that if the Pope giveth judgment against them, they will hie them to *Bohemia* and stir up the heretics to disbelief in the Church and the Pope, and will thus be avenged of their wrongs. Oh, my good Herr *Ortwin*, counsel them that they act not thus, for it would be a dreadful heresy! Yet I trust 'tis a lying rumour. Nevertheless I have thought within myself, "Peradventure the Preachers utter these threats against the Pope, seeking to intimidate him, that he might say to himself, 'Lo, if

I pronounce not judgment in their favour, they will be held in sore contempt and laughed to scorn, and the whole world will be their enemy, and no man will give them alms, and their monasteries will be razed; and then they will depart to *Bohemia*, or even to *Turkey*, and preach, saying that Christianity is not the true faith—and this would be a great evil.'"

Be this as it may, I trust that you Theologians will have patience, and fly not in the face of the Pope, lest ye make all Christians your foes. Fare ye well, in the name of the only-begotten son of God.

BREMEN.

LVIII

❦ *MAGISTER IRUS PERLIRUS* to
Mag. Ortwin Gratius

GREETINGS in plenty, Reverend Sir.
Your writings against *Johann Reuchlin* have reached our University. The Senior Magisters praise them highly, but the greenhorn Juniors make light of them, saying that you do but assail *Reuchlin* out of envy. And when we took counsel as to whether we, too, should resolve somewhat against the *Augenspiegel* —these Juniors, who are still void of experience, held themselves opposed to the Seniors, and declared that *Reuchlin* is blameless, and that he hath never written aught that is heretical. And thus far they continue to withstand us, and I know not what the upshot will be. I believe the University will ere long perish because of these poets who abound marvellously.

Lately one hath come here calling himself *Peter* of the *Mosel*,[61] and he is a Grecian. There is also another who lectureth on Greek, *Richard Croke* by name, and he cometh from *England;* and just now I said, "Cometh he from *England?* The devil he doth! I believe that if there dwelt a Poet where the pepper groweth, he would straightway come to *Leipsic!*"

Hence it happeneth that the Magisters have so few students that it is pitiful. I remember that in days

gone by when a Magister went to the baths more pupils
would follow him than now go to the Church on a
Festival.   Moreover, students then were as decorous
as so many angels; but now they run wild, and pay
no heed to the Magisters; and they are all minded to
dwell in the Town, and to have their meals without
the Hostels, and the Magisters have very few boarders.
On the last degree-day only ten bachelors graduated;
and when we held the examination the Magisters had
some talk of rejecting certain candidates.   Then cried
I, " Heaven forbid ! for if we reject a single student,
hereafter not a soul will come forward for examination, or even study for the degree—they will all be
off to the poets."   And so we made shift to let them
pass.   We found grounds of dispensation under three
heads.   First, with regard to age : for it is ordained
that a graduating bachelor must be at least sixteen
years of age, and Magisters, twenty.   Yet, if they be
not of full age, a dispensation may be granted.

Secondly, there is dispensatory power in the matter
of conduct.   For if undergraduates have not shown
sufficient respect to Magisters and graduates, they must
be rejected—unless admitted by dispensation.   And
with this view inquiry is made concerning their tres-
passes; whether they have been uncivil in the streets,
or have consorted with harlots, or have borne arms, or
have thou'd a Magister or a priest, or have made a dis-
turbance at lecture, or in a hostel.   Thirdly, there is a
dispensation in Liberal Arts, when candidates are ill-
conversant with their subjects, and have not fulfilled
the prescribed conditions.   A little while ago, during
an examination, I asked such an one, " Tell me, how
cometh it that you answer nothing ? "   He replied that
it was because he was " so fearsome."   " Nay," said I,
" I trow that it is not so fearsome, but so dulsome, that
you are."   Then he cried, " Nay, by the Lord, Herr
Magister—I have store of knowledge within me, but it
won't come out ! "   Thereupon I gave him dispensation.

It is manifest, then, that the Universities will be
sore losers.   The other day I questioned a student
about some transgression—straightway he turned upon
me and thou'd me !   Then said I, " I will store that up

for degree-day," hinting that he might suffer rejection. But he snapped back, "To the jakes with you and your baccalauriate; I shall go to *Italy*, where teachers do not cheat their pupils, and have no such mummery when they make their bachelors. If a man is learned the honour is conferred on him—if unlearned, he is treated like any other ass."

Then said I, "Thou rascal! Wilt thou belittle the degree of Bachelor, that high dignity?" He answered that he thought but little even of Magisters—"And," quoth he, "a friend told me that when he was resident at *Bologna* he observed that all the Masters of Arts from *Germany* were inducted like freshmen; not so the mere students. For in *Italy* it is deemed a disgrace to hold the degree of Bachelor or Magister of a German University."

See to what a height these scandals grow! Would that all the Universities might join hands and make an end of all these poets and humanists who are their bane. Mag. *Langschneyder*, Mag. *Negelin*, Mag. *Kachelhofen*, Mag. *Arnold Wüstenfeldt*, and Dr. *Ochsenfurt* salute you. Farewell.

LEIPSIC.

LIX

❧ *JOHANN LÖFFELHOLZ sendeth greeting*
to Magister Ortwin Gratius

YOU desired me to inquire of the merchants who flock hither from all parts during the fair, concerning that complot you have heard of; to wit, the conspiracy entered into by sundry poets and jurists to defend *Johann Reuchlin*, and write against the Theologians of *Cologne* and the Dominicans, unless they forthwith leave the aforesaid *Johann Reuchlin* in peace.

You must know, therefore, that I made great diligence in inquiring and searching out, and at last I lighted upon a bookseller from the Oberland who told me many astonishing things. He named me sundry of

the conspirators, and said that he had seen the writings
that they send to one another.

In the first place he declared Doctor *Murner* to be
the head of the junto, and he assured me that this
fellow was the author of a book concerning the misdeeds of the Friars Preachers, and of another in defence
of *Reuchlin*. Then he mentioned *Hermann Busch*,
and said that he had seen a letter of his, in which he
promises his companions that he will not be backward,
but will stand up boldly for *Reuchlin*. Next he speci-
fied the Graf *von Neuenar*,[62] Canon of *Cologne*, as being
of the plot; this man hath concocted wondrous accusations against the Theologians, and they are shortly to
be published.

Then there is *Wilibald*—something or other—who,
I suppose, lives at *Nuremberg* ; he hath uttered many
threats ; declaring that he will send all the Theologers
packing with his writings. Then quoth I :—

"Qui moritur minis, Ille compulsabitur bombis ;"

that is to say :—

"Wer vom Drohen stirbt, dem soll man mit Fürzen zu
Grabe läuten."

"He who by empty threats is felled,
With airy bounces shall be knelled."

Then he named to me one *Eoban Hesse*, of *Erfurt*—
a young man, it seemeth, and a poet of great skill.
He hath a comrade, *Petreius Aperbach* by name, and the
twain are now composing certain books that they will
forthwith publish unless the Theologians make peace
with *Reuchlin*.

Then there is at *Leipsic* an Englishman—I know
not what his name may be, but I trow that it is he who
two years ago dwelt at *Cologne*—and he also is one of
them. Besides these, there is *Vadianus* at *Vienna*, who
is said to be a woundy great poet. At the Cardinal's
Court, too, there is one *Caspar Ursinus*,[63] who knoweth
how to make Greek verses, and hath promised *Reuchlin*
his aid : he is among the band.

The bookseller moreover told me that he had heard

that *Philipp Melanchthon*,[64] and *Jakob Wimpheling*, and *Beatus Rhenanus*, and *Nicolas Gerbellius*, were all of the plot.   He averred, moreover, that they write letters to *Ulrich Hutten*, who studieth at *Bologna*, seeking that he should join them.   Besides these he had heard of none.   Then I enquired in other quarters whether *Erasmus* of *Rotterdam* taketh their part ?   And a certain merchant answered, saying, " *Erasmus* taketh his own part ; but, be assured he will never be the friend of those Theologians and Friars ; and he hath evidently, in his words and writings, defended and vindicated *Johann Reuchlin* and hath addressed letters to the Pope on his behalf."

From others I learnt that *Paul Ricius* is also of the number.   Some say that *Johann Speisshammer* and *Konrad Peutinger*—who are in high favour with the Emperor—also consort with this crew, and do all in their power against the Theologians of *Cologne*, and in honour of *Johann Reuchlin*.   A certain student of *Erfurt*, a friend of mine, tells me that *Konrad Mutianus* is the bitterest of all, and that Theologians are so hateful to him that he cannot endure to hear those of *Cologne* as much as named ; he saith, too, that he hath seen full twenty letters of his, in which he urgeth certain students to join the Reuchlinists.

This is all the information I have gathered so far ; when I learn more, I will impart it to you.   Farewell in Christ.

FRANKFORT-ON-MAIN.

LX

❡ *MAG. WERNHER STOMPFF* to *Mag. Ortwin Gratius* greeting

SIR, I would have your magnificence to know, that when I received your letter I was affrighted beyond measure, my face mantled and the hair of my head stood up.   And I doubt whether I stood in greater dread in the Red Room at *Cologne* when I sought to be made Bachelor, and offered myself for examination ; for then I had grievous fears lest the Examiners should reject

me. You tell me that the Cause of the Faith fareth
ill at *Rome*. Gadzookers! what can we say? Those
Jurists and Poets will overthrow the whole faculty of
the Artists and Theologians; for even here, in our University, they would fain brow-beat the Magisters and
the Divines. A fellow here claimed of late that a
Bachelor of Law should take precedence of a Master
of Arts. Then quoth I, "That is impossible. I can
prove that Masters of Arts rank higher than Doctors
of Law. Doctors of Law are learned in one science
only—namely Jurisprudence; but Magisters are Masters
of the Seven Liberal Arts, and therefore are the more
learned. "Go to *Italy*," said he, "and tell them that
you are a Magister of *Leipsic*, and see how they will
bait you!" But I made answer that I could defend my
Mastership as well as any that cometh out of *Italy*. And
so I departed, thinking within myself that our faculty
is sorely maligned, and this is a crying shame. For it is
the Masters of Arts who should rule the Universities,
and now the Jurists claim to govern them, which is a
thing most indecent. But I bid you be of good cheer,
and call not in question the victory of the Cause of the
Faith. May the Lord provide for you. And now, fare
ye well—so long as *Pfefferkorn* abideth a Christian.

PRINCE'S COLLEGE, LEIPSIC.

LXI

❡ *PETER LIEB*, *Cursor in Grammar, and Professor of Logic, sendeth greeting to Magister
Ortwin Gratius*

REVEREND Herr Magister—two drinking-bouts
a day are the custom here at *Vorpech*, or *Vorharz*.
The first is called the Burgher-bout, which beginneth
at noon and is kept a-going till four or five of the clock:
the second is the Night- or After-bout; this beginneth
at five, and lasteth until eight, nine, or even ten of the
clock—nay, it is sometimes kept up till midnight or one
of the clock in the morning. Well-to-do folk, and the
burgomasters and the guildmasters, when they have sat
drinking long enough at the first bout, pay their scores

and go home; but the younger folk, and good fellows who care not much what the corn costs, sit long at the After-bout, and drink for dear life.

Now it happened that we were of late thus making merry, and there was with us Herr *Peter*, a friar of the Order of Preachers, who is mightily well disposed towards you by reason of *Jakob van Hoogstraten* the Inquisitor at *Cologne;* and between ten and eleven at night a warm dispute arose concerning the derivation of your name. I held the opinion that you were named after the Roman *Gracchi*. But Herr *Peter*, who is pretty well versed in humane letters, declared that this was unapt, and that you were named *Gratius* after the grace that cometh from on high.

Now there was a braggart there who spake very crinkly Latin, so that I could not understand half he said, and he declared that you were called *Gratius* neither from Grace nor *Gracchi;* and he spake such a deal of superfluous nothing that I asked him, saying, " Whence then cometh *Gratius?* Very learned men have held high dispute over the matter, and have determined that the name proceedeth either from *gratia* or *Gracchi*." Quoth he, " They who discussed the matter were friends of Magister *Ortwin Gratius*, and they therefore interpreted his name in a favourable sense, but their opinions do not affect the naked truth." Then said Herr *Peter*, " What is truth ? " and he thought that the fellow would hold his peace, as our Lord did when *Pilate* put this question to him. Yet he did not hold his peace, but continued, " There is a hangman in *Halberstadt*, Herr *Gratius* by name, and he is *Ortwin's* maternal uncle, so it is after him that *Ortwin* was named *Gratius*." Then I could not contain myself, and cried, " Fellow ! that is a vile outrage, and I protest against it ! Herr *Ortwin* must not let that pass: I know you say this out of envy, since you are at enmity with him. A child receiveth his name and surname from his father and not from his mother. Wherefore then hath this worthy Magister been named after his mother and his maternal uncle, and not after his father like other folk ? " Then he replied, speaking loudly so that all should hear, " What you say is true enough, but he cannot, in honour, mention his father, because his father is a priest, and if he were named after his father all folk would know that he was the son of a priest and a whore—and a bastard if ever there were one!" Then again I cried aloud, saying, " How can this thing be? Is he not a Magister of *Cologne?* Hath not the University a statute which declareth that no man may graduate unless he be legitimate? Therefore—" Then saith he, " Whether graduates must be legitimate or illegitimate, the fact remaineth that Magister *Ortwin* is a bastard, and a bastard he will remain world without end!" Then said I, " But what if the Pope hath perchance given him dispensation? Then he would be legitimate after all, and you would be in grievous error, speaking against the Church of *Rome!* " Then said he, " It matters not if he had a thousand dispensations —he would not be legitimate for all that."

Then he cited a case in point, " Take the case of a Jew baptised with the water of baptism: if the Holy Spirit be absent, the water profiteth nothing, and he is still a Jew. So it is with those bastards who are the sons of priests and whores—for priests cannot lawfully enter into wedlock with whores, and therefore a dispensation profiteth their children nothing." Then I asked him, saying, " What opinion holdest thou concerning Herr *Johann Pfefferkorn?* " And he answering said, " I firmly believe that he is still a Jew." And in reply to the citations made he further quoted Matthew iii., where it is written, " Unless a man be born again of water and of the spirit he shall not enter into eternal life." " And since," saith he, " *Pfefferkorn* was not born again of the Spirit, the water profiteth him nothing, and he will abide a Jew for ever." Then I could no longer answer him, and we arose, Herr *Peter* and I, and went home to bed. And now I hear that this reprobate boasteth himself that he hath overcome us in disputation, and is more learned than Herr *Peter* or myself. Wherefore I pray your worthiness to write and tell me how those arguments about dispensations and Herr *Johann Pfefferkorn's* baptism may best be met, and how this rascal may be hoist with his own petard.

May I deserve your favour all my life long. Farewell.

LXII

*❦ MAGISTER GRATIUS, Uprooter of Tares,
that is, Quarterer of Traitors, Scourger of Forgers
and Slanderers, Incinerator of Heretics, and much
besides, sendeth many salutations to Magister
Ortwin, his sister's son*

DEARLY-BELOVED nephew, and most Reverend
Herr Magister, inasmuch as many years have now
passed by since we set eyes on one another, it hath come
into my mind that it would be a good thing to send you
a letter. I hear marvellous tidings concerning you—
how that you are of high repute, and are known to all
who have even a scantling of learning, not only in
Cologne, but beyond *Elbe* and *Rhine*, and even throughout *Italy* and *France*.

It is the Colognese, however, who honour you most
for that singular learning displayed in your writings
in defence of the Catholic Faith against one *Johann
Reuchlin*, Doctor and secular poet, and they set such
store by you that when you walk in the streets they
point at you with their fingers and say, "There goeth
Magister *Ortwin* who trounces the poets!"

Methinks that if they but knew that you were my
nephew they would respect you yet more. For here I
too am of high renown, and I exercise my art amidst
great crowds of people; and folk honour me in like
manner, and when I walk in the streets they point
at me, as they do at you at *Cologne*. And I exult
greatly that folk thus think not a little of both you
and me.

I hear, too, that there are others in *Cologne* who are
friendly to you, and also write in opposition to Doctor
Reuchlin—to wit, *Jakob van Hoogstraten*, and Magister
Arnold von Tongern, Regent of *St. Lawrence* Hostel.
All men deem you three to be the true lights of the
Catholic Faith, and they look upon you as three great
candlesticks, or lanterns. There are some, indeed, who
add a fourth light, or, as it were, a hanging-lamp, which

doth not shine quite so brightly, to wit, Herr *Johann Pfefferkorn*.

And I verily believe that if you four, with all your knowledge, were bound together to a stout stake, in an exalted position, on a pile of dry wood, there might straightway be kindled a light of the world, brighter even than that which blazed at *Berne*. But, dearest nephew, all this is naught save a merry jest of mine, and—quips apart—I hope you four will become a true light of the world: it is impossible that such learning as yours can long remain sunk in the mire.

It hath come to my ears that not long ago you would fain have bussed, after dark, an old trot who selleth pots hard by the fountain at *Cologne*, but she lifted up her voice, and folk came around the house with lanterns, and discovered you. Pardy! I highly esteem such fine pranks of yours, for they smell of my art, which pointeth too in some sort at Theologians also.

There hath of late been a rumour here that a poet hath appeared in *Cologne*. He alone holdeth you for a fool, and calleth you *Porkwinus*—that is, meet dweller in a pig-sty. Pardy! if I could only scrape acquaintance with that same poet, right gladly would I hang him without fee!

And now, in conclusion, beloved nephew, I would earnestly beseech you to strive with great diligence to spread your renown throughout the whole earth, were it not that I well know such counsel to be needless. For this you well know of yourself, and have received it from your grandparents—ay, and from your great- and great-great- and great-great-great-grand-parents; and especially from your mother, my dearly-beloved sister, who had no sooner heard that bastards are ever more the favourites of fortune than the true-born, than she straightway betook herself to a priest, and let him work his will, that there might be begotten such a man as you, whom some day all the world shall hear of! Farewell.

From HALBERSTADT.

LXIII

❡ *JOHANN VON SCHWEINFURTH*, Master
of the Seven Liberal Arts, sendeth a thousand greet-
ings, and a few more, to the scientifical, learned, and
enlightened Ortwin Gratius, who masterly teacheth
the Greek and Latin tongues at Deventer[65]

PREMISING all honour and submissive respect due
to a teacher skilled in sundry branches of knowledge.
You wrote to me of late concerning your victory
gained at *Rome* over *Reuchlin*, who so temerariously
opposed you and *Johann Pfefferkorn* not long divinely
enlightened in the Christian Faith. You told me, too,
how that the Pope hath imposed silence upon him, for-
bidding him to write more, "lest a worse thing happen
to him," as saith our Lord in the Evangel. For formerly
in the *Augenspiegel* he wrote in a fashion so uncouth
that the Doctors could not understand him. Nevertheless they declared him a heretic—since it standeth not
in their books as he hath written, nor hath that new
theologian whom God raised from the stones to be
the child of *Abraham*, (as saith the scripture), *Johann
Pfefferkorn* to wit, knowledge thereof by divine vision
or revelation, or from the authentic intelligence of his
wife; and she, I have heard, hath also the spirit of prophecy. But of this you know much better than do I,
for you have ofttimes consorted with her when *Johann
Pfefferkorn* was not at home. I know not in what
manner *Reuchlin* was put down by you or by the Pope.
For now they have instituted a new faculty, besides the
four faculties we used to have; and they all praise
Reuchlin and call themselves his disciples; and they
pay no regard to the Faculty of Arts, for they say that
the Artsmen are so many conceited asses—and that
they can scarce speak three or four Latin words—and
that, shame to them! these beasts seduce many innocent youths, who after they have wasted a long time,
and are, as it were, immersed in this vile sink of barbarism, return to their homes, having learned nothing

save " Arguitur," " Respondetur," and " Quaeritur," and having for their Gods Tartaretus, and Versor, and Perversor, and Buridan and Bruxellensis and the like, differ not from the vulgar herd.[66]

Nevertheless it is a strange thing for a mere student —a greenhorn—to know more of *Aristotle* than a candidate for a Bachelor's or Master's degree, who hath attended the courses, and is fully qualified. Moreover they are not respectful to the Magisters, and when they meet one they fail to touch their caps, as would be seemly, and they are perpetually to be found at that house you well wot of. Moreover they never listen to the " Consequentias " of *Marsilius,* nor the " Suppositiones," nor the " Parva Logicalia " ; so that it is not possible that they should be duly trained to take part in disputations. But let this pass. I must now tell you some news : *Jacob Wimpheling,* who is half a Reuchlinist, hath been roundly taken to task by a certain Monk, *Paul Lang* by name, who hath told him plainly that he hath not written the truth in a book of his intituled " De Integritate "—to wit, in saying that learning is not only to be found beneath a cowl. For *Paul* the Monk wrote another book to refute this, which was approved by the Chapter, or Synod, of the Order of *St. Benedict* at *Reinhardtsbronn,* in the year of our Lord 1509. It is fine Latin, withal—almost as good as *Alexander's Doctrinale,* it hath been said; and I rejoice greatly that such Latin is to be found among monks. They say themselves that it superlatively excelleth the style of *Cicero*—but this I scarcely believe, for that striketh a high note. Nevertheless it argueth learnedly against *Wimpheling* in verse, and in prose, and in rime ; and it holdeth, rightly as I think, that all learning lieth under a cowl—that is, with the monks. For, to proceed from things small to great, the monks have written commentaries on grammatical rules, on *Donatus,*[67] on *Peter of Spain,* upon the Physics and the Metaphysics and the Ethics, and have thus submerged them in their comments, and have become masters of all knowledge.

Yet, by your favour, I would fain distinguish. First, with regard to the word " cowled," for that is an equivocal term. First, as applied to the Bohemians, who go about with long hoods down to their middles, and yet have no learning, but, rather, heresy. Secondly, as applied to the Jews, who also are cowled, and yet are ignorant, for they are without the pale of the Church. Thirdly, as applied to Magister-nosters, who are illuminated — but not in the highest degree. Fourthly, as applied to monks; and they have knowledge supereminent, as you have.

I beseech you, therefore, aid that monk—for you also are of his party, being cowled after the third fashion—that he may defend his writings against *Wimpheling*. For I hear that *Wimpheling* hath many followers, and those at *Strasburg* were lately named to me. There is one *Jakob Sturm*, a noble, who is said to be a good Latinist; and there is *Ottomar Nachtigall*, who knoweth Greek as well as *Reuchlin*, and can quote from the *Extra Decretum* and the Digests and likewise from the Bible—which is not to be wondered at, seeing that he studied at *Paris*. Then there are *Lucas Hackfurt* and *Johann Ruserus* and *Johann Witz* and many others, all of whom desire to aid *Wimpheling* against the monks and to trounce them with their writings. They all declare that *Paul* is unsound in his views, and hath deviated from the Rules of his Order in nine particulars, and that he is a mischievous windbag, as *Trithemius* himself hath averred in a letter to *Hieronymus Tungersheim* of *Ochsenfurt*—and that it is a great shame for anybody to waste paper and ink, and time too, as he hath done. They also declare that *St. Jerome* once wrote to a monk as followeth: "Never let the Psalter depart from your hand or from before your eyes;" yet if this were true the prohibition would be binding continually and for ever. And it would follow that monks ought to do nothing save read the Psalter. This I am sure is untrue, for *St. Jerome* himself was a monk, and would not write against them. I lately heard a woundy long rigmarole from a disciple of *Wimpheling*. I said boldly to his face, "Your master, *Wimpheling*, erreth greatly, who hath written in opposition to the Abbot *Trithemius*, and against the monks, who are notable both for their learning and

their sanctity, and mightily useful: the Church's only
pillars are the monks." Then quoth he, "I divide
monks into three classes. The first are holy and useful,
but they are in heaven. The second are neither profitable nor wholly useless—you will see them painted
in the churches. The third are still alive, and they are
mightily noxious and are by no means saints. They
are as vain-glorious as any laymen. They take delight
in storing up wealth and having fair ladies around
them. Not long ago I was at *Heidelberg;* now there
liveth near *Heidelberg* a great Abbot—a fat, surly
rascal—and he drove out all the monks from St.
Jacob's College, saying that he would brew fine broth
for them, and naught beside. But they said that
they believed that he acted thus—the good brother!—
because the Count Palatine was about to introduce
new methods, and that a Poet was coming to *Heidelberg* who would make the monks and other students
talk the new-fangled Latin. And so the fat Abbot
quickly perceived what the event of the jest would be;
and, quoth he, 'My monks must not learn the new
Latin, for then they would grow proud of knowing
more than I, and I should cut a fine figure among
them—like an overfed jackass in a rout of monkeys!'"

But of a truth this argument seemeth irregular, for
it lacketh a pair of premises and therefore reacheth no
conclusion.

I send you *Paul's* book, which you ought to have
printed, for it containeth a store of good things in
opposition to *Wimpheling* who assaileth the monks;
but he will change his tune when he readeth that
Christ was a monk—an Abbot, to wit—and *St. Peter* a
prior, and *Judas Iscariot* a cellarer, and *Philip* a porter,
and so of the rest according to *sub et supra;* all of
which this illuminated and learned monk *Paul Lang*
so masterly proveth, that *Wimpheling* and his disciples cannot open their lips against him. Yet a fautor
of *Wimpheling's* withstood me to my face, and swore
that the monks lied like so many scurvy tapsters
who would fain make out that Christ was therefore a
portentous animal—a cowled beast! And they cried
out against me in His name. Then was I sore afraid,

and fell into such a pickle that I savoured ill in the
nostrils of those who stood by. But, be this as it may,
I firmly believe that sooner or later they will all stand
dismayed by *Paul's* learning, and will say, " Of a truth
the Devil hath brought this monk against us : who else
can have instructed him thus canonically in all knowledge ? How can this be save by inspiration ? He
hath resided in no University, and is naught but a
mere bejan ; and nevertheless he is fit and more than
fit to graduate Master— by the leave of our illustrious
Magisters." *Thomas Murner*, himself a monk, and a
right subtle Doctor, once solemnly declared in the
pulpit that Christ our Lord was a monk—and power-
fully argued thereon. But one of *Wimpheling's* disciples declared that he would not believe in Christ if
he were a monk, and made the following verses :—

> " In Christ himself beneath a cowl—
> That cloak of guile—I'd not believe :
> Let the S. Francis feigned at Berne
> Show all how monkish wiles deceive ! "

What skills it if he believe not ? Then he will be
a heretic like the rest of them who were condemned,
with *Reuchlin*, by *Paris* and *Cologne* and the other
Universities.

Now I beseech you to imprint in the book the
verses that follow, which I have made in praise of
the book and its author *Paul Lang* the Monk. With
great labour have I composed them, for the most part
in the night-time when I lay in meditation on my bed,
for then in my dreams I became, so to say, a poet, as
you will now perceive :—

> " This book, which worthless Wimpheling boldly baits,
> Hath been by Paul miraculously wrought—
> Langius, we mean, who with poetic art
> And craft rhetorical hath soothly proved
> That every Science lurketh 'neath a cowl :
> Trithemius said the like, and Eberhard
> De Campis, Volzius (Paul), and Schurer too ;
> Johann von Miltenberg, and Jacob Si—
> Berti, and Roger who Sicamber hight—
> All learned men, and hooded monks withal.
> Now Jacob is o'erthrown, and crushed to earth
> With Wimpheling, Gerbelius, and Bebel,

> Sturmius and Spiegel, Nachtigall, and he
> Of Rhenus named; Ruserus, Sapidus,
> And Johann Guida, with Bathodius;
> All bite the dust, and dare not 'Cuckoo!' cry.
> And weltering thus, they have no leg to stand
> Upon; no Greek or Poet can they find
> Who dares to learned Langius answer make!"

Farewell, O man most illustrious, and mine own right learned teacher! Hold me, in return, within your heart, in that I thus perpetuate your fame world without end.

From the Imperial City of *Schnersheim*, in the High Street, where the swains make merry on a Sunday, when their hearts o'erflow. In the Year of the World one.

LXIV

⁅ *HERR VOLLWEIN VON GROSSFLA- SCHENBERG to the Reverend Magister Herr Ortwin Gratianus endless greetings*

REVEREND Sir, although, as it hath been told me, you know naught of secular Latin—for the which I highly esteem you—and you pay no heed to those high-sounding words that the poets delight in, nevertheless you know well enough where to lie a-night, as the Wise Man saith in his Proverbs.

And it is no great matter to us what those innovators in Latin do, such as *Erasmus* of *Rotterdam* and *Johann Reuchlin*, neither heed I them. It concerneth not the essence of Holy Scripture—even if they and the rest are ever ready to attack the old Theologians with that Literature of theirs. I know not how they presume to ever be mingling that heretical literature with the New Testament and the works of *St. Jerome*; notwithstanding that *Paul* saith that the Greeks are always liars, and hence it seems to me—saving our exalted Magisternosters' presence—that their literature is nothing else than a lie. Hearken now to my syllogism: whosoever desireth to overturn Holy Scripture with lies is a heretic; therefore—but they know well

enough what followeth, and it would be uncivil for me
to openly prove them to be heretics. Oh, if they but
knew the subtlety that I possess they would not shew
themselves before my face. But keep silence till the
end, and then it will be perceived in what key the tune
goeth.

No longer can I put off telling you the news.
Lately, I know not when, I sat at a feast, and there
were many vain-glorious youths present; and certain
folk from other parts joined in the symposium—one
from *England,* another from *Strasburg,* another from
Vienna, another (*Angelinus* by name) from *Wimpfen,*
another from *Rome,* who was well nigh half a Curialist;
and there was that mighty chatter of many mouths, that
you well wot of. At last we fell to discourse upon
that business of *Reuchlin's.* And one fellow set himself in opposition to me when he heard I was no good
Reuchlinist. Quoth he: "Let no Abecedarian Theologian from *Cologne* come across my path, else will I
geld him—Magister *Ortwin* in particular."

Thereupon, I held my peace. Then spake one who
was out at elbows, and who had failed in many an
attempt at the Curia to gain a benefice, and was at
loggerheads with most of the Curialists; and many a
strange thing he said, as followeth:

"By my soul, I have ofttimes marvelled that those
fellows in great hoods who call themselves Theologians,
and who abound in that city where are printed Questions
on Donatus according to the use of *St. Thomas,* and
Grammatical Rules according to the use of the
ancients, with this verse:

"'Accipias tanti doctoris dogmata sancti,'

why the monks, I say, who ever yearn to declare
others heretics, and stir us up against them, and hold
an inquisition concerning heretical pravity on them—
yet hold so many benefices, one, six; another, ten;
another, twenty or more; and heap up so much money,
and sideboards with bottles and goblets—as though
they were the sons of counts or princes—and keep
harlots or concubines within their doors at a great cost,
with chains on their necks, and rings on their fingers,

and mantles fit for the wives of knights. Sometimes one of them holdeth three Canonries at one and the same time, and putteth dues in his purse from all three; whence he is able to enjoy many a drinking bout. And yet he can stand in but one choir and not in the others. So in some choirs there is no canon, and no substitute to praise God and pray for the quick and the dead. Can this be right? Wherefore are they not inquisitioned, and asked before a cloud of notaries and witnesses—as of yore at *Mainz*—'What do you believe? Yes, or no? Do you believe, or do you not believe? What is your belief concerning the sacraments in the Church of God? Tell us, how many are the Sacraments? What do you believe in your heart concerning the Sacrament of the Eucharist? Are the body and blood of Christ present in it? If you believe this, why then after you have read mass— if, forsooth, you read it once in the year—do you go home, and consort with a concubine who hath the manners and aspect of a harlot, at the table or in your chamber? Tell us if you believe the fruit of the mass to be so great and so pleasing to God as that which abideth in the Decretals and the Tractates of the Theologians. Wherefore do ye hold so many benefices, enough to maintain five or six devout priests, who would joyfully read masses, and who with a willing heart would preach to the people and the clergy, and are able to give good counsel for the glory of God, the salvation of souls, and the liberty of the Church—who would chide evil-doers, and beseech God for our Lord the Pope, for the King, for the Bishops and other Christian folk—and offer that prayer for Peace and Prosperity that in the Low Mass standeth after the *Sanctus* and the *Te igitur clementissime Pater*? If you believe that so much good proceedeth from the Mass both to quick and dead, wherefore do you not give to others of your superfluities, and hand them over to other good, devout, and learned men—that God might hence be exalted and the souls of the dead might be the more speedily redeemed from the fires of Purgatory; and that the wrath of God against us might be stayed, so that he might no longer afflict us from on high with sore blains, nor smite our vines and our corn with hail and frost, so that the times of so great famine in the world should cease? If, on the other hand, ye do not believe these great benefits to flow from the Mass, then are ye, by the Lord, suspect of heresy; yea, ye are more assuredly heretics than *Wessalia* and Doctor *Reuchlin.*'"

Lo, Reverend Magister *Ortwin*, I have thought it well to tell you all this—that you may see how that all men hold themselves on *Reuchlin's* side against you. By my conscience I believe the Devil himself favoureth this *Reuchlin*, and we are finely bemired. And now I commend myself to you.

From *Speier*—where strange scandals are spread abroad concerning us; for all the Reuchlinists declare that the Colognese are naught but raw tyros. Nevertheless:—

> Of pride in you I have a heap,
> For you are patient as a sheep;
> And all revilings you endure
> Like simple priest in country cure.

LXV

℀ *MAGISTER BARTHEL KUTZ to the learned Master of unlawful Arts, Ortwin Gratianus, Theologian of Cologne*

RECEIVE my salutations, if you will, most learned Herr Magister *Ortwin*. Somebody, once on a time, told me, in some place or other, that you were very sick, and that when you are sick you always demean yourself as though you were crazy. This I commend in you, for it suiteth well with one who hath skill in unlawful arts—to wit how to conjure the devil into a glass, or elsewhere—for such are, almost without exception, ofttimes crazy. It is meet too that all such should likewise be bastards—and that you are one was told me by a dear friend—for they are the better tools wherewith the devil can work for his ends.

The devil, forsooth, doth not yield himself so readily

to the legitimate as to bastards, who are peculiarly
fitted for him. And if only you were a monk you
would possess every qualification for this art, and you
would be an egregious instrument of the devil—but I
know not whether you are a monk. If such you be,
then I should be right glad. Monks above all men
have this gift—that they are very obstinate, and whatever they take in hand that they carry through—as I
lately heard from one *Paul Lang* who has written
a most excellent treatise, with verses, against *Jacob
Wimpheling* and has flouted him finely. They say of
that same *Paul*—saving your reverence—that he has
run out of the cloister in nine diverse ways.

And what none else attempteth to do, he doeth. I
believe too that he is crazy at times, and is base-born.
The third condition abideth in him. I rejoice greatly
that he also resembleth you who have dealings with
the devil—but, let this pass, with all respect. I have
here a notable necromantic formula that I would gladly
communicate to you openly—but I am afraid lest when
you are crazy your servant may find this letter and read
it, and then the devil would fetch both him and me.
Therefore I will proceed according to my wont, for
when I deal with secret matters I write upon paper
without ink, and then none save a bastard can read it,
and this I have determined to do in the present case.
The formula runneth thus :—

,   :

,   ,
                          !

You, I know, will understand this, and it is the very
truth, but I warn you, and conjure you by the virtue
of all the forbidden Sciences not to impart it to a single
soul. And now farewell; from *Ruprechtsau:* in a
little while you may expect somewhat more, and
weightier, from me if you relish these presents.

LXVI

❦ *MAGISTER ABRAM ISAAK, of the stem of Aminadab, sendeth greeting to Magister Ortwin Gratius*

EXALTED Master of Arts good and evil; may it please your worship to know that I will now fulfil the promise that I promised at your instance, when I departed from *Cologne*—namely, that I would fail not to send you all the news.

Before all things you were desirous that I should notify you concerning that crafty Jurist, *Johann Reuchlin*, with whom Doctor *Jakob van Hoogstraten* hath sharp contention concerning the Faith at the Roman Court. All these matters will I unfold, out of the love that I bear you.

In the first place, then—to relate all things from the foundation of the world—you must know that having set out for *Rome* in the dog-days, as you will remember, I met with no great misadventure on the way, save exceeding great thirst when I traversed the lofty mountains of *Allgäu* with my comrades.

When I reached *Rome* I engaged myself as varlet to a Cardinal, hard by the *Campo dei Fiori;* him I served with great diligence for eight months, to gain a cure of souls at *Kelbertzhausen* in the diocese of *Vollenberg*. Now, with this object, I obtained a brief with the seals of twelve Cardinals, and his Holiness prefixed his own seal for the firmer security. Thereupon with great joy I set forth to take possession —when, lo! the Incumbent was not dead after all! Then cried I in great wrath, "A thousand devils fly away with him! Am I to lose my money?" 'Twas a mighty poor prebend, too. An I had known this, I would never have left *Rome*. I reckoned that it might bring me in good twenty gulden every year. You well know that I should not think of residing in such a place. I would far rather have a prebend near home at *Deventer* of a hundred gulden, with a simple handmaid of twelve, than one of thirty gulden up

the country with a shrewish gammer of sixty.   But it is
a sinecure benefice that would suit me best of all.

Now I must tell you in the next place, Herr *Ortwin*,
that I could not get back immediately to *Rome* by
reason of the war in *Italy:* naked scoundrels were
running about in every direction; and if one of them
had taken my clothes, then should I have lost all my
poverty, as the old woman said when she broke her
eggs on *Heilbronn* bridge.   So it came to pass that
I abode for two months at *Wimpfen-am-Thal* with
some jolly fellows from *Rome*.   And there I learned
a game of *Johann Grayfer*—who is mighty liberal,
for he once gave six comrades, whereof I was one,
seven eggs to eat, and no fewer.   This game is named
in the Italian tongue *Trent uno*.   I never saw it
at *Rome*, but this is in no wise strange, for I had
always to be dancing attendance on the mule in the
stables.

You shall hear how we spent our time: We often
went to *Wimpfcn-am-Berge*, where the best of good
fellows foregather.   There was one among them,
Gregory Spiegel by name, who is a great authority
de modo supponendi.   He expoundeth this as clearly
as you were wont to unfold Alexander's Third Part,
concerning Versification.

So liberally spake he concerning that matter that
carnal stings assailed me.   Much did I learn from him
—saving your presence, 'tis but Nature's province.   I
would give, pardy! a carlin for you to master such
amicabilities, if it were but on account of Frau *Pfefferkorn*, since I well know she affecteth you above all
the Theologians of *Cologne*.   In good sooth, that Art
which you once showed me in a little book written
backwards is of no avail.

But to proceed; they once asked me over the wine
—seeing that I was from the Curia—how matters stood
in the Cause of the Faith between *Johann Reuchlin*
and the Colognese.   Quoth I, " I fear me greatly that
Johann Reuchlin, good man, is too poor to bring the
case to an end.   The Preachers can go further with
their sacks of cheese than a lone man with his money."
Then said one: " Sonty !   What villains are those

same cheese-collecting monks! Not long ago Brother
N., of the monastery here, came to my cottage, and
would fain have forced my sister. He pursued her
up the steps into the house, and threw her down, and
would have worked his will, but my sister cried 'Herr
N.! Herr N.! desist, or I will scream that all the
world shall hear, and then will the Devil shend you.'
'Body o' me!' cried he, 'Cry not out, and I will
give you handsel, if it cost me half a gulden!' Then
came her mother, and he stinted. (His foiled fury!
dangerous as a harrow-tine under a clout!)." Then
said another who sat near, "If the cullion had treated
my sister thus, I would have stoned him, and sent the
other monks pickled cod for feast-day." Then replied
the other: "Pardy! I can forgive them, for they are
ever cloistered. I trow an ass with a kirtle on would
scarce find security—how then a wench?" Another
straightway sware that *Johann Reuchlin* was minded
to put down in a book all the evil deeds of the monks
throughout *Germany*. This he will present to his
Holiness with these words: "Wherefore doth not
Hoogstraten cast out this licentiousness from among
his brethren?" The fellow would have it, too, that
monks savour like sweating he-goats, and that in his
country they have tainted all the trulls, so that upon
occasion he might believe a cowl was at hand, by reason
of that odour of sanctity.

Now you, Magister *Ortwin*, are their fautor: Take
heed lest, to mend matters, there be added to the
Inquisitor of Heretical Pravity, an Inquisitor of Libi-
dinous Depravity. Let them at all events work their
iniquities privily in their cells, like their betters, where
none can see; all might then go well, but open vice
is a scandal to the whole Order. Beware lest evil come
upon you.

After all, I have again betaken myself to the Court,
and await Heaven's favour. Farewell.

From ROME: in the Refectory of the Chapter-House.

LXVII

❡ *BROTHER NOLLERIUS STECH of Calabria to Magister Ortwin Gratius*

MY devout prayers I desire you, by way of greeting. Your Theological Excellency knoweth that I am as it were a pilgrim from Mount *Sinai*—but you know not of the ills that I have suffered since I departed from you at *Cologne*. Though it would be tedious to tell you all, yet have I no other friend remaining to me to whom I may pour forth my woes, save you.

When I open my lips in the monastery they forthwith cry, "A pretty monk art thou, who desirest to lead an easy life!" As for the ungodly, it is not so with them. I cannot guess what may be the root of it all, unless it be the ill-fortune of Doctor *Jakob van Hoogstraten* in consuming so large a sum of money in the Roman Curia on behalf of the Christian Faith that *Johann Reuchlin* the worthless hath overthrown in his *Augenspiegel.* All our monasteries, I trow, ought to send him money, for he must needs be liberal and give bribes at large to the Cardinals, that they may give judgment in his favour, and not for *Johann Reuchlin.* Hence it cometh that the Superiors abate our wine, notwithstanding that *Solomon* saith in Proverbs xii. 1, "Song, woman, and wine rejoice the heart of man!" As for song, I am for ever at it—chanting and howling Psalms in the Choir, so that it hath neither grown rare nor precious. Concerning women, it is a grief for me to speak, for I never see any, save when I go to market with our steward to buy eggs. Even when I go to the villages round about to collect turnips and greens, and the flesh assaileth me with a wench hard by, she will have naught to do with me. Now therefore that our wine is minished, what solace is left us? Would that we had but one half of the comforts of life enjoyed by other orders—or by the priests with us who are vowed to the Holy Ghost.[68] With this order, I think, you are well acquainted; they wear a double white cross on their habit, and are not all shaven and shorn as we are; and when any relaxation is taken away from them—for instance, if their wine be docked for some transgression —then have they other solace, for they can procure doxies by the aid of lame *Johann* the wood-cutter who crawleth on his hands and knees. You may say, " Such a dissolute life is not permitted to the Sanctispirituales." But I tell you that I have heard for sooth that their Superior—who, though old, lame, grey, and blear-eyed, is nevertheless avid in that matter, but not always the man he was—is wont to keep a laced-mutton in his study; and when he casteth her aside he provideth her with a husband, and giveth her a good dowry out of the treasury of the Holy Spirit, which never runneth low, for it abideth by the mere grace of the Spirit. Then he getteth another wench and doeth as I have said, and thus the order increaseth and multiplieth in secret. And now will I cite a proverb: " Whensoever the Abbot—that is the Father Superior—throweth the dice, the friars can play." That is, since our old prelates are so licentious, and lead such loose lives, it followeth that we underlings may imitate them. This is a sound conclusion, for I have seen in a tractate " De Suppositionibus" that " Prelatus supponit personaliter," but, according to *Marsilius*, " Supponit inferius materialiter." And now to the main point: I would that if Doctor *Jakob van Hoogstraten* cannot win his cause against *Johann Reuchlin*, he would obtain for us a milder Rule, such as that aforesaid. For the flesh will be served, and I know full well that my days will be short in the land if I may not at some time or other cast out the old leaven that I have derived from those cheeses. Pardon me in that I speak to you cordially, that is out of my inmost heart. I am ever in dread lest that Cause should have a bad end—as did the Cause at *Berne*. You well know what I mean.

Herr Magister-noster *Johann Eimerich* desireth you many greetings. He hath become a very holy man. He is now our preacher, and everybody praiseth him. He is mighty fine at signs and symbols: in the year of Our Lord 1516 he preached on the Passion, and he took with him a staff into the pulpit, and when he read

Pilate's sentence he drew forth the staff from his cowl, and brake it in halves, as though it were a judge's wand.   It was a dreadful sight to behold, and the old women wept as bitterly as did *Peter* when he heard the cock crow near the fire.   Farewell, and commend me to the Doctor when he returneth from *Rome.*

LXVIII

❡ *JOHANN TEXTORIS sendeth his own Peter Schwinkoncius as many greetings as there are drops in the sea, and atoms in the sun*

I MUST tell you, dearly beloved friend, that I have received a letter in the which you write to me concerning *Erasmus* of *Rotterdam,* desiring to learn what I think of him.

Now, you must know of a truth that in the days of my youth I read many works in humane letters—and as for *Stephanus Fliscus,* and the Graecist, and *Sinthen,* and the *Facetus,* and the *Floretus,* and those ancient poets—I knew them all by rote, at my fingers' ends—and in proof thereof I compiled a book styled " Florista," in the which you may discern my learning and much else—if I desired to make boast thereof.   I tell you this merely that you may not think I lie, and to show you that I am well able to judge concerning this *Erasmus* I have also examined *Reuchlin's Augenspiegel,* and his *Gabala,* as you are aware.

Now, not to be tedious, I avouch that I have no good opinion of *Erasmus.*   He is an enemy of the monks: he speaketh much ill of them; he saith they are clumsy jackasses, who hate polite letters, and they can do naught save guzzle, and swill, and mumble psalms.

Yet he lieth in his throat when he saith these things. He himself is the jackass.   He is a sound Latinist, and writeth fair Latin—but he knoweth naught else.   He hath written many books—notably the *Ship of Fools* and a commentary on *Jerome*—and in these he doeth

naught but belabour the Regulars. I warn him, pardy,
that if he refrain not his hands from them we will do
to him as to *Reuchlin*, though he were in a hundred
ways favoured by the Pope and King *Charles*. We
have seen many men as arrogant as he, and yet we
have suppressed them.

I will tell you somewhat—but blab not thereof, or
the devil may confound me. Doctor *Jacob van Hoogstraten* and all the Doctors in *Cologne* and *Cambridge* are
now examining his commentary on *Jerome*, and I hear
it will go woundily hard with him. I would not stand
in his shoes for a hundred florins, for they say that he
hath sowed many tares there, thinking that no one
would mark it. But the Divines are not such fools
as that—they know well enough where the snake lurks
in the grass, as *Alexander* hath it. I cannot call to
mind all that they found, but I remember somewhat;
he declareth that Saint *Jerome* was not a Cardinal—
and this is high treason; he is heterodox concerning
St. George and *St. Christopher*, and relics of Saints,
and candles, and the Sacraments of Confession; moreover in many passages he speaketh blasphemy, inasmuch as he speaketh against the Holy Doctor and the
Subtle Doctor. He declareth that their Theology is
nothing worth. Now all these things the Magisters
have collected into a volume, and they will undo him
as they did *Johann Wessalia* in *Mainz*. And if he
barketh at them, and writeth invectives against them,
they will wait till he is dead, and then they will condemn all his works; this, forsooth, is the Magisters'
design.

As you ever joy in hearing the news, I must tell
you that the Minorites now have a General of Observance, a privilege that they purchased from *Rome* for
sixteen thousand ducats. The nuns of *St. Clara*, of
the Minorite Order, are in parlous fear lest they should
be reformed, and they have fled into the country and
lie miserably on bare boards. Some say that Dr.
Murner hath had to do with them—but this cannot be
true, for he is an emasculate capon. But of other
Regulars I have my doubts, since they thus pursue
them. A curialist hath just died in the country who

held twenty-two fat livings, and the Poets thereabouts have composed many verses concerning him. This is all I know—except that may the Lord preserve you until a man can outrun a hound. Farewell.

From STRASBURG.

LXIX

⁌ *MARKULPH SCHULZ* to *Johann Bimperlebumpum of Rorbach*

SALUTATIONS infinite and eternal. Beloved *Johann*, you lately sent me news that was but ill hearing—to wit that *Johann Reuchlin* hath gained for himself great renown among those Poets of his by writing a book intituled "Gabellistica," or "Gabala," and that he is in high favour with the Pope. I would fain know what "Gabala" may mean, but though I have long sought for it in my *Catholicon* and *Gemma Gemmarum*, as well as in *Briton*, I cannot discover its signification. I addressed a letter thereon to Magister *Ortwin*, but he hath sent no reply. Nevertheless the Divines have held a great council, and have examined that book, and—as I heard from them at a rouse one night, when we drank so deep that each had to pay three groschen for his shot, and I had no more money in my fob—it will of a surety go ill with him : for in that book he hath set down certain passages in opposition to the Holy Doctor and his disciples, and he saith that the son of God is made of the Father. It containeth much else, and perverteth the Theological terms "beget" and "make," and others likewise ; and it payeth no heed to the arguments and questions and sophisms of the Holy Doctor. Therefore are they resolved to burn that book—because they declare they cannot understand it, and what they do not understand, that they burn. Q.E.D.

For every Doctor of Theology is a rabbi and a light of the World.

The book moreover containeth many sayings of *Pythagoras*, who was a necromancer ; but necromancy

is an unlawful art—as saith LXVI, Quest. X, Chap. O,
and in the Canon beginning "O ye asses!" and the
Holy Doctor agreeth therewith—as well as *Aristotle*
in the Ninth of his Physics, "Of Ignorance." There
is moreover in the book much Hebrew, which the
Divines cannot read, and much Greek; but inasmuch
as they pay no heed to vanities such as these, but medi-
tate on higher things, they have appointed *Johann
Pfefferkorn*—Christian, yet half Hebrew, for he is oft
ebrious—to examine it, lest mayhap poison should lurk
beneath the honey.

But of this anon, for we shall know all about it
come *Frankfort* fair, and then we can discuss these
matters with Doctor *Ortwin*, who goeth thither, as the
emissary of the Divines, to buy any new books exposed
for sale there, that they may examine them.

I have none other news to tell you, save that a
Doctor of the Order of Preachers in Strasburg, who
was always called Doctor *Jesus*,[69] hath fled from the
Convent, and many evil things are said concerning him
of which I dare not speak, and many scurrilous scrib-
blers write verses to vilify him, and drop them in the
market-place and in the church. This disquieteth me;
would that they would refrain themselves, lest they
fall into disfavour with the Preachers. Amongst
others, I picked up the lampoon following:—

> "Thief, slanderer, sink of crimes unspeakable—
> Worthy of life-long fetters, or the stake—
> Hater of pious priests, effeminate,
> Thy coward soul doth e'en in exile quake.
> A holy abbess victim of thy snares—
> Satan's best tool a monk doth ever make!"

See, now, what these gallows-birds are doing! They
have respect for no man, and by the Lord, the cause of
this is none other—"non facit hoc aliud," as *Alexander*
very truly putteth it—than that evil habit of theirs of
writing and making verses concerning everything that
happeneth at *Strasburg*. Anon I will write to you
more fully concerning this matter.

From SCHLETTSTADT.

LXX ⁷⁰

❦ *MAGISTER HÄMMERLEIN, in Paradise, without flowers of Rhetoric, to the world-renowned Mag. Ortwin Gratius, Champion of Barbarism and Mouthpiece of Cologne, who brayeth after the manner of a jackass against Poets and Scholars, and Greeks whose tongue he knoweth not*

SUCH wondrous boasts and such soaring scurrilities, Herr *Ortwin*, have I never heard in my whole life as those put forth by yourself and the Doctors of *Cologne*—saving your presence—against that most honourable and learned of men, Herr *Johann Reuchlin*. Nevertheless when I heard thereof great wonder possessed me—seeing that you are all double-headed asses, and natural philosophers, to wit born fools, "zwanzig zentner über einen tollen Fantasten"—that you strive so meanly and so scurvily to assail men so pious and learned. Moreover I marvelled greatly who taught you so craftily to pervert and falsify the pious opinions of such an upright man. At last I concluded in my mind that it could be none other than one sprung from the seed of *Judas*—like father like son—and of such is *Johann Pfefferkorn*. Small wonder that ye are all friends of this man, for "birds of a feather flock together."

To the gallows then with you all, to a man, whither the hangman and his men will hale you, while you howl "Pray for us!" Now inasmuch as all these my words are very sooth, I address them to you privately and especially, and you may impart them to the rest who sit with you in the seat of the scornful, as saith the Psalmist. But let not these matters be published abroad, lest all the righteous discern what manner of men ye are.

Nevertheless, by all the saints! a great dread falleth upon me; a fear lest the printer hath stolen a copy of my letter—for, if this be so, God help you! Then I can in no wise hinder it. Yet will I give you good counsel. Down on your marrow-bones, and pray without ceasing for eight days, and invoke, fasting, St. *Helena* who recovered the true cross. In like manner may I recover that letter. Then once more will you abide in security.

Lo, all these things have I done out of brotherly love toward you—for we are brothers all. Farewell.

From *Heidelberg*; at the house of the Lame Man at *Leipsic*, who heedeth not though a man's nose be shut in the postern. Would that you were with him. You would have no need of spectacles, for 'tis said he supplieth them without charge.

SELECTED NOTES

Part I
(*pages 5-100*)

[1] An Inception banquet given by the newly made Masters to the other graduates. The Statutes of the University of Leipsic contain several references to this festivity. For a sumptuary ordinance issued in 1496, regulating the quality and quantity of the viands and wines, see *Die Statutenbücher der Univ. Leipzig,* Leipsic, 1861, p. 25. The junior students seem to have been in the habit of intercepting "cibaria et potagia" while being conveyed to the table; and a warning to the undergraduates against interfering with the attendants was issued in 1534.

[2] An ignorant Carmelite monk, of whom H. Cornelius Agrippa wrote: "Of like clay they moulded another instrument; an untaught illiterate fellow—crafty and adroit withal, and therein the fitter for their machinations—a certain Carmelite monk, who, merely because he was useful in spreading those calumnies of theirs against Reuchlin that all Christendom wots of, the Cologne Divines rewarded with a Theologian's crown (Theologica sua aureola remunerarunt)." *Epp.* vii. 26.

[3] Legate, not of the Univ., but of the Theological Faculty only. H. Glareanus, in 1514, assures Reuchlin that the University, as a whole, was not in opposition to him—"unless the theologians constitute the University." *Epp. Ill. Vir. ad Reuchl.*

[4] A follower of Duns Scotus; as opposed to follower of Thomas Aquinas.

[5] Andreas Epistates, or Delicianus, was rector of the University of Leipsic in 1513 and 1519.

[6] The four "nations" at Leipsic University were usually known as the Bavarian, the Polish, the Saxon, and the Misnian. See Rashdall, *Univ. of Eur. in the Mid. Ages,* ii. 256.

[7] Of Arnold von Tongern, apart from his connection with the Reuchlin controversy, we know but little. Variously known as Arnoldus Luydius, A. Tungris (Tungaris, Thungaris), he was born at, or near, Tongres, in what is now the Belgian province of Limbourg. In 1494 he became Dean of the Faculty of Arts at Cologne, and held a prebend at the Cathedral, which he resigned on being presented to one at Liège by his patron, and former pupil, the bishop of the latter see. The derisive attacks made upon von Tongern in the E. O. V. are bitter and unscrupulous. He died at Liège, 1540, and was buried in the Cathedral, where his epitaph may still be read.

[8] It was not until the XIIth Cent. that a serious attempt was made to distinguish mortal from venial sins, but thenceforward the Schoolmen exercised a vast amount of ingenuity with reference to the matter. Thomas of Walden, in re-

sponse to Wiclif's challenge upon the subject, said, "Nothing is clearer than the difference between them, nothing more obscure than the line of demarcation." While to those who held that "an infinity of venial sins did not amount to a single mortal sin," it was clearly of the utmost importance to distinguish them accurately, insuperable difficulties arose, not only from diversities of classification on the part of authorities, but also from the incalculable effects of extenuating, or aggravating, circumstances in removing a sin from one category to the other. For an exhaustive historical account of the whole question, see H. C. Lea, *Hist. of Auric. Conf. and Indulgences,* vol. i.

[9] "Reserved cases" were sins for which the parish priest had no right to grant absolution, and were ranked as "episcopal" or "papal" when reserved to the bishop or the Holy See respectively. St. Antonino, *Confessionale* (1450), gives a list of thirty-six papal reserved cases and fifty-seven episcopal, thus leaving very few for the priest.

[10] The Jews had been obliged, throughout Western Europe, to wear a distinctive garb or badge since the XIIth Cent.

[11] The grievance that Jews were permitted to dress like Doctors of Divinity was an old one. In 1248 we are told that "the Jews of the diocese of Maguelonne [near Montpellier] and the surrounding districts affect large round capes after the fashion of the priests, so that it often happens that travellers and strangers pay them the respect due to clerics." *Reg. d'Inn. IV.,* ed. Berger, No. 4123. John Evelyn, *Diary,* May 6, 1645, relates a closely parallel mischance that befell a dignitary of the Church: "The Jewes in Rome wore red hatts till the Cardinal of Lions, being short-sighted, lately saluted one of them, thinking him to be a cardinal, as he passed by his coach;

on which an order was made that they should use only the yellow colour."

[12] The Commentary upon the first and second parts of the *Doctrinale* of Alexander Grammaticus. This dreary treatise on Latin grammar comprises 2645 lines of doggerel verse. Its popularity was extraordinary.

[13] Luther's friend, Frederick the Wise, Elector of Saxony.

[14] *i.e.* Ulrich von Hutten.

[15] Peter Meyer, or Mayer, was *plebanus* (parish priest) of St. Bartholomew's, Frankfort-on-Main: a bitter opponent of Reuchlin and the humanists. Ever at strife with his fellow-citizens, he seems to have made Frankfort too hot to hold him, and in 1525 left it, never to return.

[16] Peter the Lombard, one of the greatest of the Schoolmen, was born at Lumelogno, near Novara, in Lombardy, about 1100 A.D. The fame of his *Sententiarum Libri IV.* led to his being usually styled the Master of the Sentences. This "Book of Sentences" is a classified collection of opinions of the Fathers on various doctrinal points, with objections and replies from other authors also. Innumerable commentaries on this work appeared (more than 150 in England alone) from the XIIth Cent. down to the Reformation. Among the commentators appear such great names as Albertus Magnus, Alexander of Hales, Duns Scotus, William of Occam, and Thomas Aquinas. Peter the Lombard became Bishop of Paris A.D. 1159, and died in the following year.

[17] "If I am not mistaken, he was a native of Verulum (Veroli) in the Campania di Roma. . . . He flourished towards the end of the XVth Cent. His commentary upon Lucan's *Pharsalia* was pretty good for the time. La Croix du Maine . . . calls him John Sulpitius of S. Alban."

[18] Heinrich Quentel, or Quentell,

252

a native of Strasburg, set up a printing-press at Cologne about 1479, and upon his death in 1503 the business was carried on by his heirs, where the Hôtel du Dôme now stands. Ortwin Gratius acted as editor and corrector of the press to the firm for several years.

[19] Valentin von Engelhard, Canon of Cologne and Rector of the Univ. in 1503. He was nicknamed the "fox-hunter," or "student-trapper," in consequence of the assiduity with which he sought students for his hostel.

[20] Karl Mennicken (Carolus Virulus). He was author of a very popular, if inept, treatise on letter-writing," "Epistolae Karoli."

[21] *a poena et a culpa: culpa,* the guilt; *poena,* the penalty still to be undergone when the guilt had been pardoned. The strictly orthodox view always had been that the guilt is pardoned by the Sacrament, while the indulgence remits only the temporal penalty. But for ages the popular belief was that plenary indulgences absolved *a culpa et poena.*

[22] Zwickau, a city of Saxony, about 80 miles SW. of Dresden. In 1520 Thomas Münzer was appointed pastor there, and put himself at the head of a band of frenzied fanatics known as the prophets of Zwickau. Hence originated the worst follies and abominations of Anabaptism, culminating in the establishment of the New Zion at Münster, and the ruthless suppression of the mania by armed force in 1535.

[23] Under the name of *cullagium* there is abundant evidence to show that throughout the Middle Ages a tax was exacted from priests in return for permission to keep what was euphemistically termed a *focaria,* or fireside companion. Unavailing protests against this practice were made from time to time.

[24] Hermannus Buschius—Hermann von dem Bussche—(1468-1534) is described in the Register of Cologne Univ. as "equestris ordinis." As a boy, he was a pupil of Hegius at Deventer, where he was a fellow-student of Ortwin Gratius. In 1486 B. proceeded to Italy, where he remained for five years, and enjoyed the friendship of the eminent scholar and antiquary, Pomponius Laetus. In the Register of Wittenberg Univ. for 1502 Buschius is first entitled "Pasiphilus" —*quasi πᾶσι φίλος*—a name ever after associated with him. The young scholar soon became known as one of the most ardent champions of the New Learning. Attacking with the utmost vivacity the errors and futilities of the scholastic text-books, ever at loggerheads with the defenders of medievalism, Buschius flitted restlessly from city to city throughout Germany and the Netherlands. He did not, however, at first throw in his lot with the Reuchlinists, and wrote an *Elogium* for von Tongern's "Articuli." But in 1514 Mutianus writes gleefully, "Buschius has sung his palinode!" and henceforward the latter is to be found in the foremost ranks of Reuchlin's defenders.

[25] Reuchlin's *Augenspiegel* was publicly burnt by H. and the Theologians at Cologne, on Feb. 10, 1514, as "offensive, and dangerous to religion."

[26] "Leo X.," says Fra Paolo, "displayed a singular proficiency in polite literature. . . . He would, indeed, have been a perfect pontiff, if to these accomplishments he had united some knowledge in matters of religion, and a greater inclination to piety." Erasmus, it is true, lauds Leo's attention to theology, amongst his other studies. But Erasmus was not free from obligations to the pontiff.

[27] The *Summa Contra Gentiles* is divided into four books. "Its principal practical aim, at the time it was written, was the enlightenment of the Moors, the Saracens, and the Jews of Spain; and also

to bring into prominence those arguments from reason for the establishment of Christianity which were beginning to be undermined by the rationalistic spirit of the age." *The Life and Labours of Saint Thomas of Aquin,* by Archbishop Vaughan, London, 1875, p. 473.

[28] Alexander of Hales, a native of Gloucestershire, who became Professor of Philosophy and Theology in Paris, ultimately joining the Franciscan Order. He was an uncompromising supporter of Papal supremacy, and consistently intolerant of all heretics.

[29] Giovanni di Fidenza, better known as St. Bonaventura—the glory of the Franciscan Order, whose general he became in 1256. The fervid writings of St. Bonaventura are mainly concerned with mystical theology, appealing not at all to the "Bonus phisicus."

[30] Thomas Aquinas.

[31] Porphyry, originally Malchus, was one of the most eminent of the neo-Platonists. He was the pupil of Longinus and Plotinus, and teacher of Iamblichus. His chief work, now lost, was directed against Christianity, but among the schoolmen his fame rested chiefly on his *Isagoge.*

[32] The decision of the Bp. of Spires, March 29, 1514, that the *Augenspiegel* was not heretical, and that Hoogstraten should pay the costs of the appeal.

[33] Ulrich von Hutten. In the summer of 1511 Hutten, in a state of destitution, journeyed by way of Bohemia and Moravia to Vienna. That city already held many supporters of the New Learning. Vadianus (Joachim von Watt), Peter Eberbach of Erfurt, and others lived there in a *contubernium,* or community (usually of poor scholars), and hospitably received the wanderer. The account given by Krabacius is probably founded on fact; be this as it may, Hutten

suddenly vanished from Vienna in the autumn of 1511.

[34] The Humanists disdained academical degrees because they despised the Universities that granted them. Johann Lindholz, Dean of the Faculty of Philosophy at Frankfort-on-Oder, declared that he conferred the degree of Bachelor on Hutten: this the latter denied.

[35] Joannes Rhagius Aesticampianus (1460-1520), the Latinised name of Johann Rack, of Sommerfeld. Visiting Italy in his youth, he entered the ranks of the Humanists, and on recrossing the Alps he proceeded to Paris. He is next heard of successively at Freiburg-im-Breisgau, Cologne, Cracow, and Frankfort-on-the-Oder —where he reckoned Ulrich von Hutten among his pupils. For three years, 1507-10, he lectured publicly at Leipsic on Pliny, Plautus, and other classical authors. The barbarians of Leipsic, however—as Fabricius puts it—could not brook the Humanities, and Rhagius was driven out, not without a parting bolt in the shape of a fiery oration: "You have overthrown Aesticampianus," he cried, "after assailing him with every kind of weapon. What Humanists will visit you in the future? Not one, by Hercules, not one! You will live out your sordid lives, uncivilised and contemned—*damnati omnes immoriemini!"*

After teaching the Classics for three years at Freiburg, A. was attracted to Wittenberg by the offer of a handsome stipend from Frederick, Duke of Saxony, and there resided until his death.

[36] "The Seven Liberal Arts" consisted of the *Trivium,* viz. Grammar, Rhetoric, and Dialectic, and the *Quadrivium,* viz. Music, Arithmetic, Geometry, and Astronomy. "Grammar" included what we should term classical studies, and "Rhetoric" included poetry. During the Dark Ages the *Quadrivium* was almost lost sight of.

[37] In allusion both to Reuchlin's Hebrew studies, and the writer's ignorance of Greek.

[38] George, Count Palatine of the Rhine, was appointed bishop at the age of 28, in June 1513.

[39] The Univ. of Mainz and Cologne had pronounced, in 1510, the opinion that the Talmud should be destroyed. See H. Graetz, *Hist. of the Jews*, 1892, iv. 475.

[40] For a good account of this extraordinary case, see E. Belfort Bax, *German Society at the close of the Middle Ages*, 1894 (App.). See also "The Tragical History of Jetzer: or, a Faithful Narrative of the Feigned Visions, Counterfeit Revelations, and False Miracles of the Dominican Fathers of the Convent of Berne . . . to Propagate their Superstitions. For which Horrid Impieties, the Prior, Sub-Prior, Lecturer, and Receiver of the said Convent were Burnt at a Stake . . . 1509. Collected from the Records of the said City by the care of Sir William Waller, Knight. Translated from his French Copy by an impartial Pen . . . London, MDCLXXIX."

[41] Referring to the alleged poisoning of the Emp. Henry VII. in 1313.

[42] Stephanus Brulefer (the name is spelt in several ways), born at St. Malo, in Brittany, in the middle of the XVth Cent. He entered the Franciscan Order, became a pupil of Gulielmus Vorilongus, and obtained the Doctorate of the University of Paris. He was a "Scotist," and taught his master's scholastic theology at Mayence and Metz.

[43] It does not appear that O. ever published such a work; but the Obscure Men are never tired of girding at his poetic ambitions.

[44] The treatise *De Disciplina Scholarium*, though frequently printed with the *De Consolatione Philosophiae*, was not the work of Boethius, but was probably written by Thomas Cantimpraten-sis, author of a work entitled *Bonum universale de proprietatibus apum*.

The book Ortwin is asked for is some edition of *Boetius de consolatione philosophie necnon de disciplina scholarium cum commento Sancti Thome*.

[45] Von Hutten's *Tri. Capn.* was not actually published until 1517, under the pseudonym of "Eleutherius Byzenus"; but a copy had apparently been shown to Erasmus as early as 1514. Whether this is identical with another *Triumphus*, by "Accius Neobius," ascribed by Mutian to Buschius, is uncertain.

[46] Jacobus Locher, the translator into Latin (1497) of Sebastian Brant's *Narrenschiff*, and successor to Conrad Celtis in his professorial chair at Ingolstadt.

[47] This, however, is Dollenkopf's own blunder, for "Thomas Wallensis" interprets the nine Muses as "the nine orders of Angels" (*Met. Ov. Moral.*, Paris, 1509; fol. vii). We are reminded of the scholar, who, being asked, "What are the twelve Signs of the Zodiac?" replied, "They are seven in number, and are called East, West, North and South."

[48] Maximilian had written to Leo X. (Oct. 23, 1514) asking him to silence the hostile theologians.

[49] Bild von Rheinau (Elsass) (1485-1547), "than whom I have no more faithful friend," wrote Erasmus. Studied at Paris under George Hieronymus Spartanus, and then, after visiting Strasburg, attached himself to the famous printing office of Johann Froben at Basle. He edited Tertullian, Tacitus, Livy, Pliny, and Velleius Paterculus. His epitaph at Schlettstadt commemorates his "innocentia, humanitas, frugalitas, pudicitia," as well as his learning.

[50] *Cursor*: a Bachelor who had to give courses of lectures on selected books of the Bible.

[51] Beguines, a semi-monastic sisterhood, formed in the XIIth Cent.

in the Netherlands. Bound by no vows, they devoted themselves to works of charity, and were at times persecuted as pietists by the Mendicant Orders. The Beguinage of St. Eliz. at Ghent is still famous.

[52] An imaginary book; perhaps a comic perversion of "Comestor."

[53] Matthew Schürer, of Schlettstadt, a printer of Strasburg, and a man of letters. He was the author of *Grammatica Nova,* publ. in 1501, and between the years 1506 and 1521 issued many works, including several by Erasmus and Wimpheling.

[54] The compilation known as *Mamotrectus super Bibliam,* attributed to Joannes Marchesinus, was a very popular work in the XVth Cent. The word is very variously spelt, and is found in the form Mammothreptus, which St. Augustine (in Psalm xxx. serm. 2) explains as "a child too long unweaned." Erasmus said that the M. had more faults than a leopard had spots.

[55] Joannes C. (1460-1551), educated under Hegius at Deventer. At Cologne he taught Greek, and, among other works, edited Pliny's Nat. His. He was a warm supporter of Reuchlin, and died in great poverty at Cologne.

[56] A popular medieval remedy, made of the chalky excreta of hyenas and other carnivora.

[57] R. de Mediavilla; Richard Middleton, an Englishman, *ob.* 1307. He is supposed to have been a teacher of Duns Scotus, on whose tomb in the Church of the Minorites his name is inscribed. He wrote a Commentary on the Sentences of Peter the Lombard.

[58] The *Bundschuh,* or rough shoe of the Swabian peasantry, borne on their banners in the Peasants' War, had been adopted as a device as early as 1493.

[59] Guillaume Haquinet Petit, Confessor and Preacher to Francis I., as he had been to Louis XII. An eminent theologian, and "pride of the Dominicans" as Budé calls him, he had earned the wrath of the Reuchlinists, and his consequent inclusion among the Obscure Men, by his adverse influence with Louis. See *Budé to Erasm.,* Paris [1517]. Epp. clxviii.

[60] William (not John), Grocyn, *c.* 1446-1519, born at Colerne, Wilts, and educated at Winchester, and New College, Oxford. In 1488 he visited Italy, and studied Greek under Chalcondylas. Returning to Oxford, he was probably the first publicly to lecture upon Greek in that university. Among his pupils were Sir Thomas More and Erasmus. Though a firm upholder of the New Learning, Grocyn never swerved from the strictest religious orthodoxy.

[61] Thomas Linacre, *c.* 1460-1524, born at Canterbury; Fellow of All-Souls College, Oxford, 1488. Like Grocyn, he visited Italy and studied Greek under Chalcondylas, and moreover counted More and Erasmus among his pupils on his return to England. L. was King's Physician under Henry VII. and Henry VIII., and may be regarded as the founder of the Royal College of Physicians. He took priest's orders about four years before his death.

[62] Richard Croke, *c.* 1489-1558; born in London; graduated at Cambridge in 1506. He studied Greek under Grocyn at Oxford, and under Hieronymus Aleander at Paris, and lectured successively at Louvain, Cologne, Leipsic, Dresden, and Cambridge. In 1529 he was sent by Cranmer on a mission to Italy concerning the king's divorce. It is known that he was at Leipsic in 1515. Mutianus writing to Reuchlin, in 1515, remarks that Croke calls himself an Englishman, but that he should have judged him a Greek, such was his graceful fluency in that tongue. Croke was on very friendly terms with Reuchlin: "My Capnion," he calls him in an extant letter.

[63] The Landsknechte were so called, not from the long lance with which they were armed, but from those German serfs who fought for their lords on foot.

[64] At Marignano (now Melegnano), near Milan, was fought, on Sept. 13, 1515, the sanguinary battle between the French army of Francis I., aided by German levies, and the Swiss. The struggle was fierce and protracted, and although it ended in the decisive defeat of the Swiss, the losses of the victors were very heavy.

[65] Card. Grimani ordered the *Augenspiegel* to be newly translated into Latin, and on comparing the result with the transl. previously submitted by Hoogstraten it was found that the latter was grossly garbled.

[66] Reuchlin had pointed out, two years before, that Hoogstraten was a Netherlander and had but a poor acquaintance with High German.

[67] Originally subtle and elaborate theological arguments, they had degenerated into trifling, and often indecorous, discussions.

[68] *Hossus* (1487-1540). A detailed account of his life, from his birth under a tree in a cornfield, will be found in the *Narratio de H. Eob. Hesso,* by Joach. Camerarius, Norimb., 1553. Melchior Adam (*Lib. de Vit. Phil. Germ.*) compares him to Homer, while Moreri drily remarks that he was neither so blind nor so great as H., but could drink the greatest topers in Germany under the table. He was a facile writer of Latin verse, from translations of Homer and Theocritus, to a poem on the gout. See Martin Hertz, *H. E. Hosse,* Berlin, 1860.

Urbanus: a member of the Erfurt circle, afterwards a Cistercian monk. He has been strangely confused with Euricius Cordus by Melchior Adam and many subsequent writers.

Eurit.: Euricius Cordus (1486-1535), poet and physician. Visited Italy in 1521; studied medicine at Ferrara, and afterwards resided at Marpurg and Bremen. Besides poems, he wrote *Colloquium de Herbis,* and other botanical works.

Spalat. (1484-1545): Georg Burkhardt, of Spalt, Bavaria. One of the humanists of the Erfurt circle; later, chaplain and adviser of the Elector Frederick the Wise, and close friend of Luther. Author of the *Annales Reformationis* and other historical works.

[69] Believed by Böcking to stand for "Martin Luther."

[70] H. Septimellensis, or Samariensis, who in the XIIth Cent. related the vicissitudes of his own lot in a poem, "De diversitate fortunae et philosophiae consolatione."

[71] Hermann van Beck of Zwoll, one of the Brethren of the Common Life; a Commentator on Virgil—but not on the Æneid; neither is Ganymede referred to in his *Elucidarium Poeticum.*

[72] For an account of the *bacchanten,* or begging students, see *The Autobiography of Thomas Platter, a schoolmaster of the XVIth Cent.* Transl. from the German (by E. A. M'Caul), London, 1839.

[73] Jacques de Molay and the residue of the Templars were seven years in prison before they met their fate (1314). See H. C. Lea, *Hist. of the Inquisition,* vol. iii., 1888.

[74] Johann Ruchrath of Oberwesel, near Bingen, accused by the Dominicans of suspicious intercourse with the Jews, and, through their influence, unjustly condemned at Mainz for heresy in 1479 by the Cologne inquisitor. Sometimes confused with the much more famous Johann Wessel of Groningen.

SELECTED NOTES

Part II
(*pages 103-248*)

[1] In all Editions, from 1556 to 1830 inclusive, the ensuing lines occur in so confused an order as to be almost unintelligible.

[2] *Rota:* a tribunal, of twelve members, instituted in 1326 as the supreme court of justice and universal court of appeal for the Church.

[3] Thos. M., Franciscan (1475-1537); born near Strasburg; he led the life of a wandering scholar in France, Germany, Bohemia, and Poland—studying theology at Paris and law at Freiburg. In 1505 he received a poet's crown from Maximilian. Though later the bitter opponent of Luther, none attacked the abuses of the Church more violently than M. He is best known by his rhymed sermons, the *Narrenbeschwörung* ("Exorcism of Fools") and the *Schelmenzunft* ("Rogues' Guild"), 1512, and his satire, *Von dem grossen Lutherischen Narren,* 1522, against the Reformation. M. resembles Brandt, but his works are somewhat more poetical in form, and he attacks knaves rather than fools.

[4] P. in his *Defensio* boasted of having converted fourteen of his brother Jews.

[5] Friedrich III. in 1492 made a grant of arms to R. "imperialis consistorii comiti," and Maximilian frequently speaks of him as "consiliarium nostrum."

[6] "His eyes were large, round, and prominent, even to a defect; inso-much that he could not discern distant objects without the aid of a glass, by the assistance of which it was observed that in hunting . . . he saw to a greater distance than any of his attendants." Roscoe, *ut sup.,* p. 377.

[7] A friend of Luther, Melanchthon, and Spalatinus.

[8] Philipp Engelbrecht von Engen, author of *Divi Lamberti Episcopi Trajectensis . . . Vita,* Basle, 1519.

[9] Memorable to Ulr. v. Hutten for his ill-treatment by the Lötzes, recorded in his *Querelen.*

[10] Tutor of Ulrich von Hutten.

[11] Joannes and Alexander von der Osthen, to whom Hutten dedicated his *Ars Versificatoria.*

[12] S. Anthony's fire—erysipelas.

[13] Paulus Gereander, of Salzburg, to whom Melanchthon dedicated his ed. of Terence.

[14] F. Stadianus, the friend and teacher of Melanchthon.

[15] Johann Kierher, Canon of Spires, a friend of Erasmus.

[16] Paulus Seidensticker, of Schlettstadt.

[17] Corrector of the press at the printing-office of Th. Anshelm, at Hagenau.

[18] Johann S., printer, of Hagenau.

[19] Martin Gröning, a native of Bremen, and Doctor of Laws of Sinigaglia, translated the *Augenspiegel* into Latin, on behalf of Reuchlin, and proved the version

PART II

presented by Hoogstraten to the Curia false in many passages.

[20] Jacob Aurelius von Q., a native of Freiburg, in Saxony, the Pope's private secretary, had been Reuchlin's firm friend ever since they had made acquaintance in Italy in 1492.

[21] The book, publ. in 1514, *s. l.*, usually known as the *Praenotamenta Ortwini Gratii*, directed against the *Augenspiegel*.

[22] Heinrich Bebel, 1472-1516, humanist. Laureated by Maximilian in 1501. Author of *Ars versificandi, Commentaria epistolarum conficiendarum . . . contra Epistolandi modos Pontii, Triumphus Veneris,* &c.

[23] The *Reichskammergericht*, or Supreme Court of Justice, consisting of a president and sixteen assessors, was first set up in 1495, on the proposal of Berthold, Ahbp. of Mainz; it soon ceased to meet, but was revived at the Diet of Constance, 1507, and after many wanderings finally settled down at Wetzlar.

[24] Paulus Ricius, a converted Jew. He was acquainted with Latin, Greek, and Hebrew, and Erasmus eulogises his learning, zeal, and modest bearing (Erasm., *Epp. L. B.*, 1706, col. 191). R. was appointed physician to the Emperor Maximilian in 1518; lectured on philosophy at Pavia, and translated a work on the Cabbala (*The Gates of Light*) into Latin: to this work Pico della Mirandola and Reuchlin were indebted.

[25] "Sie hat ein Hufeisen verloren" —"she has cast a shoe"—is still said of a girl who has lost her honour.

[26] Dietrich von Bern, *i.e.* Theoderic the Great, King of the Goths, as represented in German legend: *von Bern*="of Verona." The amphitheatre at V. has been ascribed to him. He enters, mythically, into many Middle High German poems, including the *Nibelungenlied*.

[27] Ioannes Baptista Hispaniolus (Spagnoli), 1448-1516, a native of Mantua; at an early age he joined the Order of Carmelites, and rose to be the head of that body. Baptista, who is said to have left 55,000 verses, is extravagantly eulogised by Trithemius (Scr. Eccl., p. 387).

[28] This meeting of Leo X. and François I. took place, however, in Dec. 1515, and before the death of Bapt. Mant.

[29] Montefiascone, however, produces Muscat wine, and not Lac. Christ, which is a product of the slopes of Vesuvius.

[30] Thomas Aquinas. His *Tractatus de Ente et Essentia* had been printed several times before 1517.

[31] P. in his *Defensio* pleads that he did not preach "pontificaliter," but merely exhorted the Jews, at Frankfort, standing outside the church.

[32] Maximilian's campaign in Northern Italy.

[33] An adaptation of the Italian "strappata di corda"; the punishment of the *strappado* consisting in raising the victim to a height, and letting him fall suddenly so as to suffer a violent jerk from the suspending rope.

[34] *The Institutes of Justinian*. The introductory part of the *Corpus Juris Civilis*, the other portions being the *Digest*, the *Code*, and the *Novellae*.

Infort.: a portion of the *Digest*, comprising Books XXIV. (3)-XXXVIII, and coming between the *Digestum Vetus* and the *Digestum Novum*. This division is quite arbitrary, and seems due to the mere accident of an ancient copy having been split at the points indicated. The entire *Digest* consists of fifty books.

Reg. canc.: a collection of papal mandates, regulations, ordinances, &c. These were reissued and confirmed by successive Popes, and numerous editions had appeared before 1517.

[35] Perhaps by Wilhelm, third son of Francesco Accorso (Accursius). He was born in 1246, and ended his

days as Professor of Jurisprudence at Bologna.

[36] Richardus de Mediavilla, *i.e.* Richard Middleton, fl. 1280, a Franciscan monk, supposed to have been born either at Middleton Stoney (Oxf.) or at Middleton Cheyney (Northants). He rose to eminence in canon law and theology, and was perhaps the teacher of Duns Scotus. Middleton's chief work was a Commentary on the Sentences of Peter Lombard, which appeared in many editions.

[37] This Ep. is based almost entirely on passages from Pfefferkorn's *Defensio*.

[38] A copy of the kerchief of St. Veronica, which bore a miraculous image of Christ's face.

[39] Bernardino Caravajal, Bp. of Ostia. To him Hoogstraten addressed his *Defensio scholastica principum Almaniae . . .* 1511.

[40] Petrus Tommai, Franciscan, author of a popular book on mnemonics, *Foenix Divini Petri Ravennatis memoriae magistri,* Venet, 1491, and of a compendium of the civil law.

[41] But the *Augenspiegel* had been burnt Feb. 10, 1514.

[42] The name would be familiar, as the mediaeval transliteration of Yūhannā ibn Māsawaih, an Arab writer on Medicine, many of whose works were translated into Latin.

[43] A fiend holding a candle appears on the title-page of the *Lamentationes Obscurorum Virorum,* 1518. The phrase occurs in Pfefferkorn's *Defence*.

[44] The piazza known as Campo dei Fiori, near the Palazzo Farnese, now a market-place, was the scene of "the most terrible of the Autos da Fe, instituted by the Dominicans, in which many Jews and other heretics were burnt alive." A. J. C. Hare, *Walks in Rome* (1887), ii. 181. In 1600 it was the place of execution of Giordano Bruno. The inn there was a favourite haunt of German pilgrims.

[45] Hermann von dem Busche writes to Reuchlin, Sept. 30, 1514: "I find that the Theologians have lately sent Jakob Hochstraten, through the bankers at Rome, fifteen hundred crowns—not for maintenance, for monks should be frugal—not for necessary legal expenses, for these, I think, would amount to a much smaller sum—but I strongly suspect (bad luck to them!), for purposes of bribery; to obtain, for gold, votes that they could not hope for in the interests of justice."

[46] Almost certainly Jacobus Aurelius von Questemberg. Von Q., who was a liberal-minded and learned man, proved a valuable "friend at Court" for Reuchlin during the hearing of Hoogstraten's appeal, and, as one of Reuchlin's biographers puts it, "his influence was of more service to Reuchlin than all the letters commendatory of Kings and Princes." Maius, *Vit. Reuchlin,* p. 214.

[47] In allusion, of course, to the legend of "Pope Joan," universally credited throughout the XVth and XVIth Cents. The development of this vague myth into an accepted fact of history is a remarkable phenomenon, resulting as it did in the accumulation of a vast evidential structure upon the flimsiest of foundations.

[48] Raffaello Riario, Cardinal of S. Georgio, was degraded for conspiracy against Leo X. in 1517, but was soon restored to favour. Dominico Grimani, Cardinal of S. Marco, had been appointed by the Pope to cite Reuchlin to appear, personally or through an advocate, at Rome. Adrian di Castello, Cardinal of S. Chrisogono (to be carefully distinguished from Adrian of Utrecht, afterwards Pope Adrian VI.), was also one of the conspirators against Leo X., and to avoid the penalty fled from Rome. He was an accomplished scholar, and to him Reuchlin dedicated one of his works on Hebrew grammar. Adrian, who was in high favour with Henry VIII., was Rector of

St. Dunstan-in-the-East, and held successively the sees of Hereford and Bath, which latter he farmed out to Wolsey.

[49] At Bologna the *promotor* was the graduate who presented candidates for degrees.

[50] Jacques Lefevre d'Etaples, of lowly birth, a forerunner of the Reformation. His *Commentaries on S. Paul's Epistles* (1512) anticipated some of Luther's conclusions, but the Sorbonne took no proceedings against him till 1521, when he escaped by the aid of François I.

[51] Heinrich Loriti, *Glareanus* (of Glarus), 1488-1563. Swiss humanist. Laureated by Maximilian, 1512. Founded a school at Freiburg-im-Breisgau. A commentator upon Livy, Caesar, Horace, Sallust, &c. "The shadow of Erasmus," he favoured the Reformation at first, but afterwards held aloof.

[52] Where the *Augenspiegel* was burnt.

[53] The Greek text, with a new Lat. transl. and notes. Dedicatory epistle, dated Basle, Feb. 1, 1516. "The effect was a spiritual earthquake. . . . A single candle shone in the universal darkness. That a Pope should have been found to allow the lighting of it is the most startling feature in Reformation history." J. A. Froude, *Life and Lett. of Erasm.*, 1894, p. 128.

[54] Johann von der Wiek, afterwards Syndic of Bremen and Munster, and ultimately (1533) a martyr in the cause of the Reformation. See Erasm., *Ep.* MDCXX. *J. Caesarius to Erasm.*, Cologne, July 30, 1517.

[55] Conrad Muth, 1472-1526, pupil of Hegius at Deventer, the leader and guide of the Erfurt circle.

[56] Wilibald Pirckheimer (1470-1528), one of the most notable figures of the period. Born at Nuremberg, he spent seven years in Italy. On his return to N. he led the life of a wealthy scholar, patron of art and literature, and man of affairs. Not an extremist,

he lamented the faults and excesses of both the defenders and assailants of the Church. The fatuous "nescio quis" is a quotation from Pfefferkorn's *Defensio*.

[57] Jacob Wimpheling (1450-1528) was born and died at Schlettstadt, in Elsass. He was an ardent educational reformer, of the school of Gerson, but no supporter of the Reformation. His treatise, *De Integritate*, in which he assailed monkish pretensions, and incidentally remarked that Augustine was not a Regular, brought down on him the wrath of the Augustinians, just as his poem in honour of the Immaculate Conception did that of the Dominicans. W. was a friend and collaborator of Sebastian Brant.

[58] Sebastian Brant (or Brandt) (1457-1521), a native of Strasburg, and the author of the famous *Narrenschiff*, which has passed into English literature in the form of Barclay's paraphrase, *The Shyp of Folys of the World*, 1509. The allusion in the text is to B.'s association with Wimpheling in the Immaculate Conception controversy.

[59] The *Rationale divinorum officiorum* of Guillaume Durand (1237-1296), Bp. of Mende. It was one of the first printed books (Mainz, 1459), and is a work of great importance in liturgical history. "Le dernier mot du moyen âge sur la mystique du culte divin." See Ul. Chevalier, *Répertoire des sources historiques du moyen âge*, 1883.

[60] Francesco Accorso, c. 1180-1260, Professor at Bologna, a famous Italian jurist. His chief work was a collection of glosses on the Roman Law, known as "The Great Gloss." All the derivations given in this Ep. are to be found verbatim in the glosses.

[61] Peter Schade, of Bruttig, or Pruttig, on the Mosel (1493-1524), succeeded Richard Croke as teacher of Greek at Leipsic, 1517.

[62] Hermann, Graf von Neuenar, c. 1491-1530; pupil of Caesarius, with whom he visited Italy. Himself a man of letters, and Dean of the Canonical Chapter at Cologne, he was a liberal patron of the humanists of his day, and a strenuous upholder of Reuchlin. By many of the earlier critics he was believed to have had a hand in the E. O. V.

[63] Caspar Ursinus Velius, 1493-1538, a precocious scholar who wrote Latin and Greek verse fluently in his boyhood. There are frequent references to his accomplishments in the letters of Erasmus, and he was laureated by Maximilian. He was author of a biographical work, *Chronicorum mundi epitome,* 1534; and *C. U. V. Poematum libri quinque,* 1522. V.'s life came strangely to an end; he was missing one morning, and was never seen again.

[64] It was on Reuchlin's recommendation that M. was appointed Prof. of Greek at Wittenberg.

[65] But O. had been at Cologne for ten years.

[66] *Petrus Tartaretus:* a contemporary theologian of Paris, author of many commentaries on Aristotle and his commentators.

Versor: another Parisian theologian of the XVth Cent.

Perversor: Reuchlin in his *Defensio,* 1513, called Ortwin, "Artium perversor, volui professor."

Burid.: Jean Buridan, *ob. c.* 1358. Pupil of William of Ockham, Rector of the Univ. of Paris, 1327; a writer on philosophy, best known from his association with the sophism of "Buridan's Ass" (though a similar "case" is mooted by Dante, Par. IV.).

Brux.: Georgius B., a XVth Cent. nominalist.

[67] Ælius Donatus, a grammarian of the IVth Cent., whose *Ars Grammatica* was used as a school textbook in the Mid. Ages so widely that "Donat" became a synonym for "grammar," or the elements of any science. The early Donatus was the only block-book without illustrations.

[68] The Order of the Holy Ghost, established in 1178, was divided into Knights Hospitallers and Canons Regular, the former being abolished in 1459.

[69] One Johann Burkhardt, a Dominican, Dean of Strasburg, whose scandalous proceedings are sufficiently explained in the text.

[70] In this Ep. the satiric mask is torn off, and open scorn and derision of Reuchlin's opponents are made manifest. Erasmus, referring to the belief of many monks that the E. O. V. were written in good faith and in their defence, says: "Nec hodie deprehendissent, ni quidam, *addita epistola,* lectorem admonuisset rem non esse seriam." In the edd. from 1599 to 1858 this Ep. is ascribed to "Rupertus Cuculus."

ӈaRpeR ⚡ ԵoRcӈbooKs

HUMANITIES AND SOCIAL SCIENCES

American Studies

JOHN R. ALDEN: The American Revolution, 1775–1783.¹ Illus. TB/3011

RAY STANNARD BAKER: Following the Color Line: An Account of Negro Citizenship in the American Democracy.‡ Illus. Introduction by Dewey Grantham, Jr. TB/3053

RAY A. BILLINGTON: The Far Western Frontier, 1830–1860.† Illus. TB/3012

JOSEPH L. BLAU, Ed.: Cornerstones of Religious Freedom in America. Selected Basic Documents, Court Decisions and Public Statements. Enlarged and revised edition with new Intro. by Editor TB/118

RANDOLPH S. BOURNE: War and the Intellectuals: Collected Essays, 1915–1919.‡ Edited with an Introduction by Carl Resek TB/3043

A. RUSSELL BUCHANAN: The United States and World War II. † Illus. Volume I TB/3044
Volume II TB/3045

ABRAHAM CAHAN: The Rise of David Levinsky: a novel. Introduction by John Higham TB/1028

JOSEPH CHARLES: The Origins of the American Party System TB/1049

T. C. COCHRAN & WILLIAM MILLER: The Age of Enterprise: A Social History of Industrial America TB/1054

FOSTER RHEA DULLES: America's Rise to World Power, 1898–1954.† Illus. TB/3021

W. A. DUNNING: Reconstruction, Political and Economic, 1865–1877 TB/3073

CLEMENT EATON: The Growth of Southern Civilization, 1790 1860.† Illus. TB/3040

HAROLD U. FAULKNER: Politics, Reform and Expansion, 1890–1900.† Illus. TB/3020

LOUIS FILLER: The Crusade against Slavery, 1830–1860.† Illus. TB/3029

EDITORS OF FORTUNE: America in the Sixties: the Economy and the Society. Two-color charts TB/1015

LAWRENCE HENRY GIPSON: The Coming of the Revolution, 1763 1775.† Illus. TB/3007

FRANCIS J. GRUND: Aristocracy in America: Jacksonian Democracy TB/1001

OSCAR HANDLIN, Editor: This Was America: As Recorded by European Travelers to the Western Shore in the Eighteenth, Nineteenth, and Twentieth Centuries. Illus. TB/1119

MARCUS LEE HANSEN: The Atlantic Migration: 1607–1860. Edited by Arthur M. Schlesinger; Introduction by Oscar Handlin TB/1052

MARCUS LEE HANSEN: The Immigrant in American History. Edited with a Foreword by Arthur Schlesinger, Sr. TB/1120

JOHN D. HICKS: Republican Ascendancy, 1921–1933.† Illus. TB/3041

JOHN HIGHAM, Ed.: The Reconstruction of American History TB/1068

ROBERT H. JACKSON: The Supreme Court in the American System of Government TB/1106

THOMAS JEFFERSON: Notes on the State of Virginia.‡ Introduction by Thomas Perkins Abernethy TB/3052

WILLIAM E. LEUCHTENBURG: Franklin D. Roosevelt and the New Deal, 1932–1940.† Illus. TB/3025

LEONARD W. LEVY: Freedom of Speech and Press in Early American History: Legacy of Suppression TB/1109

ARTHUR S. LINK: Woodrow Wilson and the Progressive Era, 1910–1917.† Illus. TB/3023

BERNARD MAYO: Myths and Men: Patrick Henry, George Washington, Thomas Jefferson TB/1108

JOHN C. MILLER: The Federalist Era, 1789–1801.† Illus. TB/3027

PERRY MILLER & T. H. JOHNSON, Editors: The Puritans: A Sourcebook of Their Writings
Volume I TB/1093
Volume II TB/1094

GEORGE E. MOWRY: The Era of Theodore Roosevelt and the Birth of Modern America, 1900–1912.† Illus. TB/3022

WALLACE NOTESTEIN: The English People on the Eve of Colonization, 1603–1630.† Illus. TB/3006

RUSSEL BLAINE NYE: The Cultural Life of the New Nation, 1776–1801.† Illus. TB/3026

GEORGE E. PROBST, Ed.: The Happy Republic: A Reader in Tocqueville's America TB/1060

FRANK THISTLETHWAITE: America and the Atlantic Community: Anglo-American Aspects, 1790–1850 TB/1107

---

† The New American Nation Series, edited by Henry Steele Commager and Richard B. Morris.

‡ American Perspectives series, edited by Bernard Wishy and William E. Leuchtenburg.

* The Rise of Modern Europe series, edited by William L. Langer.

** Researches in the Social, Cultural, and Behavioral Sciences, edited by Benjamin Nelson

§ The Library of Religion and Culture, edited by Benjamin Nelson.

Σ Harper Modern Science Series, edited by James R. Newman.

º Not for sale in Canada.

TWELVE SOUTHERNERS: I'll Take My Stand: *The South and the Agrarian Tradition.* Introduction by Louis D. Rubin, Jr.; Biographical Essays by Virginia Rock   TB/1072

A. F. TYLER: Freedom's Ferment: *Phases of American Social History from the Revolution to the Outbreak of the Civil War.* Illus.   TB/1074

GLYNDON G. VAN DEUSEN: The Jacksonian Era, 1828-1848.† Illus.   TB/3028

WALTER E. WEYL: The New Democracy: *An Essay on Certain Political and Economic Tendencies in the United States.‡ Introduction* by Charles Forcey   TB/3042

LOUIS B. WRIGHT: The Cultural Life of the American Colonies, 1607-1763.† Illus.   TB/3005

LOUIS B. WRIGHT: Culture on the Moving Frontier   TB/1053

Anthropology & Sociology

BERNARD BERELSON, Ed.: The Behavioral Sciences Today   TB/1127

JOSEPH B. CASAGRANDE, Ed.: In the Company of Man: *20 Portraits of Anthropological Informants.* Illus.   TB/3047

W. E. LE GROS CLARK: The Antecedents of Man: *An Introduction to the Evolution of the Primates.*° Illus.   TB/559

ALLISON DAVIS & JOHN DOLLARD: Children of Bondage: *The Personality Development of Negro Youth in the Urban South***   TB/3049

ST. CLAIR DRAKE & HORACE R. CAYTON: Black Metropolis: *A Study of Negro Life in a Northern City.* Introduction by Everett C. Hughes. Tables, maps, charts and graphs   Volume I   TB/1086
    Volume II   TB/1087

CORA DU BOIS: The People of Alor. *New Preface by the author.* Illus.   Volume I   TB/1042
    Volume II   TB/1043

LEON FESTINGER, HENRY W. RIECKEN & STANLEY SCHACHTER: When Prophecy Fails: *A Social and Psychological Account of a Modern Group that Predicted the Destruction of the World***   TB/1132

RAYMOND FIRTH, Ed.: Man and Culture: *An Evaluation of the Work of Bronislaw Malinowski*** °   TB/1133

L. S. B. LEAKEY: Adam's Ancestors: *The Evolution of Man and his Culture.* Illus.   TB/1019

KURT LEWIN: Field Theory in Social Science: *Selected Theoretical Papers.*** *Edited with a Foreword by Dorwin Cartwright*   TB/1135

ROBERT H. LOWIE: Primitive Society. *Introduction by Fred Eggan*   TB/1056

BENJAMIN NELSON: Religious Traditions and the Spirit of Capitalism: *From the Church Fathers to Jeremy Bentham*   TB/1130

TALCOTT PARSONS & EDWARD A. SHILS, Editors: Toward a General Theory of Action: *Theoretical Foundations for the Social Sciences*   TB/1083

JOHN H. ROHRER & MUNRO S. EDMONSON, Eds.: The Eighth Generation Grows Up: *Cultures and Personalities of New Orleans Negroes***   TB/3050

ARNOLD ROSE: The Negro in America: *The Condensed Version of Gunnar Myrdal's An American Dilemma. New Introduction by the Author;* Foreword by Gunnar Myrdal   TB/3048

KURT SAMUELSSON: Religion and Economic Action: *A Critique of Max Weber.*** ° *Trans. by E. G. French; Ed. with Intro. by D. C. Coleman*   TB/1131

PITIRIM SOROKIN: Contemporary Sociological Theories. *Through The First Quarter of the 20th Century*   TB/3046

MAURICE R. STEIN: The Eclipse of Community: *An Interpretation of American Studies. New Introduction by the Author*   TB/1128

SIR EDWARD TYLOR: The Origins of Culture. *Part I of "Primitive Culture."§ Introduction* by Paul Radin   TB/33

SIR EDWARD TYLOR: Religion in Primitive Culture. *Part II of "Primitive Culture."§ Introduction* by Paul Radin   TB/34

W. LLOYD WARNER & Associates: Democracy in Jonesville: *A Study in Quality and Inequality***   TB/1129

W. LLOYD WARNER: Social Class in America: *The Evaluation of Status*   TB/1013

Art and Art History

EMILE MÂLE: The Gothic Image: *Religious Art in France of the Thirteenth Century.§ 190 illus.*   TB/44

ERWIN PANOFSKY: Studies in Iconology: *Humanistic Themes in the Art of the Renaissance. 180 illustrations*   TB/1077

ALEXANDRE PIANKOFF: The Shrines of Tut-Ankh-Amon. *Edited by N. Rambova. 117 illus.*   TB/2011

JEAN SEZNEC: The Survival of the Pagan Gods: *The Mythological Tradition and Its Place in Renaissance Humanism and Art. 108 illustrations*   TB/2004

OTTO VON SIMSON: The Gothic Cathedral: *Origins of Gothic Architecture and the Medieval Concept of Order. 58 illus.*   TB/2018

HEINRICH ZIMMER: Myths and Symbols in Indian Art and Civilization. *70 illustrations*   TB/2005

Business, Economics & Economic History

REINHARD BENDIX: Work and Authority in Industry: *Ideologies of Management in the Course of Industrialization*   TB/3035

THOMAS C. COCHRAN: The American Business System: *A Historical Perspective, 1900-1955*   TB/1080

ROBERT DAHL & CHARLES E. LINDBLOM: Politics, Economics, and Welfare: *Planning and Politico-Economic Systems Resolved into Basic Social Processes*   TB/3037

PETER F. DRUCKER: The New Society: *The Anatomy of Industrial Order*   TB/1082

ROBERT L. HEILBRONER: The Great Ascent: *The Struggle for Economic Development in Our Time*   TB/3030

ABBA P. LERNER: Everybody's Business: *A Re-examination of Current Assumptions in Economics and Public Policy*   TB/3051

PAUL MANTOUX: The Industrial Revolution in the Eighteenth Century: *The Beginnings of the Modern Factory System in England*°   TB/1079

WILLIAM MILLER, Ed.: Men in Business: *Essays on the Historical Role of the Entrepreneur*   TB/1081

PERRIN STRYKER: The Character of the Executive: *Eleven Studies in Managerial Qualities*   TB/1041

PIERRE URI: Partnership for Progress: *A Program for Transatlantic Action*   TB/3036

3

A LETTER TO THE READER

Overseas, there is considerable belief
that we are a country of extreme conservatism and
that we cannot accommodate to social change.

Books about America in the hands of
readers abroad can help change those ideas.

The U. S. Information Agency cannot,
by itself, meet the vast need for books about
the United States.

You can help.

Harper Torchbooks provides three packets
of books on American history, economics,
sociology, literature and politics to
help meet the need.

To send a packet of Torchbooks [*] overseas,
all you need do is send your check for $7 (which
includes cost of shipping) to Harper & Row.
The U. S. Information Agency will distrib-
ute the books to libraries, schools, and other
centers all over the world.

I ask every American to support this
program, part of a worldwide BOOKS USA campaign.

I ask you to share in the opportunity to
help tell others about America.

EDWARD R. MURROW
Director,
U. S. Information Agency

[*retailing at $10.85 to $12.00]

PACKET I: *Twentieth Century America*

Dulles/America's Rise to World Power, 1898-1954
Cochran/The American Business System, 1900-1955
Zabel, Editor/Literary Opinion in America (two volumes)
Drucker/The New Society: *The Anatomy of Industrial Order*
Fortune Editors/America in the Sixties: *The Economy and the Society*

PACKET II: *American History*

Billington/The Far Western Frontier, 1830-1860
Mowry/The Era of Theodore Roosevelt and the
   Birth of Modern America, 1900-1912
Faulkner/Politics, Reform, and Expansion, 1890-1900
Cochran & Miller/The Age of Enterprise: *A Social History of
   Industrial America*
Tyler/Freedom's Ferment: *American Social History from the
   Revolution to the Civil War*

PACKET III: *American History*

Hansen/The Atlantic Migration, 1607-1860
Degler/Out of Our Past: *The Forces that Shaped Modern America*
Probst, Editor/The Happy Republic: *A Reader in Tocqueville's America*
Alden/The American Revolution, 1775-1783
Wright/The Cultural Life of the American Colonies, 1607-1763

*Your gift will be acknowledged directly to you by the overseas recipient.
Simply fill out the coupon, detach and mail with your check or money order.*

NOTE: *This offer expires December 31, 1966.*